Obstetric Litigation
from A–Z

Obstetric Litigation from A–Z

Andrew Symon

Quay
Books

Mark Allen
Publishing Ltd

Quay Books Division, Mark Allen Publishing Ltd,
Jesses Farm, Snow Hill, Dinton, Salisbury, Wiltshire, SP3 5HN

British Library Cataloguing-in-Publication Data. A catalogue record is available for this book

ISBN 1 85642 184 8

Printed in the UK by Redwood Books, Trowbridge, Wiltshire

Contents

Acknowledgements

This book is based on part of my doctoral studies at the University of Edinburgh. My thanks go to my two supervisors, Professor Michael Adler and Professor Kath Melia, who have both provided support and encouragement over the years. Much of the book relates to information obtained from an examination of legal files, and my thanks also go to those legal department officials at the Central Legal Office in Edinburgh and in the two English areas for their help and co-operation. As some of them were also interviewed I cannot name them, but my grateful thanks are extended to them for all their assistance.

A series of qualitative interviews is reported here. I am very grateful to all those who gave their time to be interviewed, especially since the subject matter was, for many, a painful one. I am encouraged by the fact that those who had been involved in litigation, despite having suffered from the experience, were able to share their thoughts and feelings with me. Their contribution to this book is immense, and while they too cannot be named, I would like to offer them my sincere thanks.

Research is a costly business, and I am grateful for the financial assistance of my supporting bodies. The examination of legal files was made possible by awards from the Economic and Social Research Council and the Margaret Callum Rodger award (administered by the National Board for Scotland for Nursing, Midwifery and Health Visiting). The interviews were funded by the inaugural Iolanthe Trust Research Fellowship, and study time (equivalent to one day a week over two years) was granted by the Perth and Kinross Healthcare NHS Trust. Without all this financial and organisational backing, the research would not have been possible.

A considerable amount of work has been required in order to update and augment the results which were originally submitted as part of my thesis, and I would like to thank Ray Philp, Lecturer at the School of Nursing and Midwifery at the University of Dundee, for providing helpful comments on a late draft of this book.

Lastly, I would like to thank my wife Maggie for, once again, allowing me the time and space to write.

Acknowledgements

Foreword

It is essential that a midwife has a good knowledge of the law, so that she/he understands the context within which she/he practises. This is crucial not only because of the increase in litigation, but also because of the increasing emphasis on the rights of the patient: a change symbolised by the fact that under the Human Rights Act 1998, action can now be brought in the courts of the United Kingdom for violation of the European Convention of Human Rights. A book which aims at clarifying the law for the midwife is therefore to be welcomed. This book can be of value not only to the novice, but also to those who have greater experience and knowledge of the law. In Part I of the book there is a brief explanation of the legal framework within which the midwife practices. In Part II various topics are considered in alphabetical order enabling the reader to dip into various issues, following up the leads, so that she/he develops an understanding of the law and becomes more confident and familiar with the language and concepts. The book can also be used as a ready reference when a problem or concern arises at work. Many who work in the NHS probably feel that too often we fail to learn the lessons from the past and from colleagues in other organisations. Andrew in his PhD studied hundreds of cases where claimants sought compensation for harm suffered during pregnancy and child birth. His book points out clearly the lessons to be drawn from this analysis. In addition the book draws on a series of interviews and questionnaires completed by midwives and obstetricians and is thus well grounded in practice. This book should be welcomed by the midwifery profession as another useful tool in tracing a path through a complex and daunting field.

Bridgit Dimond
Emeritus Professor, University of Glamorgan
December, 2000

Introduction

This book aims to explain the nature of litigation within maternity care in Britain. Litigation is one of the health service's most pressing concerns, and obstetric litigation has been one of its most prominent features.

The book stems from doctoral research based at the University of Edinburgh, and follow up interviews which were originally intended to be part of the PhD. Due to reasons of space these were not included in the final thesis, but funding for these had been secured from the Iolanthe Trust and they were duly carried out. Some parts of the book draw upon two series of articles which appeared in the *British Journal of Midwifery* from 1997–99; others draw upon other published and unpublished data. Those parts which draw upon published articles have been augmented and updated.

An *Obstetric Litigation from A–Z* is just that: it is not intended to be the definitive account of this developing area (even if such were possible). Instead it is an attempt to expose areas of the subject which my own experience as a health service practitioner tells me are important, but which would not be collated together in a standard text book. In this way I am trying to make the subject 'alive' and relevant for those who may at some stage (whether directly or indirectly) become involved in litigation.

Methods of enquiry

The 'windows' which I have used to shed light on this subject are an examination of legal files, and in-depth interviews with a number of people who have either a personal experience of litigation, or particular knowledge of this field. Large scale postal surveys of midwives and obstetricians also constituted part of the doctoral research, and reference is made to 'the postal survey' throughout this book. These two surveys were collated and published in 1998. The citation in the reference list is Symon (1998).

The book's approach is broad, being socio-medico-legal. The eclecticism of socio-legal enquiry is well known, and while this creates some difficulty in establishing a narrow definition of socio-legal research, its diverse and inter-disciplinary nature is also held to be one of its main strengths. Its empirical character contrasts with the more theoretical sociology of law, and it is hoped that the discussion in this book will help to promote a clearer understanding of the experience (as opposed to the theory) of litigation in maternity care. The intention is to open up the subject and make it relevant to those working in clinical areas. It will provide answers to some questions about the extent and significance of litigation, but equally it raises other questions.

The examination of legal files was carried out in the premises of the Central Legal Office in Edinburgh (which deals with all aspects of health service litigation in Scotland), and in the legal departments of two English areas (one a former health authority, the other a large city hospital). More detail about these files is given in *Appendix II*. Given the lack of an existing model of enquiry regarding medico-legal files, the approach most closely resembled that of grounded theory. This allowed for a multi-dimensional picture to be constructed from a sequential analysis which made use of both quantitative and qualitative data. The assembled picture comprises aspects which relate to clinical management as well as organisational policy and the civil justice system. This inevitably makes for a rather complex portrait and, in an attempt to shed further light on a number of the topics which had been identified, a series of interviews was arranged.

In all 30 people were interviewed, 21 of whom had responded to the earlier postal survey (these had all indicated that they were prepared to be contacted with a view to being interviewed at a later date). These 21 comprised 16 midwives (including a midwifery manager, a labour ward manager, a senior lecturer, and one who practised independently) and five obstetricians (a medical director, three consultants and one registrar). These were chosen because of their varying experience of and views concerning litigation. Added to this purposive sample were another consultant obstetrician, a neonatologist, three lawyers (including a Queen's Counsel), a legal department official, and three representatives from consumer groups (two from Action for Victims of Medical Accidents [AVMA], and one who stressed that she spoke in a personal capacity).

Occasional reference is also made in this book to earlier interviews which were conducted for an undergraduate dissertation (Symon, 1992). An opportunistic sample of 14 midwives and two consultant obstetricians was augmented by another two midwives known to have a direct experience of litigation. A discussion surrounding the findings of some of these interviews was later published in the *British Journal of Midwifery* (Symon, 1994).

Qualitative research is usually small scale, and the intention was not to reflect a representative sample but to explore a range of subjectively-held positions. A phenomenological approach aims to provide an accurate description of 'lived experience'; in this case the experience (or the fear) of litigation. The intention is that these views and experiences should help to promote a more informed debate about the true significance of perinatal litigation.

As a health service practitioner working in a maternity unit throughout the course of this research, and with an academic background in Social Policy and Law, it is only right that I should admit to bringing a level of experiential knowledge to this research. No research is value-free, and it is intellectually dishonest to pretend that an investigator with background knowledge and experience could discount all of this when analysing and interpreting results. Far from being a hindrance, this allows for a considerable degree of 'engaged reasoning' – interpreting the significance of the findings from an existing understanding of the subject.

Proposals for each part of the research were submitted to the Research Committee of the Department of Social Policy at the University of Edinburgh. This committee concluded that neither the examination of legal files nor the survey of clinical practitioners and others involved in the legal process required specific approval by an ethics committee.

Structure of the book

The whole topic of medical litigation is one which is developing rapidly, and it is impossible within one volume to cover every area comprehensively. Indeed, the subject matter of many of the chapters may be books in their own right. Given the enormity of the subject matter, any attempt to explore it will leave some areas covered only thinly. However, in an attempt to cover the subject in reasonable depth I have selected 26 different aspects for particular discussion.

Briefly, *Part I* sets out the theoretical basis for negligence litigation within the health service. It examines the nature of accountability as it applies to professionals in the NHS (particularly obstetricians and midwives), contrasts the various types of accountability, and directs the reader to the related discussions in *Part II*. *Part I* sets the background to litigation, and is largely theoretical. *Part II*, by contrast, widens the discussion, and from the findings of the research noted above, evaluates obstetric litigation from a number of different angles.

Part II is set out in an A–Z format which is, of course, an artificial construct, that may appear as if there is no logical sequence to the chapters. However, getting a consensus of opinion on what would be a logical sequence is impossible: what one person might consider a logical starting point (I have started with accountability) might not be to everyone's taste. For some the debate about cerebral palsy or why people sue might be where to start. The subject is more like a series of overlapping circles than a linear narrative. Since civil litigation aims to restore a successful claimant to the position(s) he would have been in had the adverse event not occurred (ie. the status quo ante), I conclude by asking whether this zero sum game has been attained.

The chosen format allows for a wide discussion of various features of obstetric litigation, and there is inevitably some overlap between different parts of the book. I have tried to minimise repetition within the discussion in each chapter, but not all the topics included in this volume separate out easily into discrete chapters. For example, one incident may be included in discussions relating to fetal monitoring, supervision, documentation, or cerebral palsy. Because of this, some quotes appear more than once. It is intended that this multiple focus approach makes the discussion accessible to those who have an interest in the reality and consequences of legal claims as they are experienced 'on the ground'. In this respect the book is aimed largely at clinically-based practitioners, and those with a knowledge and appreciation of the clinical setting. It is not intended that it should be read cover-to-cover; instead the reader is invited to consult different chapters as the relevance of each becomes apparent, either in day-to-day practice, or in discussions elsewhere. Because some of the discussions overlap, reference to earlier and later chapters is made throughout.

This is not a standard legal text book. While *Part I* sets out the essentials of the theory of medical negligence litigation, it is comparatively brief. *Part II* (the bulk of the book) is concerned with the experience and significance of litigation, since an understanding of these is essential in today's health service. By and large healthcare law is very well reported in standard texts (some of these are cited in the reference list at the end), although one area which is not always well reported is the distinction between Scotland and England in matters of law. While these are rarely of great consequence in terms of medical litigation, there are differences (for example the 'Bolam test' is not used in Scotland), and this does lead me onto an important feature of my research.

Most of the research reported here took place in Scotland, although two areas of England were also examined (several interviewees came from these two areas). This might be seen as a limitation; it cannot be said with certainty whether Scotland and England have significantly divergent experiences of medical litigation, although some of these are discussed in *Chapters 7* and *24*, and in *Appendix II*. Some of the data presented here suggest certain differences, but whether the two English areas under observation are typical of England as a whole I cannot say. There is plenty of scope for future research in this area, but whether anyone will enjoy the range of access which I secured to legal files is (for many reasons) doubtful. In this respect, Scottish litigation (in which all the claims are currently dealt with by a central body) is rather easier to study. For ease of reading for (I presume) the majority of readers I have adopted Anglo-American legal terminology except where this is explicitly inappropriate.

A note about other terminology

In this book I have used the term 'patient', which some readers will dislike. The word has unfortunate connotations (critics claim it connotes sickness when pregnancy and labour are essentially normal physiological life events), but it is at least widely used and universally understood. Most of the alternative terms can be criticised for being either too cumbersome ('user of maternity services') or inappropriate. While 'client' is undoubtedly gaining currency, I feel this connotes a generalist fee-for-service relationship which, like 'customer' and 'consumer', does not apply in publicly-funded health care. I acknowledge the deficiencies of 'patient', and indeed have enjoyed a stimulating correspondence with a lecturer who criticised my use of this term in an article (some of our correspondence is summarised in *Appendix I*). I am not convinced that the term 'client' represents an improvement, and so am reluctant to jump out of the patient's frying pan into the client's fire merely for the sake of change.

Andrew Symon
Perth, April 2000

Part I – Accountability and the law

Section 1

The basis for litigation

Why is there litigation? Litigation is based on the concept that individuals are responsible for what they do – in other words, they are accountable. There are three particular features of accountability as it applies to health service workers which may be termed,

- professional
- contractual
- legal.

Although this book is concerned primarily with litigation under the civil law, I start with a general evaluation of what accountability is. A discussion of professional accountability follows (*Section 2*), looking at the nature of professional misconduct. A short discussion of contractual accountability (*Section 3*) is followed by an explanation of accountability under the civil law (*Section 4*). Several other features of the law which require some initial explanation are covered briefly in *Section 5*.

What is accountability?

We can start by asking what accountability is, and why anyone should be concerned about it. It may seem self-evident that accountability is a good thing, but how may it be described? Greenfield (1975: vii) accepts the definition of accountable as meaning 'subject to giving an account; answerable or capable of being accounted for; explainable'. Accountability, then, is the state or quality of being accountable.

In a modern democracy accountability is highly prized: our elected leaders and many of those in positions of power are held to be answerable for their actions. Greenfield notes that accountability is an ex post concept, in other words it is retrospective; yet as Etzioni (1975) points out, it is not always equally applied – those groups with higher status or more power are able to make any system more accountable to them.

In *Chapter 2* there is a discussion of the claim that we inhabit a 'blame culture' in which we are all too ready to demand that someone is held to account whenever something goes wrong. This is linked to the belief that contemporary society has high expectations (see *Chapter 8*).

Accountability can be linked to the notion of justice: in the formal-rational legal model we are all held to be accountable for our actions (and sometimes for our failures to act). Mashaw (1983: 25–26) considered three types of administrative justice which he described as 'bureaucratic rationality', 'professional treatment' and 'moral judgement'. Whereas moral judgement uses subjective considerations of deservingness, and bureaucratic rationality uses 'instrumentally rational routines designed to render transparent the connection between concrete decisions and legislatively validated policy', (*ibid*: 28) professional treatment is harder to examine, for it involves a mixture of clinical intelligence and scientific knowledge. While this often appears opaque to the lay person, 'the mystery of professional judgement is, nevertheless, acceptable because of the service ideal of professionalism' (*ibid*: 28).

As stated above, there are three types of accountability which may apply to health service workers: professional, contractual, and legal. These are examined in turn. In relation to professional accountability we consider whether Mashaw's claim that professional judgement in matters of accountability is acceptable. Contractual accountability is considered only briefly, since it plays a comparatively minor role in terms of litigation. The law of medical negligence, by which clinical practitioners are held accountable under the civil law, is explored in more depth, and within this section the reader will find directions to much broader discussions and debates which are to be found in *Part II* of this book.

Section 2

Professional accountability

The concerns of professional accountability are two-fold. Firstly, there is the need to ensure that the standards of the profession are maintained so that the general public may benefit and thereby have confidence in it and continue to accord it professional status; and secondly, there is the need to protect the public from practitioners who are not of a competent standard. The General Medical Council (GMC, 1989: 5) sums this up:

> *The primary concerns are to protect the public and to uphold the reputation of the medical profession.*

The United Kingdom Central Council for Nursing, Midwifery and Health Visiting (UKCC, 1989: 6–7) states that the practitioner:

> *should recognise that the interests of public and patient must predominate over those of the practitioner and profession... silently to tolerate poor standards is to act in a manner contrary to the interests of patients or clients, and thus to renege on personal professional accountability.*

It further stresses that advocacy – promoting and safeguarding the well being and interests of patients and clients – is a crucial element of professional accountability.

* Accountability is a critical feature of professionalism. The need for practitioners to accept this is stressed in the discussion in *Chapter 1*.

Professional misconduct

The regulation of professional accountability in medicine and midwifery is very similar: allegations of professional misconduct are notified to the statutory body concerned (GMC or UKCC), as are criminal convictions. Anyone may make such an allegation to the relevant statutory body, although there is a practice within the GMC whereby staff may suggest to the person making the allegation that NHS complaints procedures are invoked instead. Montgomery (1996) notes that this practice has no statutory basis and has, unsurprisingly, attracted criticism.

The Medical Act 1969 states that the GMC must investigate allegations of 'serious professional misconduct'; this definition replaced the earlier definition (from the 1858 Medical Act) of 'infamous conduct in a professional respect'.

> *Any abuse by a doctor of any privileges and opportunities afforded to him or any grave dereliction of professional duty or serious breach of medical ethics may give rise to a charge of serious professional misconduct.*
>
> (GMC, 1989: 9)

Examples include the neglect of professional responsibilities, the abuse of professional skills or privileges, self-promotion or canvassing, or such personal behaviour as the misuse of drugs or alcohol. These are seen as 'habits which are discreditable to the profession and may be a source of danger to the doctor's patients' (*ibid*: 13). The misuse of drugs or alcohol is the single most common cause of reports to the GMC, and it clearly presents a potential danger to the patient which no professional body could ignore.

Procedure – doctors

Allegations concerning doctors go initially to a preliminary screener who is a doctor, and who has, since 1990, been assisted by a lay member of the GMC. If they both agree, the case may go no further. In 1993 half the cases referred to the GMC did not get past this screening stage (GMC, 1993). If it is felt that there is insufficient evidence to establish serious professional misconduct but there are still grounds for concern, the doctor concerned may be asked to make comments on the allegations. In such cases the lay and medical screeners may decide to issue advice to the doctor, so avoiding formal disciplinary proceedings (Payne-James and Smith, 1996).

Those cases which are believed to warrant further investigation next go to the GMC's Preliminary Proceedings Committee. This Committee can dismiss the charge; request further investigations before making a decision; send a letter of advice to the doctor concerned; or refer the matter to the Professional Conduct Committee (PCC) or the Health Committee, in which case it can order immediate interim suspension or immediate conditional registration, stipulating which conditions must be met.

The Professional Conduct Committee can dismiss the case; order erasure from the register, or suspension for up to 12 months; make registration conditional for three years; or can postpone its decision for one year (this acts like a deferred sentence). Periods of suspension and conditional registration may be extended, and the latter penalty may follow on from the former. Conditions may include not practising privately or undertaking further training.

Having been convicted in a court of criminal law (and all criminal convictions are automatically reported to the GMC), a doctor cannot plead innocence before the GMC's Professional Conduct Committee, although it may hear a plea in mitigation (Leahy Taylor, 1982). Any appeal against the decision of the Professional Conduct Committee must be made within 28 days, but an application for restoration to the register cannot be made before ten months have lapsed, and it is usual to wait much longer. The proceedings before the Professional Conduct Committee are very similar to those of a court of law, and a legal assessor (an advocate or barrister) with at least ten years' experience is always present to ensure the legal formalities are observed.

The Health Committee, which was created under the Medical Act 1978, is concerned with protecting the public from doctors who are, through either physical or mental illness, unable to work to an acceptable standard. It can suspend registration for up to 12 months, or make registration conditional for up to three years.

Over the years there has been criticism that the GMC is not able to self-regulate effectively. This was voiced particularly over the Harold Shipman case in 1999. One criticism is that there is no charge less serious than 'serious professional misconduct' which can be made to the GMC. This was addressed by the Medical (Professional Performance) Act 1995, which gives the GMC powers to investigate allegations of 'seriously deficient standard of professional performance'. Those doctors who do not meet the performance standards laid out in the GMC's *Good Medical Practice* (GMC, 1998) may be required to undertake retraining and reassessment. However, there are still concerns that the procedure for examining cases are slow. Weaver (2000) claims that there is a massive backlog (of up to two years) of cases awaiting the fitness to practice procedures.

Procedure – midwives

In the case of allegations referring to midwives the initial proceedings are carried out by a Preliminary Proceedings Committee (PPC) (Heywood Jones, 1999). Until 1992 this stage was carried out by the relevant National Board, of which there are four: one each for Scotland, Wales, Northern Ireland and England. The PPC may decide to close the case with no action; refer the matter to the Professional Conduct Committee (PCC); issue a caution; or refer the case to a Panel of Screeners, who will decide whether the case needs to go to the Health Committee (UKCC, 1998a).

The UKCC Professional Conduct Committee and Health Committee have the same rights of sanction as those of the GMC; erasure from the register is the ultimate sanction of the Professional Conduct Committee which, according to Dimond (1990: 7) is 'concerned with protecting the public from an irresponsible practitioner; its intention is not to punish...', although the removal of livelihood must feel very like punishment.

An appeal to the High Court/Court of Session from the UKCC's Professional Conduct Committee is available, but must be made within three months. The court's decision is final, and it is generally held that a court will only rarely contradict the conclusion of the professional body's own disciplinary process.

Such a case did occur in 1988, however, when a judge ruled that the removal of a nurse from the register was unreasonable, amounting to a breach of natural justice (*Hefferson v UKCC*). The nurse had given the wrong drug to a child, but had realised her mistake quickly and had informed the doctor; no adverse effects were noted in the child. The Professional Conduct Committee believed that the nurse should have informed her nurse manager, but Lord Justice Watkins ruled that 'no reasonable body concerned with the discipline of the profession could have reached this conclusion' (ie. removal) since there had been no danger to the public, and the nurse had not been allowed to cross-examine the child's mother, nor to challenge allegations made about her past conduct after she had been found guilty. Allowing witnesses to be heard after the verdict was a 'quite extraordinary process', the trial judge said. This failure to observe proper legal procedures made the case against the nurse fundamentally flawed.

The UKCC Professional Conduct Committee prides itself on working in a legal manner, and its hearings are held in public. Its procedures are set down in law, and the proof it has to establish must be 'beyond reasonable doubt', as in any court of criminal law. Legal advice is given by an experienced advocate or barrister, as in the GMC's Professional Conduct Committee, and the practitioner in question is entitled to legal representation. Witnesses may be subpoenaed and are sworn in.

If the facts alleged are not proved, the case is dismissed; similarly, if the facts are proved but they do not amount to professional misconduct, the case is dismissed. The PCC may postpone judgement, and may order interim suspension pending the hearing if this is felt to be in the public interest. If the allegations are held to have been proved, and if they amount to misconduct, the PCC has a range of options. It may order indefinite removal from all or parts of the register; it may suspend the practitioner for a specified period, after which (s)he may apply formally for restoration; it may refer the case to the Health Committee if this is thought appropriate; or it may issue a caution. Exceptionally, it may postpone its judgement to allow the respondent to produce further information (UKCC, 1998a). Further details of the procedures of the UKCC Professional Conduct Committee can be found in Dimond (1994a).

The Health Committee is more informal and meets in private. If it decides that a practitioner's fitness to work is not impaired by ill health, it will dismiss the matter; alternatively it can postpone judgement pending further details, in which case interim suspension may be ordered; it can refer the matter to the PCC or Panel of Screeners; and in very serious cases can order suspension or removal from the register.

By allowing investigations into alleged misconduct which do not occur in the workplace, the UKCC attempts to ensure that all those who are entitled to practise are deemed worthy of the public's respect, whether or not the practitioner is currently employed. The UKCC's Code of Professional Conduct (UKCC, 1992: 1) begins with this instruction:

> *Each registered nurse, midwife and health visitor shall act, at all times, in such a manner as to justify public trust and confidence, to uphold and enhance the good standing and reputation of the profession....*

Such an aim may be thought to be a lofty one, but misconduct is viewed very seriously and removal from the register is for 'conduct unworthy'. Carson and Montgomery (1989: 41) point out that 'evidence of dishonesty or drug abuse is often taken as sufficient justification for removal from the register'. The professions are concerned that their image is good, and they use the threat of removal from the register to encourage good behaviour.

Section 3

Contractual accountability

Contractual accountability concerns employment law, and relates to the mutual accountability of employer and employee. An employer is accountable to its employees in that it must provide a safe working environment. An employee must work in a safe and competent manner, having due regard for colleagues and patients/clients, and failure to do so may mean that the terms of the contract have not been met.

A contract of employment will determine the mechanisms of the grievance and disciplinary processes. By invoking the appropriate mechanism, either employer or employee may hold the other accountable. It is worth bearing in mind that there is no single contract of employment which covers health care workers in any particular discipline, and that terms and conditions may therefore vary from one employer to another.

Contract law has in the past been used in terms of litigation concerning alleged negligence. Most practitioners in maternity care are employed by the NHS, and so contract law no longer arises. However, for those practising independently or privately, there is a contract between patient and practitioner, and an action under contract law may also be brought. Before the advent of the NHS this was clearly more commonplace.

In what Cameron (1989: 9) calls 'the male chauvinistic society of former times' the question of title to sue was relevant. In *Lanphier v Phipos* it was held that although it was the woman who had suffered from the negligent care of a 'surgeon and apothecary', both the husband and the wife had to pursue the action because it was the husband who had employed the medical man. This defence was attempted in *Edgar v Lamont*, where the doctor claimed that he did not have a contractual relationship with the woman since her husband had employed him, and that therefore she did not have a title to sue; it was held, however, that the woman had a good action in tort/delict against the doctor.

Carson and Montgomery (1989: 6) claim that there is no basis for negligence litigation in contract law: 'Nurses give services to their patients but patients do not give anything in return. Praise and boxes of chocolates do not count.' Most authorities would agree with this view, although in a textbook on 'Delict' (tort is the equivalent in the English legal system), Walker states:

> *Where patients call in a doctor participating in the NHS these facts may raise a contract between them.*

(Walker, 1981: 1057)

Blackie (1985) points out that the relationship is non-contractual, since the doctor is performing an obligation under the NHS Acts, a view leant weight in the case of *Pfizer Corporation v Ministry of Health*. In practice, when someone brings an action alleging negligence by a doctor, nurse or midwife, it is usual for the employing authority to be sued (see below).

Section 4

Legal accountability

Legal accountability may apply in either a civil or a criminal context: while liable in a civil sense for issues of negligence, a hospital employee is as liable to prosecution for a criminal offence as anyone else. There is an old obstetric case in which a doctor was both sued and prosecuted: in *R v Bateman* a doctor, who was also sued in the civil courts, was prosecuted for manslaughter after an unsuccessful attempt at instrumental delivery, and an attempted internal version which was followed by a stillbirth. The woman became very ill, and was transferred to the infirmary five days later, but died on the seventh day. It was held that the doctor was negligent – he was found guilty of the charge of manslaughter, and was sentenced to six months imprisonment (this was quashed on appeal).

More recently this issue has been resurrected. In *R v Prentice and Sullman* two young doctors were found guilty of manslaughter after they had wrongly injected a drug into the spine of a 16-year-old who had leukaemia, and both received suspended sentences of nine months. The prosecution in this case succeeded in its assertion that the doctors' action amounted to 'criminal failures'. A further case in 1997 was referred to the Crown Prosecution Service after an obstetrician allegedly pulled too hard and too long during a forceps delivery, as a result of which the baby died some hours after birth (Henderson, 1997).

Most legal actions concerning allegations against clinical practitioners are brought under the law of negligence, and indeed this is the only means whereby a patient may secure financial compensation. The law of negligence is part of the common law, and is a fundamental feature of a modern civil society. Accountability, in a social as well as a professional context, determines that we are responsible for what we do, and at times for what we fail to do.

In order to secure compensation it is necessary to establish three things. The first is whether the practitioner concerned owed a duty of care to the patient; the second is whether this duty was breached (the standard of care argument); and the third is whether damage flowed from this breach (this is known as causation).

The duty of care

The 'duty of care' principle stems from the judgement given in the case of *Donoghue v Stevenson* 1932, where it was stated that a duty of care would be owed, for example, by me to 'persons who are so closely and directly affected by my acts that I ought reasonably to have them in contemplation as being so affected when I am directing my mind to the acts or omissions which are called in question' (from Lord Atkin's judgement). For this reason this test is sometimes known as the 'Good Neighbour' test. It will be remembered from the chapter above on contractual accountability that an employer and employee owe each other a duty of care.

As it applies to the law of medical negligence this requirement, in practice, causes little argument. It is rarely denied that a practitioner owed such a duty to a patient, although this may be questioned in the situation where a woman goes into labour in a public place. A passing obstetrician or midwife who had had no reason to meet the woman before might claim that they owed no duty of care to her. Probably the most common example of a challenge to the claim that a duty of care was owed relates to the victims of an accident. There is no legal obligation to render assistance in such a situation, although it might well be claimed that there is a moral or indeed a professional obligation to do so (UKCC, 1996;

GMC, 1998). In practice most obstetric claims relate to care given under the NHS, and the question of the duty of care is not an issue.

The standard of care

The next question is whether the practitioner(s) concerned acted properly. The legal test in England and Wales by which a practitioner's actions are judged is known as the Bolam test (from *Bolam v Friern HMC* 1957); in Scotland the equivalent is *Hunter v Hanley* (1955). In Bolam it was held that:

> *A doctor is not guilty of negligence if he has acted in accordance with a practice accepted as proper by a responsible body of medical men skilled in that particular art.*
>
> (per McNair J @ 121)

In *Hunter v Hanley* the judge, Lord President Clyde, stated:

> *The true test for establishing negligence on the part of a doctor is whether he has been proven to be guilty of such failure as no doctor of ordinary skill would be guilty of if acting with ordinary care... it must be established that the course the doctor adopted is one which no professional man of ordinary skill would have taken if he had been acting with ordinary care.*

The two definitions of medical negligence are not identical, and there is a view which holds that the test for establishing negligence in Scotland is that much harder (Howie, 1983). By and large, however, the two judgements are considered to approach the question of clinical culpability in the same way. The Bolam test holds that a practitioner's actions are safe as long as they are in accordance with a responsible body of medical opinion (and in this discussion the term 'medical' covers the field of midwifery). Not all jurisdictions allow professions this much latitude in determining an acceptable standard of practice. Phillips (1997: 20) notes that:

> *Australian law may be setting an example in asserting the primacy of the court's view of acceptable practice, diminishing the impact of common practice, in the recent decision in Rogers v Whitaker.*

✳ Some of the recent criticism of the Bolam test is explored in *Chapter 23*.

It may be asked how standards are maintained within health care, and a number of answers are traditionally offered. Some see health service work as vocational, there being a moral imperative on the part of each practitioner to do his or her best. Some argue that the fear of disciplinary action or litigation is a deterrent against substandard practice: indeed, it is one of the claims of a tort system that it has a deterrent aspect. Others will argue that effective training, post-registration education and supervision are the most effective guarantors of good clinical practice. There has certainly been a growth in the awareness of the need to regulate practice: the Medical (Professional Performance) Act 1995, the establishment of the National Institute for Clinical Excellence (NICE), and the statutory requirement for midwifery supervision, all point towards the desire to maintain clinical standards.

✳ The work of NICE and the Commission for Health Improvements is discussed in *Chapter 16*, while supervision is considered in *Chapter 19*.

The law also recognises that within health care there is room for differences of opinion over clinical practice, and that a court's preference for one body of opinion over another is no basis for a conclusion of negligence. This was stressed by the House of Lords in *Maynard v West Midlands RHA* in 1984.

In determining what is a reasonable standard of care, the court will often examine local or national protocols and guidelines. It is generally held that providing these are research or evidence-based, and providing that they have been adequately disseminated to the relevant practitioners, then it is reasonable to expect that clinicians will adhere to them. Clinicians have a professional responsibility to keep up-to-date with local protocols, although there may be circumstances in which a practitioner would be justified in not following a protocol or guideline.

* The debate about the growth of protocols and guidelines and possible justifications for not following them, is discussed in *Chapter 16*.

The failure to make an accurate diagnosis is not of itself evidence of negligence, but the failure to take steps to make such a diagnosis is more likely to be. In *Wood v Thurston* it was heard that a Casualty Officer had neither examined nor X-rayed a patient who came in with a history of having been seen under a moving lorry; the man was smelling strongly of alcohol and did not complain of any pain and the doctor sent him home. He died the following day, and at post mortem it was found that he had eighteen fractured ribs and extensive lung damage; the failure even to take steps to diagnose this was held to be negligent. From this it may be inferred that there is a 'reasonableness' test involved, and this is a line which is taken up by Norrie (1987: 93):

> *The law expects the experienced to show more skill than the inexperienced... the concept of reasonableness allows the court to reflect that expectation.*

Once the plaintiff has shown that no reasonable practitioner would have acted as the defendant did, the burden of proof shifts to the defendant to show that he did not cause the injury.

While many cases of negligence relate to specific acts by one or more practitioners, negligence may also result from an omission, for example in communication. In *Coles v Reading HMC* the failure to impress on a man who had presented at a cottage hospital with a crush injury to his finger that he should go to the nearest general hospital to receive a tetanus injection, was held to be negligent. The man had gone to see his GP instead, had not received a tetanus injection due to poor communication between the GP and the cottage hospital, and had subsequently died of tetanus.

Liability cannot be inferred simply when something goes wrong (the question of fault and no fault liability are discussed in *Chapter 11*). This view was given express approval in *Rolland v Lothian Health Board* in 1981. The judge, Lord Ross, stated:

> *If medical and nursing staff were to be found liable when anything untoward occurred, that would have an adverse effect on the medical and nursing professions and on the public generally.*

Brazier (1987: 76) picks up on this point of muzzling innovation: 'If liability in negligence automatically followed once harm resulted from the adoption of a novel method of treatment, medical progress would be stultified.'

There is the possibility of suing successfully even where the exact nature of the alleged negligence cannot in fact be proven, under the doctrine of *res ipsa loquitur* (roughly, 'the thing speaks for itself'). This may be used when the events alleged by the plaintiff are held to establish a prima facie case of negligence. The favourite textbook examples of this doctrine in relation to medical negligence claims are cases where swabs have been left inside a patient during an operation (eg. *Mahon v Osbourne* 1939; *Cooper v Nevill* 1961). Another example is seen in *Cassidy v Ministry of Health* in which a man went into hospital for an operation on his left hand because of two stiff fingers. When he was discharged he had four stiff fingers and his hand was useless. Of this Lord Denning said:

> *I am quite clearly of the opinion that that raises a prima facie case against the hospital authorities... they have nowhere explained how it could happen without negligence.*

Experts

In most cases the question of whether the standard of care has been met is determined by the opinions of expert witnesses. In a legal case each side nominate one or more experts who will produce an opinion based on the available evidence (usually this consists of the case notes, the importance of which is discussed in *Chapter 14*).

One of the hallmarks of a profession is that it reserves the right to decide just what is acceptable. Klein (1973: 3) notes that, 'It is for professional colleagues, not the user of the services, to judge the appropriateness and the competence of the skills applied.' This view does not go unchallenged, however. Norrie (1985: 137) claims that medicine should be just as accountable as other occupations, 'It is nothing short of dangerous complacency to assume that they (doctors) are safe from legal criticism if they do only as their neighbours do.'

This view seemed to be backed up by Sir John Donaldson MR when he gave judgement in the case of Sidaway:

> *The definition of a duty of care is a matter for the law and the court... in a word, the law will not permit the medical profession to play God.*

Despite this, courts in Britain appear to have been happy to accept, within the bounds of reasonableness, that in medical matters medical people are best placed to decide what is a satisfactory standard of care. The expert's opinion will state whether it is believed that the relevant practitioner's conduct fell within the scope of acceptable clinical practice. If the experts from each side cannot agree, the case may have to go to the court stage. In this event the experts may be required to give evidence, and the case will be decided by a judge.

The opinion should not take into account any information which was not known to the practitioner at the time. Advances in knowledge or developments in clinical practice since the time in question must not form part of the expert's opinion. Given that there is frequently a long gap between an event and subsequent legal investigation (see *Chapter 15*), it may be difficult to determine exactly what was felt to be an appropriate standard of care. This is discussed further in *Section 5* on 'Limitation'.

A problem does however occur when 'expert witnesses' disagree with one another; in *Whitehouse v Jordan* it was felt that 'expert opinion' must be seen to be the independent expert opinion of a specialist, and not partisan.

> *While some degree of consultation between experts and legal advisers is entirely proper, it is necessary that expert evidence presented to the court should be, and should be seen to be, the independent product of the expert uninfluenced as to form or content by the exigencies of litigation. To the extent that it is not, the evidence is likely to be not only incorrect, but also self-defeating.*
>
> (Wilberforce LJ, cited by Hodgson, 1981: 2)

* Some of the debate about the role and expertise of experts is considered in *Chapter 5*. In *Chapter 25* the question of the use of experts by some solicitors is also discussed.

Causation

The final test which determines whether compensation can be awarded is known as causation. Once it is established that the duty of care exists and has been breached, it must be shown that this breach led directly to a recognisable form of damage. Heads of claim (in other words the claimed 'damage') are detailed in *Chapter 7*. This is summed up in *Miller v Minister of Pensions* (1947):

> *... but for the defendant's fault, on the balance of probability, the injury complained of... would not have occurred.*

The debate in many legal cases centres on the question of whether the practitioner's conduct caused the condition which is the subject of the litigation. A causal link between event and outcome ought not to be assumed and, in many legal cases causation has been one of the most critical features associated with obtaining compensation. Was the practitioner's act (or failure to act) the cause of the plaintiff's condition? In this 'the plaintiff' denotes whichever member of the family is the subject of the legal action: this could be the mother, the child, or the father. This is a wide area, covering issues as disparate as brain damage in the child, severe pain or bodily injury in the mother, and psychological trauma in the father. It should be noted that this last situation may be problematic, but this head of claim has apparently become more common in recent years (Bradley, 1998).

The causal connection is crucial within a fault-based legal system: without it a plaintiff cannot successfully claim damages. Given its legal importance, much time is spent by both plaintiff and defendant arguing over the question of causation which is determined on the balance of probability. This requires a 51% onus of proof, which creates its own anomalies: 'one percent separates the "good doctor" from the "bad doctor"... the same margin separates plaintiffs awarded millions from those who lose out entirely' (Akazaki, 1999: 9).

In New Zealand, which has introduced no-fault compensation for medical accidents, the question of causation is still very pertinent: damage must be shown to flow from the accident. It would be a mistake to conclude that removing the need to establish fault (as advocated by the British Medical Association) would circumvent this particular legal argument.

* The debates about balancing fault and need, and the question of no-fault compensation are discussed in *Chapter 6*.

In an English case in the Court of Appeal, which subsequently went to the House of Lords, (*Bolitho v City & Hackney HA*) there was an attempt by one of the judges to restrict the scope of expert witnesses to determine the question of causation. He distinguished applying the Bolam principle (equivalent to the *Hunter v Hanley* principle in Scots law) to the standard of care criterion, and applying it to the question of causation. Had this move been successful and become an established legal principle, considerable leeway would be given to the courts to disregard the evidence brought on behalf of a defendant – a prospect which some lawyers clearly relish. Goldrein (1994) claims it is surprising that the courts have allowed the medical profession to retain this sovereignty over evidence when they (the courts) have jealously asserted their rights to determine such matters in other fields.

However, as the law stands, considerable weight is given to the views of expert witnesses with regard to the question of causation as well as to whether the practitioner's conduct constituted a breach of the duty of care. Supportive opinions will be sought by each side, and negotiations made based on these reports. Since this matter is so crucial to the chances of success of a legal action, it is instructive to explore the difficulties sometimes encountered in establishing causation.

In order to establish a causal link between a clinical incident and a pathological or psychological condition, several requirements must be met. Before any case can proceed, the plaintiff must show that such a condition does exist, and usually this must be confirmed by medical opinion. The condition may be well known, for instance a child may have been long diagnosed as suffering from cerebral palsy. Other conditions too may be obvious and well documented for that individual: an Erb's palsy in a baby, for example, or an area of alopecia on a child's head; in a mother a postpartum haemorrhage or postnatal urinary or faecal incontinence would be easily diagnosed and beyond serious dispute. The least disputable circumstances are the discovery of a gauze swab which has been accidentally left inside the patient after a procedure is completed. Such cases are considered under the term *res ipsa loquitur* ('the thing speaks for itself').

In other situations, establishing that a pathological condition exists may be more problematic: nerve damage may cause relatively non-specific symptoms, including backache; spinal or pelvic injuries may be attributable to a pre-existing condition or a previous trauma; and diminished or absent eyesight in a child may not be assessable for some time. Until a condition can be established, and a causal connection made between that and a clinician's negligent conduct, a case cannot be settled nor damages quantified. In the case of cerebral palsy the diagnosis may not be made for some time after the child's birth, and parents who have had a baby who was asphyxiated at birth and who suspect that the child may be handicapped as a result may well wait with trepidation to see whether the child shows signs of cerebral palsy in the months following delivery. Perhaps hardest of all to assess and quantify are the psychological effects of a traumatic delivery or other incident. In order to obtain compensation under this head of claim it is not enough to demonstrate that the person in question has experienced emotional distress. Bradley (1998: 227) notes that 'gruesomeness is an important factor', and that the response to the event may include 'intense fear, helplessness, or horror' (*ibid*: 226).

✳ Some of the difficulties with establishing causation are considered in *Chapter 13*.

Litigation

There is certainly a strong perception, going back some time, that litigation has increased and that this is a world-wide phenomenon (Jakobovits, 1996). In 1983 Howie (1983: 193) claimed: 'One of the more notable developments in the field of medical law has been the marked increase in the number of actions brought against doctors and other health service staff for professional negligence.' Such received wisdom is difficult to verify, for as Blackie (1985: 563) states, 'reliable accurate information as to the number of claims for damages, the success rate, the amounts paid and their mode of disposal is unfortunately unobtainable.' Nevertheless, the impression of a high incidence of claims is created by the RCOG, whose booklet *How to avoid medico-legal problems in Obstetrics and Gynaecology* notes at the start that:

> *There are few practising obstetricians and gynaecologists who have not experienced allegations of medical negligence against them.*
>
> (Sharp and Chamberlain, 1992:1)

Sheikh and Hurwitz (1999: 554) note that studies in Australia and the USA have estimated that errors occur in between 4% and 45% of hospital admissions, and conclude that 'such widely varying rates (reflect) to a large degree differences in definition.' Ham *et al* (1988: 8) found that figures for 'accidents' were not routinely collected. Before NHS indemnity was introduced for NHS hospital doctors in 1990, the Department of Health (DoH) left the concerns of medical litigation to the Medical Defence Organisations. If the rate of medical error is not known, its relationship to litigation is impossible to ascertain, although Dingwall *et al* (1991) claim that only a small proportion of iatrogenic events result in litigation. This claim is confirmed by studies in California and New York State, which are discussed in *Chapter 21*.

Despite this apparent reluctance to sue (and possible justifications for suing are discussed in *Chapter 10*), data released by the medical defence organisations (MDOs) suggested a rapidly increasing number of claims – and subsequent cost of litigation – in the 1980s (Ham *et al*, 1988; MPS, 1989). However, for reasons of commercial confidentiality specific figures by specialty have not been disclosed, although local studies have attempted this (eg. Law *et al*, 1996). Nevertheless, it was apparent that obstetrics and gynaecology was the specialty most heavily implicated in rising levels of damages (quantum is discussed in *Chapter 17*).

However, until very recently there has been no systematic central collation of incidents of perinatal litigation in either Scotland or England, which has made analysis of the phenomenon problematic. Some studies have concentrated solely on certain outcomes (Ennis and Vincent, 1990), an approach which, while valid in terms of drawing lessons for risk management, may misrepresent the true nature of the problem. Several studies have been conducted which have obtained data from a limited number of files (Hawkins and Paterson, 1987; Capstick and Edwards, 1990; Doherty and James, 1994), and while many of their conclusions are eminently sensible, it is not known how representative these samples were. Dingwall *et al* (1991) note that the 'long tail problem' – the time it takes to initiate an action – makes discerning a trend problematic: in the USA, year-to-year fluctuations have been noted in some States.

In *Appendix II* the incidence of obstetric litigation in Scotland from 1980–1995 is detailed. The rate of litigation, measured in deliveries per legal claim, is also shown and a limited cross-border comparison (based on a smaller sample of English files) is described.

Section 5

Features of the law

There are a number of aspects of the civil law as it relates to medical negligence claims which need briefly to be discussed. The reader will be directed to further discussions and considerations in the main part of this book. The four topics covered here clearly do not represent comprehensive coverage of health-related law. At the end of this section are references to medico-legal texts.

Consent

A fundamental basis for health care treatment in terms of maternity care is that valid consent exists. While litigation which concerns allegations of negligence rarely involves issues of consent, it is nevertheless such a vital factor in all forms of treatment that a short explanation is required.

Consent rests on the question of autonomy. While an autonomous person has the right to consent to treatment, (s)he may also refuse treatment, even if that refusal will lead to death. In the case of a pregnant woman there is also the question of the unborn baby, but this does not alter the right of a pregnant woman to refuse any treatment. The unborn baby has no legal rights as such, only potential rights. This was the view of the court in the Appeal Court case of *re* MB, where it was explicitly stated that a mentally competent pregnant woman may refuse any treatment even if that will result in her own death or that of her baby. Her refusal does not have to appear sensible to health care professionals.

Failing to secure consent to any treatment may leave a practitioner open to an accusation of trespass. A trespass may be considered 'battery' if there is actual touching, and 'assault' if there is a perception of unlawful touching. These issues are covered, respectively, by the civil and criminal law. Securing valid consent is a complete defence to either charge. It is not necessary for harm to be caused: in itself the trespass is sufficient grounds for an action.

There is no explicit form of consent required by the law. 'Consent forms', routinely used prior to surgical procedures, merely formalise the taking of consent. Consent may be given by other means – verbally, or by implication. If there is a dispute about whether or not consent has been given, written evidence may of course carry considerable weight.

Consent touches issues of negligence when it is claimed that consent could not properly be obtained because of a failure on the part of a practitioner to fulfil his/her duty of care in terms of giving information. Negligence may be alleged that a doctor or midwife owes a duty to inform a patient of certain risks. The question then turns on how remote a risk must be mentioned. This was the basis of *Sidaway v Bethlem Royal Hospital*, in which one of the House of Lords judges said that deciding which risks should be explained, and the manner of doing so:

> ... *is as much an exercise of clinical skill and judgement as any other part of the doctor's comprehensive duty of care to the individual patient.*
>
> (per Lord Diplock @ 659)

In other words the Bolam test concerning the standard of care applied and the court rejected the notion of 'informed consent' (which was seen as an American formulation). There are certainly difficulties with ensuring that a patient has understood the implication of a particular course of action, particularly if the practitioner in question has difficulty in either understanding or conveying a sense of the degree of risk (see *Chapter 18*).

* Several descriptors (implied, rational, informed) may be attached to the term 'consent'. These are considered further in *Chapter 3*.

Limitation

There are many problems associated with the typically lengthy legal process. These include distress to practitioners which is compounded by the long gap between event and investigation (examined in *Chapter 9*); and problems with investigating the relevant events because the case notes are inadequate or missing (*Chapter 14*), or because memories are poor (*Chapter 22*).

The Limitation Act 1980 seeks to restrict the time in which a legal action can be brought: in most cases this is three years. The three-year period begins on the date on which the alleged injury occurred, or three years from the date on which the affected person could reasonably have been expected to know that a legal action was possible. In one respect this limitation is practical: it effectively excludes a potentially large number of claims which could otherwise be brought by any person over injuries which are alleged to have been caused in the distant past. The difficulties in pursuing such legal actions would make most cases impractical.

As far as obstetric litigation is concerned, this protection is only partial. The three-year time period does not start until the age of minority has been exceeded, which is at age 18. This means that legal actions can be initiated up to 21 years after the birth in question, and courts have the discretion to extend the period of limitation.

By the time the period of limitation has expired, the plaintiffs must have lodged a writ if they are to have any chance of obtaining compensation. After the writ has been lodged, the legal process may still take many years to run its course.

* Some of the particular problems with lengthy legal actions are examined in *Chapter 15*.

Cerebral palsy

A detailed discussion of cerebral palsy, and of the various possible markers which might help practitioners to predict its occurrence, is given in *Appendix III*. Of all the clinical procedures used in maternity care, cerebral palsy is probably most closely linked with electronic fetal monitoring.

* The importance of such monitoring is evaluated in *Chapter 13*.

Costs

Compensation is the ultimate goal of litigation (although there are other claimed motives as well, see *Chapter 10*). It is largely because of the costs involved that obstetric litigation has received so much attention. Costs are escalating: a recent Court of Appeal case has ruled that 'damages for pain, suffering, and loss of amenity for the most severely injured claimants should go up by a third from the previous maximum of £150,000' (Dyer, 2000: 891). As the upward trend in costs continues it becomes ever more important for the health service to contain litigation. It is estimated that in both England and Scotland as much as 65% and 70% respectively of the total cost of NHS negligence litigation is attributable to obstetric claims (personal communications: CNST; CLO). It is, of course, the cerebral palsy claims which account for this.

* Compensation is awarded under a number of different headings (including pain and suffering; and past and future financial losses), and these are detailed in *Chapter 17*.

Part I of this book has been concerned with covering the essentials of the law related to medical negligence claims. Negligence litigation is only one part of health care law, and those who wish to examine its many other aspects are directed towards the references and further reading below.
    Part II now takes obstetric litigation and examines it from a number of different angles.

References and further reading

Dimond B (1994a) *The Legal Aspects of Midwifery*. Books for Midwives Press, Hale

Dimond B (1999b) *Patients' Rights, Responsibilities and the Nurse*. Quay Books, Mark Allen Publishing Ltd, Salisbury

Mason K, McCall Smith R (1999) *Law and Medical Ethics*. 5th edn. Butterworths, London

Montgomery J (1997) *Health Care Law*. Oxford University Press, Oxford

Norrie K (1987) Reasonable: the keystone of negligence. *J Med Ethics* **13**(2): 92–94

Payne-James J, Dean P, Wall I (1996) *Medico-legal Essentials in Healthcare*. Churchill Livingstone, New York, Edinburgh, London

Part II – Obstetric litigation from A–Z

Chapter 1

A Accountability

Since accountability is one of the key features of litigation, it is worth exploring some of the debate about what it actually means. In the earlier series of interviews, one respondent noted:

> *I have to think of litigation because I am a midwife, and therefore I am accountable for my own actions.*

This sums up very neatly the relationship between accountability and litigation. It also demonstrates an acceptance of the implications of accountability. However, not all practitioners would appear to have such a forthright grasp of these implications, and there are various aspects of accountability which are not always as straightforward as they might at first seem. This chapter discusses some of these and, as with the discussion in *Part I*, directs the reader towards related discussions contained in later chapters.

We can start by asking in what ways practitioners are accountable. Doctors qualify after a five or six-year spell at university, but must complete a year in clinical practice before they are fully registered practitioners. Provisional registration during this period means that they are still accountable for what they do, but in theory they have adequate supervision so that they are not placed in the position of being required to do something beyond their competence. Both the statutory body and professional organisation for midwives are quite clear on when individual accountability begins. According to the UKCC (1993: 12), the midwife should 'assume on registration the responsibilities and accountability for her practice as a midwife', while the RCM (1992: 3) talks of, 'autonomous, accountable practitioners from the point of registration'.

There is a possible complicating factor in the role of the newly qualified midwife who under statutory definition is an accountable practitioner, but who is now being encouraged to undergo a period of supervision under a preceptorship (or mentorship) scheme. This aims to broaden and deepen the competence and ability of the newly qualified practitioner who is prepared for 'safe practice at the point of registration' (UKCC, 1992b: 3). As Jackson (1994) notes, since a midwife is deemed to be individually accountable from the day she qualifies and could quite legally set up in independent practice that day, this period of supervision is anachronistic. Recent research has evaluated the question of fitness to practice (Peach, 1999; Fleming *et al*, 2000).

This degree of confusion may account for the apparent reluctance on the part of some midwives to accept the full degree of accountability which professional status entails, a stance which – for some – apparently outlasts the period of extra supervision following registration.

Some respondents commented that there is an ostensible belief that being employed by the NHS provides an individual with some sort of special protection:

> *I don't have any more responsibility than any other midwife. I'm doing exactly the same job as they're doing. They are as responsible and accountable working in an obstetric unit as I am caring for somebody at home...*

(Independent midwife)

> *I think we all recognise deep down that we are accountable for our actions – intelligent midwives do – but you still have few who say 'The doctor will cover me.' Once you knock that out of them and say 'You can't hide behind the doctor: the buck stops with you,' that panics them. You have to say it, because they have got to realise that they are accountable.*

(Midwifery lecturer)

The NHS, as an employer, is variously liable for what its employees do while acting within the scope of their contracts. This means that the NHS will pay any compensation awarded for the negligent conduct of its employees. Given that such awards may be very high (see *Chapter 17*), it is possible that an employing authority will try to recoup these costs from the relevant employee. There is one report of a Trust hospital attempting to do just that (Dimond, 1994b), although to date such a move has not succeeded. However, given the implications of large compensation payouts for Trusts, it is possible that such moves will be attempted again. While it is not mandatory, practitioners are encouraged to be a member of a professional body or trade union, or otherwise carry insurance cover.

The present legal system is fault-based, and there is a requirement for a litigant to establish negligence in order to obtain compensation. Some of the difficulties of such a system are discussed in *Chapter 6*. There have been claims that the fault requirement is too high a hurdle and that a no-fault system would be fairer, although this is not a view shared by all. One respondent, referring to 'cavalier doctors', noted:

> *If you took away that – albeit not terribly useful – element of accountability, they wouldn't worry at all. You wonder what* (particularly consultant) *obstetricians would feel they could get away with.*

(AVMA official)

This uncharitable view, not surprisingly, was not shared by some of the medical respondents. One replied:

> *... some form of no fault insurance, a no-fault scheme, would save an awful lot of litigation... I see no reason why one couldn't maintain the accountability of individuals.*

(Consultant obstetrician 4)

There are certainly claims that accountability for practitioners has been maintained in New Zealand, which has had a no-fault scheme for over 25 years (see *Chapter 6*). The professional bodies in Britain are charged with maintaining standards, although there has been some increasing lay and state influence in these matters in recent years (see *Section 4*, 'The standard of care', *p.11* in *Part I*).

The concept of professionalism, which underpins the specific nature of accountability which relates to health care practitioners, is traditionally bound up with notions of control. While there are competing views of what constitutes a profession, a critical feature is that it claims some sort of monopoly. Professional groups, in essence, claim to be able to do something specialist which is beyond the scope of the lay person. Acquiring state recognition of this occupational monopoly is a key step (Berlant, 1975); the group then maintains its exclusivity through restricting competition from outside bodies. Medicine can be seen as the role model for other groups which aspire to professional status, and in this midwifery has copied the medical model closely. A central legislative board maintains a register of those legally allowed to use the term 'midwife', and a professional conduct committee considers allegations of misconduct against those on the register.

These elements of autonomy are a crucial feature of a profession. However, this model of professionalism is inherently hierarchical, since it claims greater knowledge than the lay person. It is ironic that, at a time when most midwives would be content to see themselves described as professionals, the notion of autonomy and control which is bound up with this concept of professionalism is being challenged. Some see these challenges as part of societal shifts, with a far greater emphasis of personal autonomy and a consequent lessening of respect for established professional groups. No more is the professional to be revered or placed upon a pedestal. Such changes may be thought to account for the 'Blame culture' which has apparently grown (this is explored in *Chapter 2*), or for the increase in litigation.

The debate about how much control a professional group should have over its client base is a strong contemporary theme. Government reports in the 1990s (DoH, 1993a; Scottish Office, 1993) stressed the need to allow the pregnant woman to exercise greater control over the management of her pregnancy. The need to give women more information is critical to considerations of consent and choice, which are discussed in *Chapter 3*. While most midwives welcomed these reports and the drive behind them, the intrinsic loss of control has certainly diluted the prestige of professionalism. The whole tenor of these reforms, however, has done nothing to lessen the demands of accountability required of those in professional groups. There is no scope for 'passing the buck':

> *I think a lot of midwives don't take on board the responsibility and accountability that they actually have. They think that if they're working in a hospital they can pass the buck, the buck wouldn't stop with them...*

(Independent midwife)

These elements of accountability may have implications in either a professional or a legal sense. As noted in *Part I*, an allegation of professional misconduct may be made against a practitioner to the statutory body (GMC or UKCC), or an allegation of negligence raised under the civil law. If it is thought that these principles of accountability are being exercised more frequently, it is worth noting that in today's cost-control environment employers may also be more demanding of those whom they employ:

> *I think there are real problems because Trusts are making their consultants much more accountable for their time, as you know, and that's impinging upon writing reports and reading papers, and it's leading to delays...*

(Defence solicitor)

Delays, one of the most frustrating aspects of litigation, are considered in *Chapter 15*.

Given these considerations, it is worth noting in what pragmatic ways a practitioner may address the question of his or her accountability.

* Practitioners are accountable for updating their skills.

Health care is developing and extending almost constantly. New technologies are being introduced into many aspects of care, and while employers have a responsibility to see that suitable training and education is available, individual practitioners have a professional responsibility to ensure that they remain up-to-date in their practice. There is a requirement to provide research- and evidence-based practice, and this may entail challenging long-held practices.

One area which has attracted particular attention within maternity care is cardiotocograph (CTG) interpretation. Practitioners who use this technology must be competent to use it. The importance of monitoring is discussed in *Chapter 13*.

* Practitioners are accountable for providing continuity of care.

While each practitioner is individually accountable, contemporary maternity care is – with very few exceptions – team-based. Continuity of care was a principal theme of certain decisive government reports of the 1990s (DoH, 1993a; Scottish Office, 1993). While there is certainly room in maternity care for individual approaches, in order to ensure a reasonably consistent standard of care, policies, protocols and guidelines have been introduced into most, if not all, maternity units. Their scope and influence is controversial, and these matters are discussed in *Chapter 16*.

* Practitioners are accountable as members of a team.

Just as practitioners have a responsibility to provide consistent care, they must also liaise with relevant colleagues (of whatever grade or discipline). Indeed, midwives have a statutory duty to report abnormalities to an appropriately experienced colleague. Intra- and inter-professional communication are vital aspects of health care; and these require cooperation and mutual respect. Sadly, investigations into poor outcomes (eg. MCHRC, 1999) have found that communication failures are a factor in those poor outcomes. The importance of effective communication is explored is *Chapter 20*.

* Practitioners are accountable for keeping accurate and comprehensive records.

This point develops from the last one, since record-keeping is one of the principal methods of ensuring effective communication between practitioners. This is examined in *Chapter 14*.

* Practitioners are accountable for the information which they give to patients/clients.

A fundamental precept of health care is that it requires the informed consent of those who receive it. Only in exceptional situations is it possible to proceed without such consent. It would appear that society generally is demanding more from its health care attendants in terms of the type and amount of information it provides. Such raised expectations are discussed in *Chapter 8*, and the need for consent to be obtained is explored in *Chapter 3*.

Chapter 2

B   Blaming culture?

> *All too often a glance at the mother's notes will show that a child who is underachieving at school is the possible victim of an excessively patient obstetrician who allowed the labour to progress too long.*
>
> (Stuttaford, 1988)

When no more than a glance at something is needed in order to know where to apportion blame, then it can be said that we live in a culture all too ready to blame. In *Part I* it was noted that in civilized societies there is a fundamental right to take a civil grievance before a judge. Within the health care field this matter has acquired particular resonance in recent years with details about million pound claims aired in the media (Dyer [1998] cites one case settled for £3.3m). Compensation of this sort can only be secured once it is shown (or admitted) that negligence caused or materially contributed to harm; by this means practitioners are held to be accountable for what they do, and for what they fail to do.

There is, however (certainly in the minds of some practitioners), a blurring of the distinction between being held to account and being held to blame. While they may be two sides of the same coin, they are not exactly the same. In one case in which no negligence was established, the midwife commented:

> *The system is completely wrong, it's like a system of blame. Myself and the SHO are the people that this lady blamed because we were the ones most involved with her.*
>
> (Midwife 3)

Practitioners involved in the care of a woman and her baby will perhaps naturally become the focus of blame when things go wrong. While some explain the recourse to litigation in terms of securing explanations and apologies (in other words in terms of accountability and good manners), others feel that we now live in a blaming culture, and that this explains the apparent rise in litigation across a wide spectrum of public and private life. Osborne (1999: 16) notes that, 'There is certainly plenty of anecdotal evidence that we inhabit a "blame culture", but if so, why are we more prone to accuse? A possible answer is that the desire to blame increases as we lose a sense of how to cope with adversity.' The notion of 'blame-shifting' is echoed by Rosser, who states that midwives who have supported women in their choices may be on the receiving end of severe criticism. This happens, she notes, 'when a woman who has suffered some kind of tragic outcome, in trying to ease her suffering, assigns blame. She does this in an attempt to protect herself from the consequences of her actions' (Rosser 1999: 5).

There have been reports which indicate that many different individuals and groups have found themselves on the receiving end of legal actions: Springett and Finch (1998: 3) cite a spokesman for the Royal Institute of British Architects claiming that, 'There is a real blame society these days. People in the construction industry live in fear of litigation'. Aitkenhead (1998) cites cases involving a school being obliged to pay a former pupil whose dyslexia was not diagnosed, and a thief who obtained compensation after being chased by a police dog. In a similar vein a policeman successfully sued a car thief whose careless driving caused injury (*Langley v Dray* 1997). Dyer (1998) notes that a deputy head teacher successfully obtained £100,000 in compensation after being bullied by colleagues.

Dingwall (1994) claims that many professional groups (including architects, accountants, veterinary surgeons, engineers and even lawyers) have been affected by rising litigation. Within health care this has been attributed to rising expectations (which are examined further in *Chapter 8*):

'consumerism and somewhat unrealistic expectations about the capacities of modern medicine have combined to make patients less trusting and more willing to blame the doctor for an adverse outcome' (Robinson, 1986: 1017–18).

This view was reinforced in one of the cases examined here, in which a paediatric consultant noted:

> *Both (parents) were very angry indeed at the time of the (baby's) illness. Even at that time they were trying to find someone to blame...*

In another the legal department noted that the plaintiff's solicitors had made no specific allegations of negligence, but had proceeded on the basis that

> *An accident has happened therefore someone must be to blame.*

It may be thought quite natural to want to blame someone or something when things have gone wrong, particularly if they have gone disastrously wrong. In one case the expert report noted:

> *There is no doubt that Miss D suffered severe grief and distress. The unexplained and unexpected fetal death is disastrous. However, having said that, in my experience, when this catastrophe occurs a search is often made to apportion blame.*

In another case the employer wrote to the legal department:

> *Mrs C was noted to be depressed and ambivalent regarding her baby and husband... I see no negligence and feel this is a try by a rather unhappy lady.*

It does seem that there is a strong perception that members of the public will want to know who (or perhaps what) to blame. There are those who believe that 'blame-shifting' sometimes occurs, as in this quote from an earlier series of interviews (Symon,1994):

> *Some NCT ladies don't want any intervention, but if anything goes wrong they're the first to pull litigation out of the hat and say 'I should have been monitored', or 'I should have had an episiotomy'.*

> (Midwife)

On occasion the emotions behind the desire to blame are very raw, as in this statement by a litigant:

> *I have never suffered such torture as was inflicted on me at that moment... this so-called doctor... I will not rest until this woman faces retribution...*

On the other side of the coin there is sometimes almost a sense of resentment that patients have sought recourse in the law. In one case the expert noted:

> *I can see no basis for litigation in this case and the doctors involved deserve congratulations that both Mrs G and her baby survived.*

The emotional responses of several practitioners who have been involved in litigation are discussed further in *Chapter 9*, but it is worth noting that many practitioners do seem to feel under some pressure from the prospect of accusations of blame or negligence. The consequences, as one interviewee noted, may be critical:

> *Mistakes are made but nobody does it deliberately, nobody sets off saying 'I'm going to kill this baby'. Nobody does that, but in the end when you are blamed of something,*

your career might be ruined, you might lose your registration, that will be the end of your career.

(Obstetric registrar)

An unfounded allegation will not lead to removal from the professional register, but some have considered leaving practice because of the stress involved in litigation (see *Chapter 4*). It is perhaps unreasonable to expect parents to consider the sensitivities of practitioners when they themselves feel hard done by. The need to find someone to blame in such circumstances was stressed by a midwife in an earlier interview (Symon, 1994):

The days of having five or six kids are gone – they're down to 2.2 kids now, and the 2.2 are to be perfect... the media's given the impression that it's 'a - b - c - d', and when things don't go right... they tend to blame us.

(Midwife)

Such attitudes of course relate to people's expectations and the disappointment experienced when these are not met. This is explored further in *Chapter 8*.

Interviews with a number of practitioners who have had some experience of litigation produced some interesting responses. One summed up the way society has apparently changed:

Only two generations ago people accepted that babies died, or that even mothers died; we've come so far, and we can't push it that much further that every pregnancy is going to be successful... It maybe helps in the grieving process to find someone to blame, and the obvious point of call is the hospital.

(Midwife 4)

A senior lecturer echoed this point:

I think we're in a society where people want compensation much more than before. They want to be able to point the finger of blame, and they want to be able to say 'I got that person'. It's a societal change. In the past if a baby died or got brain damage... an explanation from the medical and midwifery staff – they would still have been angry about it but they wouldn't have pressed a claim.

(Midwifery lecturer)

There is certainly a perception that people are more ready to blame when things do not go well. Wanting or needing to blame someone may be understandable, and is often combined with other emotions, among them anger. One midwife stated:

I delivered someone whose baby, very unexpectedly came out with a low Apgar score... The mother did not realise how sick her baby was until the afternoon... she was asked if she wanted the baby to have the last rites... she feels very angry, and very angry with me, because she thinks I'm to blame, and she's taken the notes around (this city), *she's gone to two barristers, I know that, to try and find a case against me. I just feel that there is a certain thing that you've got to blame someone.*

(Midwife 2)

An obstetrician echoed this last point:

> *My general impression is that everyone expects to have an entirely normal pregnancy, an entirely normal labour. If there's anything which detracts from that there must be someone found to blame…*

(Consultant obstetrician 1)

There is a concern that this need to find a focus for blame may inhibit sympathetic communication, as one midwife noted:

> *It's very difficult to say sorry. If I say sorry am I then opening myself up to saying that I'm to blame?*

(Midwife 2)

The question of communication, and of giving explanations and apologies, is explored further in *Chapter 20*.

The general public is certainly believed to be ready to 'point the finger of blame' at practitioners. However it would be a mistake to think that practitioners stand united in solidarity against such expressions of censure or, indeed, that the internal process of audit and review is not used on occasion to apportion blame. One obstetrician noted that:

> *The problem is nobody is willing to accept the blame…*

(Obstetric registrar)

He went on to distinguish informal and formal meetings to discuss such matters:

> *Informal - that's OK. We sit together and say 'If you had done this, instead of that, then the outcome would have been different', and then it makes some sense and it educates you for the future.On the other hand, formal meetings like… we have, say, perinatal mortality meetings, I don't think they are useful.*

One consultant believed things have changed in recent years:

> *We used to have perinatal meetings when I was a trainee, which (were) very much an opportunity to allocate blame for situations. They were very uncomfortable, and I think that we've done well to get rid of them…*

(Consultant obstetrician 4)

However, this clinician went on to note that not all inter-professional and peer criticism has been removed (this is discussed further in Symon, 1999b):

> *I am saddened to see how often individual consultants can express the opinion that their colleague's performance fell below a reasonable level… Some can be quite outspoken and quite hurtful, and it is very easy to comment on other people's management because in a labour room we must be the only specialty who every day have to deal with other people's patients… It seems to me awfully easy for one doctor to say 'I think another doctor's management was wrong'. I suspect that obstetricians are more prone to say this than are physicians or surgeons… I think obstetrics is a minefield of acrimony…*

However this view was contradicted by another interviewee:

We understand that one of the problems with litigation is criticising your colleagues, and we try not to do that.

(Obstetric registrar)

From these comments it is not clear whether doctors are now more or less likely to criticise colleagues. However, several interviewees claimed that there is considerable criticism between doctors and midwives:

I think that there has always been, what shall I say, a source of friction between midwives and medical staff, or possible sources of friction. I now find that if there is any untoward event there is much greater bitterness between nursing, midwifery and medical staff, a much greater tendency to blame or to attempt to put the blame or the reasons or suggest that the medical staff were at fault...

(Consultant obstetrician 2)

The corresponding view that obstetricians blame midwives was put by a representative from a patients' rights group:

In the last few years after Changing Childbirth you've got a wee bit of a culture clash between the obstetricians and the midwives. We get a lot of cases where the midwives have fouled up, basically, not called anyone, not done the right thing, where we've got obstetric experts who are in there, they're desperately keen: 'It's the midwives, blame the midwives'.

(AVMA official 1)

It appears that it is not only obstetricians who criticise midwives. According to one experienced midwife there is within midwifery a tendency to be critical:

With medical people it tends to be 'Close ranks, OK, naughty naughty, switch off.' But the practice doesn't necessarily become enlightened. With us we (have) a knee-jerk reaction: and we go down a more horrible process much more readily. It's still that kindergarten, 'naughty girl.'... That military component is very much around still.

(Labour ward manager)

The possibility that this induces a certain defensiveness or lack of confidence was put by one midwife who had been involved in a poor outcome:

It took me a long time to get my head round it, you know, because you blame yourself, and it took me a long time to actually rationalise that I was only a small part of a whole chain of events.

(Midwife 1)

It is evident that the blaming process takes many forms, at times including self-blame. There is a strong feeling on the part of many practitioners that members of the public seem very ready to point the finger of blame whenever something goes wrong. It has also been claimed that this may include blame-shifting – displacing feelings of guilt through finding someone else to target. The views expressed here are principally those of practitioners, and it was not within the remit of this research to survey members of the public who have complained or made allegations of negligence. The depiction may, therefore, appear one-sided. However, it is possible to deduce from some of the comments that there is a perception of a need to connect a poor outcome to something or (perhaps preferably) someone. The next section looks specifically at some of the expressed attitudes towards the apparently rising tide of complaints.

Complaints

While the preceding section dealt with allegations concerning clinical negligence, allegations may be seen as a sub-set of the wider category of complaints. This section examines some of the ways in which practitioners have responded to complaints from patients and/or their families.

It is unclear what the relationship is between complaints and litigation: both reflect degrees of dissatisfaction, and a complaint may subsequently become formally legal (see *Chapter 7*). The number of complaints certainly seems to be increasing: Warden (1996) notes a 28% rise in the yearly figures for complaints to the Health Service Ombudsman between 1994 and 1995, and Dunne (1999) refers to a three-fold increase in complaints against doctors between 1993 and 1998. There is certainly greater publicity within hospitals about the mechanism for making a complaint: Rosser (1999: 5) notes that in the hospital in which she works, 'there are plaques up in all the corridors encouraging maternity service users to complain if they are unhappy with any aspect of their care.' This is not to criticise the right to complain; but the health service cannot express surprise that the public have taken up such offers.

One clinician characterised complaints as a kind of signal to practitioners to be vigilant:

> *Luckily I have not had any litigation against me, but there have been one or two complaints, and when there is a complaint you have to write a statement and everybody else has to write a statement, and that gives a sort of warning... be careful, otherwise you'll end up being sued...*

> (Obstetric registrar)

There is a popular belief that the incidence of both complaints and litigation is increasing, although, as *Chapter 9* details, the upward trend of litigation appears to have been checked. However, what does not seem to be disputed is the rise in the number of complaints to the Ombudsman (HSC, 1997). Whether or not complaints procedures are effective may be questioned: Robinson (1996) criticises the reduced time limit (introduced by the NHS Executive) for instigating a complaint. The notion that people sue at the drop of a hat is rejected by Weiler (1993), a view reaffirmed by May and Stengel (1990) who claim that those who formally sue represent just the tip of the iceberg. This view was also confirmed by one of the midwives interviewed in the course of this research:

> *I think a lot of people are put off suing who should be suing because it's such a daunting process.*

> (Midwifery lecturer)

One area which may predispose towards instigating complaints or even litigation is the perception by patients/clients of staff attitudes. Kraus (1990: 309) notes that a study by a malpractice insurance company in Tennessee found that 35% of malpractice lawsuits 'had been filed because of the physician's attitude'. In the large postal survey 41% of obstetricians (n=86) and 17% of midwives (n=294) admitted being the subject of such a complaint. Although one can not necessarily draw a line between a complaint and being sued, the existence of such dissatisfaction clearly represents a problem for the health service whether or not a complaint becomes formally legal. While many complaints may not be pursued rigorously, in a bid to obviate complacency Lamont (1993) believes that we should find out more about them.

This discussion of the views of health service staff concerning complaints aims to shed some light on the subject. Given the size of the interview sample, and the fact that respondents were selected on the basis either of their responses to an earlier postal survey or their known interest in this area of health care, this discussion may be particularly subjective. The aim is to open up the subject for wider discussion by highlighting some of the views held by people who have been involved in health service complaints and/or litigation.

While the apparent growth in complaints is seen by some as a regrettable development within the health service (one midwifery manager described the volume of such letters as being 'like confetti'), Whelan (1988: 71) points out that 'complaints procedures are effective if they provide incentives to take a proper degree of care.' Neuberger (1992: 53) points out that very often patients do not want to go through complicated or formal proceedings, but are anxious 'to get some form of apology and expression of concern'. She goes on to add that the medical defence organisations 'have been fairly negative about expressing apologies on the basis that they could, in fact, consist of being an admission of liability of some kind' (*ibid*).

Publicity about the avenues of complaint for dissatisfied patients/clients may be found in the Patient's Charter and other similar local initiatives. Many hospital Trusts now have a designated 'Complaints Officer' to whom complaints are addressed, although the background of this member of staff apparently varies. Clearly a balancing act is required from health service staff, particularly from those who deal with complaints: on the one hand deficiencies in the standard of care that have given rise to complaints must be acknowledged and acted upon while, on the other hand, managers are expected to provide a certain amount of support for their staff.

One patient group representative mentioned a reason for the alleged increase in complaints:

> *One of the strange by-products of the internal market is that... if you see it's the 'Get Well Trust' it's no longer your NHS hospital,* (which) *everyone was grateful for; however bad the treatment at least it was free. If they are seen as small businesses then people are going to treat them in the same way.*

(AVMA official 1)

This was reinforced by another representative from the same organisation:

> *As well as patients being referred to as customers and clients of the service, the whole thing about customer rights, that kind of thing, pushes people down to start questioning more because they are customers rather than being patients.*

(AVMA official 2)

The belief that hospitals are going to be seen as just another local business is certainly worrying. If health care is just another product or service, then it may be a short step from complaining to suing, particularly if hospitals are seen as 'deep pocket' defendants. There is literature from the USA which describes the debate about whether large institutions, such as hospitals or big businesses, are seen as being 'rich' and therefore more worthwhile suing (cf. Daniels 1989; Vidmar *et al,* 1994). There is, after all, little point in suing an organisation with few or no assets (Pattison, 1997).

The ease with which complaints may now be made was mentioned by one midwife respondent:

> *The system is more publicised in that there is a complaints procedure and the public are able to make complaints, whereas in the past they really had to be strong people to see it all through, and to find out who to go to, and what the procedure was. There are leaflets around the place now, and postcards to send back if there are any comments or complaints.*

(Midwife 4)

The belief that a complainant must be assertive appears to be fairly common. Another patient group representative made this point:

> *In practice the woman has to be highly motivated, well educated and articulate in order to follow a complaint through. The initial response is often fairly bland...*

This view contrasts with the perception among several respondents in the postal survey. Many midwives appeared to feel that staff are assumed to be at fault when a complaint is received. Comments like, 'In a court of law you are innocent until proven guilty. With the NHS it's the opposite' and, 'I feel both midwifery and hospital managers want staff to submit statements about complaints without referring them first to the RCM rep' make this point very forcefully. On the latter claim, practitioners are strongly advised not to write reports quickly or 'under duress' (Brown 1990: 52). Truelove (1985) warns that taking complaints at face value can be misleading: some complaints are understated, and so may not be sufficiently investigated; equally misleading is to assume that if the person appears unreasonable, the complaint must be unreasonable.

One former RCM steward claimed that her manager moved into 'disciplinary mode' as soon as a complaint was received. This was specifically rebutted by one manager (from a different unit):

> *It's* (a) *misunderstanding... I think very often you have a more junior member of staff getting very defensive.* (They) *get more irritated and more rattled than perhaps some of the more confident staff.*

(Midwifery manager)

Such complaints relate to perceived standards of care, and while these clearly must be accorded respect, in audits of complaints they can be seen as part of a more general dissatisfaction. That there is a perception of a wide range of subjects about which complaints may be made is seen from the following:

> *The awareness of the ability to complain has been put in people's minds, and sometimes it's daft things. It's nothing to do with any negligence. It's just stupid, stupid... perceptions about, you know, 'My labour didn't go as I expected it to, therefore I will complain.' People's perception of what things should happen, but it's nothing to do with negligence.*

(Consultant obstetrician 3)

> *They have complained about the chips on the enamel in the bathroom, they have complained about the paint chipping... I mean, the spectrum is from trivial and time-wasting to very* (serious) *complaints.*

(Midwifery manager)

That there can be a difference in perspective in this regard was noted by another senior midwife:

> *There are a lot of complaints that are trivial to people who are working in the service all the time, but not trivial to the patient.*

(Midwifery lecturer)

Another experienced midwife (midwife 12) believed that complaints are frequently of a non-clinical nature. She claimed that some people were saying things like,

> *'I don't want that midwife, she's rude'... They're writing to the manager saying 'I don't want that midwife.'*

When asked if this happened often, she replied:

> *It does around here... because half of them think they're private patients. In this area...*
> *a lot of them are very middle class. They've read the Patient's Charter, they're having*
> *their rights, and that's that... They're spoiled, from that point of view. It's patient*
> *power.*

There is certainly a perception that various charters have contributed to an increase in complaints:

> *I don't think the Citizens' Charter has helped, and the actual people saying, you know,*
> *this is what you can expect, whether it be reasonable or not reasonable, you know, here*
> *you are, complain if you don't get it.*

(Consultant obstetrician 3)

The task of sifting complaints is fraught with potential pitfalls. While it is clear from some of the views expressed that some complaints border on the trivial, the temptation to respond with a uniform 'We apologise for the inconvenience and are endeavouring to ensure that this does not happen again' must be resisted. It is important to distinguish clinically-based complaints from those relating to other matters (such as chips on the enamel in the bathroom). However, the seriousness of those complaints which are clinically-based may not always be immediately apparent; and investigations into such complaints must be more than superficial.

The balancing act faced by those charged with investigating complaints demands tact and insight. Disgruntled patients and their families may have a genuine grievance, but the principles of justice require both sides of the story to be heard. Some practitioners feel that they are assumed to be guilty whenever a complaint is made, and the impulse to offer an automatic apology must be checked. If an investigation finds there are grounds for the complaint, then apologies and, if warranted, meetings and/or counselling sessions must be offered.

From these views it is clear that some practitioners feel that a certain proportion of complaints are unwarranted. While there seems little doubt that many people view hospitals and health service personnel in a less reverential light than was once the case, there is also little prospect of a return to a 'golden era' when complaints were rare.

Conclusion

The health service, in common with other public institutions, faces significant change. Part of the change in culture is a demand for more openness and accountability. The apparent increase in readiness to apportion blame and make complaints may be seen as a mechanism by which practitioners can be held accountable. Practitioners are becoming more proactive in a bid to pre-empt the need to complain or sue. The 1995 Professional Performance Act (which came into force two years later) 'aims to seek and deal with substandard performance of doctors' (Mahendra, 1999: 935) and the requirements of clinical governance and NICE recommendations (see *Chapter 16)* reinforce this *approach.*

While complaints may induce dissatisfaction among health service staff (as well as other stronger emotions; see *Chapter 9),* the principle of being allowed to complain is not one with which practitioners ought to disagree. We all cherish our right to complain or, if the grievance is sufficiently serious, to take our cause before a judge. In this respect, our awareness of our civil rights, and our general expectations are higher (this is explored further in *Chapter 8).* Practitioners can minimise their risk of being on the receiving end of such allegations or complaints by striving always to improve standards of care and communication, particularly when events do not turn out as well as expected. However, this will never be completely successful and it is a fact of life that some people will want to apportion blame when things do not go well.

Chapter 3

C   Choice and consent

Choice

The subject of expectations is examined in *Chapter 8*. Briefly, it is widely thought that expectations generally are raised; this being the case, it may seem obvious that expressions of choice will be heard more often. However, choice is not as simple a matter as it might first seem: must a woman express her choice, or can she be expected to wait until someone asks her what her preferences are? Clinicians may sometimes forget that some people are intimidated by hospitals and by professional staff, and that some view the hospital as foreign territory in which they are unlikely to assert themselves. That this may be changing was noted by one interviewee in an earlier interview (Symon, 1994):

> *Eleven years ago the women would come in and say 'You're working in your professional capacity: we respect your professionalism — you do whatever you think is safe for the delivery of my baby and for me.' Today they come in and say 'I want a, b, and c, and a perfect baby... we've read Sheila Kitzinger, and we've read Michel Odent, so we know it all.'*

(Midwife)

Being assertive in this way is prospective. Those who were not assertive but wish they had been are left with the option of complaining. In one of the legal claims a complaint was made that a medical student assisted at a woman's delivery. The professor of obstetrics wrote to the legal department:

> *As a teaching hospital all the women at this hospital are aware that medical students may be present during their labour and birth, and we rely upon them to tell us if they do not wish this to occur.*

Here the presumption was that the onus lies with the woman. Such a view can easily be criticised, but legal claims are sometimes made because the woman's expressed preferences have not been overridden: in one instance the plaintiffs alleged that an elective caesarean section ought to have been carried out, despite evidence in the notes that the woman had made it quite clear that she wanted a normal delivery. Very occasionally it is the demands made by the woman's husband or partner which are adhered to: in one case a husband consistently refused to let staff examine his pregnant wife and threatened violence against anyone who attempted this. The full tragedy was that the woman developed serious complications, and subsequently died; it is not known whether this tragic outcome could have been prevented had the woman been examined sooner.

Several cases were concerned with a situation where a woman had expressed a wish for minimal intervention but, unfortunately, the outcome was a handicapped or even a dead baby. The argument usually turned on whether earlier intervention would have affected the outcome at all. Several of these cases related to a woman's desire for a normal delivery having already had at least one child by caesarean section. Given the recently vaunted scope for choice within maternity care, it is a matter of some debate whether treatment will be significantly altered in the light of such expressed wishes. In one such case a consultant obstetrician noted:

> *It may be that this enthusiasm for a vaginal delivery as opposed to caesarean section in some way influenced her obstetric management.*

When the outcome is poor it is very easy for clinicians to claim that their advice was ignored or given insufficient weight by the patient. It would appear to be tempting for some to pursue the 'I told you so' line, and use such outcomes to justify higher levels of surveillance in routine care in the future. While this may be so, these cases inevitably reflect a rather distorted picture, in that all the cases relate to an outcome which is suboptimal; those instances where a patient has successfully had a normal delivery after having had an earlier caesarean section receive less attention.

It is not always the case that the woman's expressed choice is for minimal technology and intervention; a number of cases concerned the woman's dissatisfaction that she was in fact persuaded to try for a normal labour and delivery when she wanted an elective caesarean. Such instances may be fairly rare, but it is a common perception among staff that demands by patients for either elective induction of labour or caesarean section are growing. A study of female obstetricians found a high personal preference for elective caesareans (Al-Mufti *et al*, 1997), a finding which was echoed in a study of pregnant women who were not obstetricians (Jackson and Irvine, 1998). These claims have been treated with scorn by some commentators (Robinson, 1999), and Dickson and Willett (1999) report a survey of midwives which found that almost all would opt for a vaginal delivery. Al-Mufti *et al's* findings led to a great deal of controversy (Paterson-Brown, 1998; Amu *et al*, 1998; associated correspondence cited in reference section), with many finding it difficult to justify acceding to a demand for such a procedure when there are no supporting clinical factors. One senior obstetrician noted:

> *I've got the lowest induction rate* (in this hospital) *because I don't interfere. And it's interesting, it's often the patients that want the intervention, despite what people say. The patients demand it. You look in* (city). *Their induction rate is something like 40%. They* **want** *to be induced.*

> (Consultant obstetrician 3)

With regard to the legal position, Dimond (1999a: 517) stresses that while 'a patient has the legal right to refuse recommended treatment, (she) does not have a legal right to insist on treatment which is not clinically acceptable.' The key requirement is a clinical indication for the intervention or operation. It could be argued that in a fee-for-service situation a patient could justifiably demand such an operation, but we are not yet in that situation.

With much safer anaesthesia today than has been the case in the past there does appear to be a popular perception that operations are more or less risk-free. It is possible that patients may claim that they are only exercising the choice which various government and local charters say is now theirs when they make such demands; if so, these ignore the fact that a caesarean section is still a major abdominal operation not without risks. Obstetricians may be caught on the horns of a dilemma when such requests are made, for current policy is to reduce the number of caesarean sections (which coincides with the demand for less intervention).

Informed consent

The previous section noted that choice is critical in modern health care, with an increasing emphasis on the rights of the patient/client, particularly in relation to decision-making. This section now examines the question of informed consent, which, according to Mason and McCall Smith (1999: 277) 'will always remain a classic example of the importation of a medical philosophy from across the Atlantic.' They go on to note that 'the phrase is tautologous – to be clinically and legally acceptable, "consent" must always be "informed" and the first element in the phrase is, then, redundant' (*ibid*: 278). Despite such concerns, the phrase is in common use, perhaps to emphasise that adequate information must be given to a patient.

Indeed, maternity care has seen some of the most intense debate on this subject. A recent Court of Appeal case (re MB) determined the extremely limited extent to which practitioners can override the expressed wishes of a pregnant woman, even when (to staff) her intended course of action appears unreasonable. Hewson (1997: 752) notes that a woman can 'decline medical advice and treatment, for reasons that are rational or irrational, or for no reason.' Legally, her wishes can only be overridden if it is held that she is not mentally competent. Carrying out a procedure without her consent could be construed as a trespass or an actual assault. The need for the woman's decision-making to be informed is clear because in pregnancy and labour those concerned are almost always both adult and competent. Not all are convinced that women are in fact included in decision-making, however:

> *My experience in talking to midwives about these issues, and informed consent particularly, is that quite a lot of midwives and other professionals understand by informed consent* (is) *that you tell parents what they should do and then they consent to that.*

(Consumer group representative)

There has been a growth in the need for clinicians to demonstrate that they have given adequate information to the patient, since claims have been made on the basis that patients have not fully understood the nature or possible consequences of a procedure or operation. Midwives today appear to be more aware that adequate information must be given to pregnant women, especially in labour, although, as Kirkham (1989) found out, the quality of this information can vary considerably.

Consent is required before any procedure can be carried out (with a few exceptions in cases of extreme emergency), the notion of consent being intrinsically bound up with an understanding of autonomy. There is a common acceptance that consent must be informed, ie. the decision concerning consent is only taken when the relevant facts have been considered. There may, of course, be a difficulty in deciding how much information should be imparted in order to achieve 'informed consent'. This is bound up with questions of risk, and the distinction between what is considered to be a significant level or a remote probability of risk. These are discussed further in *Chapters 11* ('Known complications', *p.99*) and *18* ('Risk', *p.150*).

There is also a separate argument which centres on whether the consent is rational. Savulescu and Momeyer (1997: 282) claim that 'what passes for respecting autonomy sometimes consists of little more than providing information, and stops short of assessing whether this information is rationally processed.' Clearly there is limited scope for such considerations in an acute emergency, and there is also the question of who determines what is considered rational. Even Brahams' (1985) phrase 'the prudent patient' invites us to ask who will determine what is considered prudent.

During a caesarean it may become apparent to the obstetrician that further action, beyond that which was anticipated, is needed. When the patient is unconscious consent clearly cannot be obtained; even when the patient has epidural or spinal anaesthesia, and is awake, it can be argued that informed consent is not possible, since there is no time for the patient to reflect on the situation before either agreeing or disagreeing. In one case the plaintiff's solicitors wrote:

> *Our client learnt that while she had been under general anaesthetic one of her ovaries and a piece of tube were removed.*
> *The standard consent form said: 'I hereby consent to the performance of any operation which may be considered necessary.'*

The consultant claimed that after the operation the woman was almost hysterical, and so explained to her husband why one ovary which appeared malignant had been removed – although histology showed it was benign. The impracticality of trying to counsel a patient in such difficult circumstances was explained by a hospital manager to the plaintiff's solicitors in another case:

> (The Consultant) *does not consider it normal practice in an acute obstetric emergency to counsel patients in detail on all the possible difficulties that might, very infrequently, arise.*

In this case damage to the fallopian tubes was caused at caesarean section, leading to secondary infertility. In a different case the obstetrician noted, again at caesarean section, that a previous section scar had ruptured; the rupture was large, and he felt that a further pregnancy would almost certainly lead to uterine rupture which would then lead to stillbirth and possibly even maternal death. To prevent further pregnancy he ligated the fallopian tubes, and was sued for an unauthorised sterilisation. This is an ethical matter as well as a legal one, but in this instance the defence of necessity appeared to be sufficient.

In another case (not concerning allegations of clinical negligence) a patient complained when a photograph of her was taken while she was in labour and without her consent. An anaesthetist wanted a picture of a patient using 'Entonox' (a mixture of oxygen and nitrous oxide) apparatus, but did not seek consent at an earlier time, and instead took the photograph while the woman was having a contraction. His explanation was:

> *In view of the self-administration of the* (Entonox) *and the effects of the labour I assumed implied consent.*

This took place in the early 1980s; such an assumption would hopefully not be made today. The emphasis is now very much on consent being informed rather than assumed. All this relates to the notion of the patient having a degree of choice in her care and treatment.

Conclusion

Consent is well enough understood by clinical staff for it to be only rarely the basis of a successful negligence action; choice, however, much vaunted in government charters, represents more of a potential dilemma. Whether or not a patient is deemed to be capable of understanding every item of information relating to a condition, or whether indeed the standard of consent ought to be 'informed' or 'rational', is a matter of debate. However an inescapable reality of current health care is that pregnant women are being told that they have the right to make choices about their care. While most clinicians welcome this development, such moves are evidently not seen favourably by all.

Chapter 4

D   Defensiveness

Never make a defence... before you be accused.

(Charles I, 1636)

In view of Charles I's fate, the wisdom of this advice may be questioned. This chapter examines defensiveness in the clinical area. 'Defensiveness' represents the idea that practice is determined at least in part by medico-legal considerations.

There have been claims in the press concerning the rising tide of litigation in a number of fields, not just health care, and these were discussed in *Chapter 2*. Within the health service such claims (eg. Tharmaratnam and Gillmer, 1995; Easterbrook, 1996) have become received wisdom, despite a lack of comprehensive supporting data which might confirm this. Indeed, in *Appendix II* it is shown that this apparently 'inexorable' rise in the overall incidence of litigation has been checked and even reversed in maternity care, in Scotland at least. Nevertheless, along with accounts about a rising tide of litigation there are claims about its consequences.

In terms of the effects of litigation, two points are worth making. Firstly, while most of the claims made about the incidence of litigation suggest it is rising, few people know exactly how much litigation there is; and secondly, in the absence of such publicly-available data, it is the fear of being sued (rather than the actual probability of being sued) that may have a critical effect on how a practitioner acts or reacts. In some senses this is comparable to the apparent effects of the fear of crime: the British Crime Survey (Hough and Mayhew, 1985) found that the fear of being mugged, particularly among some older women, far outstrips the likelihood of such an event. Knowing how likely (or unlikely) something is will not necessarily reduce the importance or effect of the fear of it happening. While there may be a discrepancy between perception and reality, it is the perception which shapes people's actions and reactions. In the context of health care, concern has been expressed that increasing litigation may have a detrimental effect: partly through its direct effects on staff, and partly through the knock-on effects on the organisation and management of health care. In the latter case it is defensiveness, particularly in clinical terms, which has caused concern.

Defensive practice is extremely difficult to define: Clements (1991: 424) claims that 'one man's defensive medicine is another man's risk management' which illustrates the imprecision of the whole subject. However, a useful working definition has been given by Black (1990) who characterised defensiveness in terms firstly of risk avoidance, and then of risk reduction. A 'risk avoidance' strategy may include practitioners '... avoiding specialties, procedures, and patients that they perceive carry a high risk of leading to a malpractice claim' (*ibid*: 36). 'Risk reduction' strategies may include practitioners undertaking 'more investigations and interventions than they would otherwise' (*ibid*: 36). This chapter looks at certain aspects of each of these in turn.

Risk avoidance

'Defensiveness' may refer to a number of different reactions, and probably the most dramatic of these is the avoidance of certain clinical specialties. Risk avoidance is believed to take one of two forms in this respect: either the prospect of exposure to litigation will adversely affect recruitment; or practitioners already in the specialty will leave. This first section discusses the second of these possible responses, since it has been claimed by some commentators to represent a serious potential threat to the provision of maternity care.

It should be stated that such concerns have mainly been expressed in the literature in relation to obstetricians, although there are claims of 'burnout' among some midwives (Bakker *et al*, 1996; Sandall, 1997). The Royal College of Obstetricians and Gynaecologists (RCOG) stressed in its evidence to the Winterton Committee (House of Commons, 1992) that recruitment to obstetrics was believed to be under threat because of its image as a litigation-prone specialty. College members appear to be aware of this perception:

> *I think that is what is being stated by our College, that it is the fear of litigation that a lot of people opt not to go into it... We certainly went through a patch of that a few years ago, but my impression is that in the past few years there has been an increasing number wanting to specialise... but there certainly had been a downturn of people coming in.*

> (Consultant obstetrician 2)

Another clinician pointed out that different units may have very different experiences:

> *From the point of view of our hospital we have never had a problem in recruiting junior staff. We're a major centre; so if we can't get staff, no one can.*

> (Medical director)

Accompanying claims about difficulties in recruitment there have been claims that retention within the specialty was difficult (Ranjan, 1993), and fears have been expressed that Britain may follow the US experience in this area. In the mid-1980s Casselberry (1985) claimed that family physicians were being squeezed out of maternity care by the threat of litigation, a finding echoed by Bredfeldt *et al* (1989). Developing this point, Acheson (1991), citing a study carried out by the American College of Obstetricians and Gynecologists (ACOG, 1988), noted that 12% of family physicians had given up practising obstetrics altogether, and that in Georgia in 1987 there were 70 counties without a practising obstetrician. While some midwives may be delighted at the thought of reclaiming ground from obstetricians, perinatal care is multi-disciplinary, and the prospect of a complete absence of obstetric provision is not a development which gives cause for celebration.

My postal survey found that a small proportion of midwives and obstetricians (5% of each sample) said that they had considered leaving clinical practice because of the fear of litigation. A further 27% of the doctors and 22% of the midwives said that they knew of a colleague in this position. It is conceded that considering leaving and actually leaving may not be that closely linked, but for even a small proportion of practitioners to have considered leaving because of the threat of litigation indicates that practitioners are discontented, and this represents a significant challenge for the health service.

That there is dissatisfaction among practitioners was noted by one interviewee:

> *Every colleague I talk to tells me that the quality of his job is spoiled by a threat of litigation. Anyone who has ever had any significant litigation brought against him – and the worst ones, the very worst ones are undoubtedly brain damaged babies and that sort of thing – they all feel like giving up without having been through the sweat... of a court case.*

> (Consultant obstetrician 4)

However, it seems that considering leaving clinical practice is not a constant. One midwife who had considered leaving said:

That was in the short term... I was quite bitter about it. I don't think it lasted that long.

(Midwife 11)

Another midwife claimed:

That was a serious consideration for quite a while actually, probably about a year anyway.

(Midwife 6)

When asked what had actually stopped her from leaving midwifery, she added:

Because I'm the breadwinner in the family, so basically the decision was made... the fact that I had the responsibility for being the breadwinner in the family made me have to bite the bullet (and) *get on with it.*

The consideration of leaving appears to strike soon after a critical incident, or notification of an intention to sue. One midwife who said that she had seriously considered leaving said:

It took me a long time to get my head round it, you know, because you blame yourself, and it took me a long time to actually rationalise that I was only a small part of a whole chain of events.

(Midwife 1)

This midwife (who had been involved in litigation) said that being taken out of a high stress environment had encouraged her to remain in practice:

(It was) *probably because I wasn't in the labour ward. I mean, I came out of the labour ward not long after that happened. I was on the change list anyway, and I came out and I went to one of the* (wards) *and that was quite good. It was very sort of normal... I think if I had still been in the labour ward I wouldn't have been working. I think I would definitely have gone...*

Most critical incidents, and most events which subsequently lead to litigation, occur in the intrapartum period. It is not surprising that the Labour Ward is an area which engenders stress and anxiety in some practitioners, and some will opt not to work there. However, it will not always be a single instance which causes such stress. One obstetrician claimed that considering leaving resulted:

Not (from) *a specific incident... there may be a number of emotional feelings: the cases themselves are distressing because there's a bad outcome... I think it takes a long time to come to terms with that aspect of the job.*

(Consultant obstetrician 1)

Clearly it is simplistic to expect that it would always be a single factor which might lead someone to take a decision as important as giving up work or opting for early retirement. A study into stress among GPs identified causes ranging from time and workload problems, to on call, patient expectations and demands, administration and paperwork, as well as complaints and fear of litigation (Young and Spencer, 1996). Among midwives there have been claims made that pressure of work, the emotional stress of poor outcomes, and particularly the demands of an 'on-call' service, have contributed to feelings of disenchantment and a consideration of alternative employment (Willis, 1996). Of course, a critical incident or the notification of a legal claim may well hasten such a consideration:

> *I've heard a number of people tell me that they no longer want to be involved in obstetrics because they're tired of the threat of litigation... I suspect that if anyone was to thump a big case against me at the moment I would feel that* (way).
>
> (Consultant obstetrician 4)

This paints a rather pessimistic picture, as if some practitioners are only working until the final straw arrives. This is, of course, a rather one-sided view: there is still job satisfaction for many people. One obstetrician noted that this helped to redress the balance:

> *Oh, there are plenty other things. Another rewarding thing comes up in the course of your* (work)*, and then you do something good... and the woman says 'Thank you very much, doctor', and that gives you another boost, and then you go on!*
>
> (Obstetric registrar)

Another midwife who had been involved in litigation and who had subsequently left midwifery, said:

> *I have now decided that I will probably never go back to midwifery. I'm not sure that it's necessarily the litigation side that's pushed me that way, but it certainly hasn't helped.*
>
> (Midwife 14)

This appears to reaffirm the notion that the experience of being sued is only one factor: a practitioner's ability to cope with the stress of poor outcomes and possible litigation may vary throughout his or her career. One obstetrician claimed that a lack of experience could predispose someone to consider giving up:

> *I would have thought that if as a junior you were involved in a serious problem, you probably would want to leave.*
>
> (Consultant obstetrician 2)

It may be concluded that increasing seniority brings a degree of self-assurance and confidence that a critical situation will improve with time; correspondingly, a lack of experience may encourage the perception that leaving is the only option. On the other hand it is possible that lengthy experience may induce a certain weariness: two other obstetricians noted that towards the end of a career the pressure of actual or potential litigation could be very significant:

> *I had an example of a chap who has since retired who gave that as a very major ground for leaving.*
>
> (Consultant obstetrician 4)

> *What can you do? When you are younger you can fight. You have got that fight in your blood... But when you are older, when you are 50+, and you have got to watch every step, then it becomes too much, and I know more now who are wanting to retire early than to carry on doing the job to 65...*
>
> (Obstetric registrar)

Once again, although litigation may be a significant factor in retiring early, it is unlikely to be the only consideration:

> *I don't think the retirement thing is simply litigation, there are more factors than that. It's the hassle in the National Health Service, the lack of progress in the*

administration, it's many other factors... I think that across the board people are thinking about early retirement. If you look at it now I'm one of the most senior people in the place and I've just hit fifty.

(Consultant neonatologist)

Another interviewee agreed that changes in the health service had resulted in practitioners retiring at an earlier age:

The age of retirement in the years I've been in the specialty has gone down dramatically, and in obstetrics and gynaecology in the UK the average age of consultant retirement is certainly well under 60. When I was training all our consultants seemed to work until they were 65. But their life was very different, and hospital practice was different. Consultants then could stand back a little bit...(they) were in such an isolated authoritarian position, that if they wanted to take life a little easier, then they could. Nowadays that's not so.

(Medical director)

Yet another consultant spoke of his own imminent retirement:

I'm just about to retire, and the most I would have said the top reason for wanting to get out as quickly as I can is litigation... the whole scene is unhappy as far as I'm concerned.

(Consultant obstetrician 2)

However, retirement is no guarantee of immunity from the emotional drain of legal involvement. One midwife who had retired, and who was subsequently informed that she had been named in a legal action, noted that she felt a 'dark cloud' had descended on her which she was 'finding hard to shake off'. A consultant reaffirmed retirement's lack of security:

There's the chap who retired four years ago, and he is now faced with a brain damaged baby case from more than twenty years ago, and his retirement is being ruined... so retiring is not necessarily a way of getting away from it.

(Consultant obstetrician 4)

Retirement may offer little in the way of protection from allegations of negligence. The 'long tail problem' – the length of time from an event to subsequent legal notification – is particularly acute in perinatal events, since there is effectively no time limit for certain actions (including many of those which concern cerebral palsy). It should be borne in mind that an allegation of negligence does not necessarily mean that negligence has occurred. While such claims are undoubtedly distressing to practitioners, there are few who would deny the right to consult a solicitor if someone feels sufficiently aggrieved.

The fears of an exodus from clinical practice, claimed by some commentators, appear to be overstated. Certainly there does not appear to be evidence to support the view that Britain is facing a crisis comparable to that experienced in parts of the USA. The situation in the USA is complicated by fee-for-service health care and the workings of the malpractice insurance industry; the rate of litigation is also believed to be higher. These factors are discussed in *Chapter 21*.

After a critical clinical outcome the initial impulse to leave diminishes with time, and is in addition affected by other considerations. Because of the complexities of a fluid employment market it is not known how many practitioners in Britain may already have left at least in part because of litigation. Certainly some clinicians, particularly in obstetrics, have claimed that retirement is an attractive option, but it has been shown that this is no guarantee of immunity from litigation. For practising midwives the best protections against legal involvement are competent practice, thorough documentation, and effective communication with patients/clients. While attaining a 'gold standard' in all these areas cannot preclude someone who has suffered a poor outcome from seeking legal advice, they are the best safeguard against being sued.

It is beyond the scope of this chapter to comment on the possible effects of the threat of litigation on recruitment. Retention may certainly be affected in individual cases, but it cannot be concluded that there is a 'haemorrhage' of practitioners. Nevertheless, apart from litigation there are other factors within the health service which appear to cause stress and burnout, and these need to be addressed. Such reactions are both individual and complex and there are no simple solutions.

Claims of an exodus from clinical practice relate to only one reaction to the possibility or experience of litigation. What follows below examines some of the allegedly defensive clinical reactions claimed to result from the threat or prospect of litigation.

Risk reduction

Black's second characteristic of defensiveness is an attempt at risk reduction: practitioners undertaking 'more investigations and interventions than they would otherwise' (Black 1990: 36). This may be developed to include the uncritical use of technology in the belief that this will somehow help to prevent a poor outcome, and the adoption of other practices in clinical care to minimise the risk of exposure to litigation. Ennis *et al* (1991: 616) claimed that 'tests deemed to be inaccurate are used in clinical practice because some obstetricians fear litigation', which, if true may constitute a significant burden for the health service. Marks (1997: 26) claims that in the USA doctors are said to be 'making decisions on what expensive tests to order as much on the basis of what would look good in court as on the basis of medical requirement.'

While some have doubts regarding the validity of claims about 'risk reduction' strategies (Baldwin *et al's* [1995] study of low risk women found no association between an obstetrician's previous malpractice experience and the use of antenatal investigations), concerns have been expressed about the financial implications of unnecessary tests, and the possible morbidity associated with the use of technology which may increase the rate of intervention. DeKay and Asch (1998: 20) assert that 'Defensive testing inevitably sacrifices the interests of patients for the interests of physicians. In other words, defensive testing is not only expensive, it is harmful to patients as well.'

This chapter now examines three such possible examples of defensiveness in clinical practice – the alleged increase in caesareans sections, and in the use of cardiotocography (CTG); and discusses a third allegedly defensive reaction – an increase in documentation. Although this section refers to the large scale postal survey, the discussion is drawn in the main from a series of interviews. It is acknowledged that the arguments may be subjective, but the intention is to draw out some of the possible implications of the apparent rise in defensive practice. Given limitations of space, only a brief examination of each area is possible; documentation and caesarean section are discussed more fully elsewhere (Symon, 2000).

Caesareans

In the postal survey an increase in caesarean sections was the most commonly cited example of defensive practice in both the midwifery and obstetric samples. This belief was echoed in the Audit Commission (1997) report, although it provided no data to support this.

There are concerns about an increase in caesareans: it is a major abdominal operation which carries an increased risk of both morbidity and mortality for the mother; while avoiding the dangers of vaginal delivery there are associated risks to the baby; and there is a large increase in cost to the health service. However, the incidence of caesarean section appears to be rising steadily (Bolaji and Meehan, 1993; Jackson and Irvine, 1998) despite attempts to reduce this. It is questionable how desirable this trend is. One obstetrician claimed that:

> *It has become much easier for obstetricians to decide to do a Caesarean section on a patient who would have been quite safely delivered by forceps...*

(Obstetric registrar)

A consultant in the earlier series of interviews acknowledged that there is pressure to perform more caesareans, but claimed to approach this from different angles. He noted:

> *People are much more ready to do a caesarean section than they would have been in days gone by; you would be very cautious about doing a 'trial of forceps', or doing any kind of moderately difficult forceps... I'd never do a vaginal breech delivery now – not even in a parous woman, ever.*

(Consultant obstetrician)

However another stated:

> *I know that for a period of time at* (hospital) *I was the only consultant who would allow a vaginal breech delivery... We have a generation of juniors who have so little experience in managing vaginal breech delivery that it has other knock-on effects, for example at the delivery of a second twin ... We've had, to my certain knowledge in* (this hospital) *in recent years at least three caesarean sections done for second twins. I don't believe that's good practice.*

(Medical director)

These claims appear to provide evidence for the view that some caesareans are unnecessary. However, a third, while agreeing that the perception of more caesareans was common, questioned whether this was in fact the case:

> *People talk about going and doing Caesarean sections much more quickly than they used to do, but I don't think we are, because we're being accused. of doing too many sections – but often those 'too many sections' are patients' requests!*

(Consultant obstetrician 3)

This view seems rather ambivalent about the actual incidence of (and reason for) caesareans. It was noticeable that in the postal survey almost a fifth of the hospital-based obstetric respondents admitted that they now performed more caesareans because of the fear of litigation. One obstetrician laid the blame for more caesareans squarely on the increased use of monitoring:

> *I think we introduced fetal heart rate monitoring away back in 1970. We made a few rules and we never really kept to them terribly well... If there's any doubt we move to a Caesar rather quickly...*

(Consultant obstetrician 4)

Higher levels of monitoring are linked with greater intervention rates, and this chapter now discusses the alleged defensive use of such monitoring.

Cardiotocography

The CTG, pioneered in the late 1950s, and introduced commercially a decade later, has since the early 1970s been introduced on a comprehensive scale in British maternity units. However, this has been done without thorough evaluation, and with the current drive to ensure that practice is research- and evidence-based it is questionable whether such an approach could be followed today. Certainly there have been critics of the widespread use of CTG (Beech, 1992), although its use is considered more or less mandatory in certain circumstances (Gaffney *et al*, 1994; Steer and Danielian, 1999).

While the limitations of a small scale study preclude a definitive analysis, the responses reported here suggest conflicting motives for using the CTG, and varying abilities in its interpretation. Many senior obstetricians in the postal survey had claimed that training for midwives in CTG interpretation was insufficient. Referring to this one senior doctor noted:

> *The consultants are condemning themselves if they say that, because it's up to them in their own hospitals to run things... If we're using CTGs, like any other observation, people have to know about them and be properly trained.*

> (Medical director)

In the postal study there were also many comments supporting the routine use of monitoring, including these two:

> *Sometimes it is easier to attach a monitor to a woman rather than stay with her.*

> *Always the worry of litigation – mothers reassured by hearing the fetal heart.*

Another midwife agreed, citing one particular case:

> (The mother's) *one comment to me was the fact that she felt she didn't hear the fetal heart, so she thought I was lying because I wasn't actually recording it. What I was doing was putting the ultrasound bit of the CTG against her abdomen, but not with the volume on. I suppose I should have done. That's made me reflect that I need to make sure that the parents* (hear the fetal heart).

> (Midwife 2)

Some may feel that hearing the fetal heart rate is a reassurance, but there is the danger that routine and uncritical use not only de-skills the midwife, but also gives a false sense of security. The fetal heart rate is only one indicator of the fetal condition, but it has become the pointer which may lead staff to diagnose fetal well-being or compromise. One midwife summed up her views:

> *Women have continuous monitoring when* (there's) *no indication for it. But people say 'Well, at least you know what's happening'. They say that it's a security which it's not... they're worried about not doing something when the technology is there.*

> (Independent midwife)

There are concerns that staff, perhaps those with less experience, may use this technology uncritically:

> *Often the junior staff will do an admission CTG and it just doesn't get taken off. You wonder 'What is the indication for this monitoring?' Maybe skills of using the Pinards are lost.* (Students) *need encouragement – it's not their first choice. If there's a sonicaid or CTG to hand they would probably pick that up first.*

> (Midwife 4)

In addition to the possibility that midwives may lose the skill of using the Pinard stethoscope, there may also be an assumption that if there is a CTG trace then staff and parents can be reassured that all is well. However, this may not be so:

> *My feeling is often that if only the midwife had listened in to the baby with a Pinards... We have a number of cases where the women have had caesareans because the trace showed a problem, and it's been shown that the baby had in fact died long before that. The fetal heart monitor was picking up the mother's heart beat and doubling it. So the mother was actually put through an unnecessary caesarean...*

(Consumer group representative)

In fact Gibb and Arulkamaren (1997) stress the need to auscultate the fetal heart with a Pinard's stethoscope prior to initiating the CTG for just this reason. However, faith in the technology appears to be undimmed. The reassurance of hearing the fetal heart rate electronically was noted by one midwife in one of the earlier interviews:

> *I would be happier if the woman I was looking after had a CTG on... it's proof I am hearing the fetus.*

(Midwife)

However, a consultant confirmed that relying on a CTG trace as evidence of well-being may be misplaced:

> *We seem to be using cardiotocography as a means of suggesting that everything is OK, and we would be comforted to have that evidence folded in the back of the case notes, so that we could at a later date, if something was wrong... we could always say 'Well, look, here is the Non Stress Test.' I don't know of any evidence that says that this is accurate, that this is evidence-based.*

(Consultant obstetrician 4)

Clinicians are called upon to ensure that their practice is indeed based on sound evidence and research, and yet this approach appears very defensive in nature.

These comments do suggest that a degree of CTG use is defensive, and that its use may contribute to increased levels of intervention. Small scale research of this nature cannot of course quantify this issue – anecdotal evidence may highlight various viewpoints within a subject and may suggest areas for further research. It is instructive to note that in the postal survey, 42% of the midwives stated that they felt the CTG to be overused generally, and yet only 8% cited increased CTG use as an example of general defensive practice. Only a tiny proportion (1.3%) admitted that they themselves used the CTG more often from a defensive point of view. However, and again from the earlier series of interviews, it seems some midwives feel there are pressures to use the CTG:

> *Here they're overused, definitely. Here it's more a doctors' hospital, and they want everybody on a monitor, and they make you very vulnerable when you don't monitor people...*

(Midwife)

> *The CTG's a sort of talisman. I think probably there is an underlying fear that if they don't have the CTG then their actions as a midwife could be interpreted as negligent.*

(Midwife)

It seems that, while many midwives believe the CTG to be over-used, relatively few see its use as defensive. Defensiveness, as a concept, is difficult to define, but if unnecessary tests are indeed being carried out because practitioners fear litigation, then there is cause for concern. Such tests have inherent costs: a financial cost borne by the health service; costs in terms of morbidity as the level of intervention rises; and emotional costs as women are subjected to instrumental and operative deliveries which might not always be justified. Without widely-accepted criteria for judging the appropriateness (or otherwise) of tests or procedures such as the CTG, it is not possible to declare how much may be justified and how much defensive. A multi-centre audit of CTG use would be a useful first step to establish these parameters. While there appear to be fairly widespread concerns about use of the CTG, few midwives feel themselves to be reacting defensively in this respect. The importance of monitoring is discussed further in *Chapter 13*.

It must be borne in mind that, while midwives have enjoyed a considerable degree of autonomy concerning CTG use – especially with regard to the length of period for which intrapartum monitoring is performed – they do not have completely free rein. Increasingly, it seems, unit protocols are dictating such matters. Risk management programmes aim to reduce the potential for exposure to litigation; these matters are examined in *Chapters 16* and *18*.

Documentation

In the postal survey an increase in documentation was the most commonly cited example of a personal defensive reaction by midwives. Poor documentation has certainly been cited as a feature in poor clinical outcomes, and the examination of legal files noted many instances in which poor record keeping inhibited the investigation of circumstances which formed the basis of litigation. The importance of good record keeping is stressed in *Chapter 14*; the remainder of this chapter looks briefly at changes in the practice of documentation, including some claims about its defensive nature.

With regard to changes, one midwife noted:

> *I can remember when we wrote just the minimum that we needed to... now basically our note taking has become very, very meticulous.*

(Midwife 6)

One obstetrician admitted to personal changes in documentation:

> *I think I certainly am more aware of writing and... putting things down in a very clear way so that it can be read afterwards... I was involved in the Scottish Office in looking at the Perinatal Mortality Review Group, but one of the things we found in looking through notes was that you couldn't determine who was who...*

(Consultant obstetrician 3)

Another senior practitioner agreed that practices had changed, and that because of the 'long-tail problem' it could be a long time before anyone realised just how insufficient the case notes were:

> *Usually the notes are so out of date; by the time litigation gets through the notes are five or ten years out of date. Now you're almost writing the notes for somebody else to read.*

(Consultant neonatologist)

He went on to note:

I'm now looking at parents and assessing them in terms of 'what are their attitudes? is there a problem here?' If it's a high risk area, and there's a baby who's been asphyxiated, then there's no doubt about it, we are documenting those extremely carefully.

This need to document more carefully was confirmed by another senior clinician:

I probably would take more time in writing down what the patient is saying and what your answers to the patient are. I think we are having to record much more detail.. and probably are still not doing it sufficiently well, for example writing down 'pros and cons discussed' may not be adequate in any particular case.

(Consultant obstetrician 2)

One midwife who had been involved in litigation thought that her clinical practice hadn't changed as a a result, but added:

It's made my documentation more precise... I write everything.

(Midwife 3)

Another, also involved in a legal claim, said that she had changed her practice in documenting:

Say you call a Sister into the room, (now) I would write on the CTG 'seen by'. ... I never used to do that. I thought... it just seems a bit much. I mean, it's covering your back, and I never did that (before), whereas I would now.

(Midwife 1)

A more senior practitioner agreed that this practice occurs, but felt it was often unnecessary:

... it got to the silly stage of, you know, 'Dr So-and-so was here', or the midwives would always write, 'Somebody popped in'...

(Consultant obstetrician 3)

Another midwife in one of the earlier interviews said:

Midwives are much more aware of documentation. A solicitor had once said, 'If you didn't write it you didn't do it.' That has really stuck with me.

Not all midwives in that series of interviews were happy about this perceived requirement to write reams:

We're documenting to say 'This is how safely we have worked.' We're needing evidence today to prove what used to be not taken for granted, but respected and accepted. I'm documenting more what the woman has to say... her requests, professional advice given, that before I honestly didn't think was required, considering I am a professional midwife. I didn't think it was necessary everyday to state that I was working in a safe professional manner.

(Midwife)

There is a possibility that an over-emphasis on documentation can in fact inhibit the delivery of good care (I have discussed this elsewhere in more detail [Symon, 2000]):

> *There is a down side as well. Sometimes we see midwives calling us to see a CTG, and we get there and you see them quite busy writing notes... that's because she is also quite worried when something goes wrong, but it takes time... but there is no other way out. You've got to put everything in black and white.*

(Obstetric registrar)

Despite the possibility that the standard of care may suffer because of a perceived need to produce thorough case notes, it does seem as if some practitioners are quite consciously aware of the possibility of litigation. In one of the earlier interviews one said:

> *We're writing, documenting: it's drummed into us...we're talking about litigation all the time – we never talked about that before.*

(Midwife)

It is difficult to know precisely how practices have changed over the years. That current practice is perceived to be different was stressed by one respondent:

> *It's quite interesting: if somebody comes back to have a subsequent baby and you've looked after them previously, and you see your level of documentation five or ten years ago...you cringe. Now I think we document something at every point of contact.*

(Midwife 4)

It is not only midwives who appear to have taken this on board:

> *I'm saying the same things to parents as I always did, but I'm documenting it more.*

(Consultant neonatologist)

The whole defensive response was summed up by one midwife in an earlier interview who said:

> *I would document things a lot more now... in case something ever came to light.*

There is little doubt that practitioners are aware of the importance of producing comprehensive and legible records. Ensuring that this concern does not supplant the need to provide good care, while difficult, is essential.

Conclusion

Defensiveness is a very broad area and this chapter has examined a number of its facets. While there may be some argument as to what exactly constitutes defensiveness, few deny that it exists. The danger that responding defensively may in fact be detrimental to patient care, either through the inappropriate use of tests or because staff are spending too much time writing and not enough in caring, is a danger that must be faced. Individual practitioners may point to a tragic event as the reason for such actions, but there is a danger on relying too much on atypical cases.

While there is little evidence that Britain has witnessed the exodus of clinical practitioners apparently seen in parts of the USA, there is little room for complacency. A deceptive sense of security surrounds the uncritical use of technology, and it is a common perception that tests and operations are being carried out without sound clinical indications. While the assertion is extremely difficult to quantify, the views expressed here suggest that defensiveness is commonplace. Whether this constitutes good clinical practice, or good risk management, is very much a moot point.

Chapter 5

E   Experts

The only evidence that can decide a case of malpractice is expert evidence: that is, the evidence of other doctors; and every doctor will allow a colleague to decimate a whole countryside sooner than violate the bond of professional etiquet (sic) by giving him away.

(Shaw 1946: 14)

Introduction

The system for adjudicating allegations of negligence has traditionally relied on an adversarial approach. In cases which concern any kind of technical knowledge such as health care, the practice has been for each side to consult an expert in the relevant field. The theory is that an 'expert' opinion will be one of high calibre, although MacDermott (1997: 642) cites an unnamed judge who claimed that 'Expert opinion is only opinion in evening dress.' The expert (usually a senior clinician/academic) will produce a report using the available evidence, and from these reports the two sides will conduct negotiations. The claim may be dropped, settled out of court, or – usually when the experts disagree fundamentally – agree to go to court, in which forum the experts may be asked to give testimony. Although having a 'team' of experts may be thought desirable, a study of obstetric claims by Bors-Koefoed *et al* (1998) found that having several defence expert witnesses was associated with a decreased chance of a successful defence. There is ample advice for midwives and doctors on how to prepare for such a role (Dimond 1996; Tranter 1996; Copperfield 1996). Lists of suitable experts are now held by the Royal Colleges, and the Law Society maintains the Expert Witness Register. Training in the art of providing expert evidence is given by the Expert Witness Institute and the Judicial Committee of the Academy of Experts (both based in London). However, this training is not without criticism: one respondent in the interviews claimed that:

> (The) *Expert Witness Institute... is an attempt to do something... but it's entirely unregulated, so we had a lot of experts getting slightly carried away.*

(AVMA official 1)

Recent proposals for reform of the civil justice system may herald a change to the use of experts. Among these are opportunities to use arbitration/mediation rather than adversarial litigation; this would involve the appointment of a single joint expert to decide on the issues at stake. It is felt that having such an expert would be more efficient, and would also pre-empt any charges of partisanship. One of the potential dangers of these processes are that the single expert will not be exposed to cross-examination by a legal opponent. The advantages of such a challenge are noted by Puxon (1996a) who cites a case in which a very senior expert conceded considerable ground when challenged in court, a move she lauded as demonstrating his true independence.

The theory

Although in theory the 'expert opinion' must be seen to be the independent opinion of a specialist, this has apparently not always been the case. The theory was reiterated in *Whitehouse* v *Jordan* (1981), in which the judge (Lord Wilberforce) said 'While some degree of consultation between experts and legal advisers is entirely proper, it is necessary that expert evidence presented to the court should be, and should be seen to be, the independent product of the expert uninfluenced as to form or content by the exigencies of litigation. To the extent that it is not, the evidence is likely to be not only incorrect, but also self-defeating'(cited by Hodgson, 1981 @ p 2). This view was reinforced by the judge in the more recent case of Wiszniewski. Referring to one of the defence experts he said: 'Professor Thomas' unwillingness to criticise was in my view unjustified and an example of his general disinclination to say much that might be adverse to the defendant's case' (per Thomas J @ 262). A senior lawyer commented on the difficulties encountered by experts:

> *I do think this notion of 'independent expert' is perhaps a more difficult notion than it is sometimes assumed to be... I understand that experts are supposed to be in some way independent, and there is very high judicial authority for that...(but) I think it is a bit difficult for an expert to be entirely independent... if you are an expert on whatever and you're asked to look at the case... it would be nice to make you feel part of a team... I think it would be unsurprising if the consulted expert didn't feel that he was part of a forensic team...*

> (Queen's Counsel)

The requirement for an expert to be disinterested in the outcome of a claim was stressed in an obstetric case (De Martell), in which one expert, initially consulted by the plaintiffs, was then subpoenaed to appear in court by the defendants. The judge noted: 'Dr. Rosenbloom was in an invidious position... Nevertheless, there is no property in a witness. He was bound to give evidence in accordance with the subpoena or, as a last resort, risk imprisonment at my hand' (per Simpson J @ 244).

Lord Wilberforce's insistence that an expert must provide testimony 'uninfluenced... by the exigencies of litigation' looks to be a tall order, and some of these difficulties are now discussed.

Difficulties in practice

Motivation

Being asked to write an expert report is an acknowledgement of expertise within a subject. However, upon being asked to provide such a report, emotions may vary, as Hoyte (1997: 18–19) notes: 'While some practitioners may have reservations about investigating the actions of clinical colleagues... many regard it as a privilege to be invited to evaluate their peers.' Symonds (1992: 3) notes that doctors are often reluctant to act as expert witnesses because of the time involved, the stress of court appearances, and the desire not to give evidence against a colleague: 'There is... an acute awareness in all but the most arrogant of clinicians that the dividing line between success and disaster in treatment can be very narrow, and there is a corresponding reluctance to sit in judgement.'

It may also be that constraints of time are a disincentive, as noted by one defence organisation to an employer:

Paediatric neurologists spend half their time on medico-legal matters, and we are detecting a marked reluctance on the part of all well-known names to take on any further cases.

As an incentive, it seems that the monetary rewards for acting in this way can be high: Stanbridge (1999: 43) a financial consultant offering courses in this kind of work, claims that 'gross fees exceeding £100,000 per annum are not uncommon for those prepared to devote time and attention to this source of income.' That such economic considerations may provide the necessary motivation was claimed by one interviewee:

> *It's serious extra money, you can charge £1,000 a report. And if you can knock a couple of them up at the weekend it's a very nice Saturday job...*

> (AVMA official 1)

Part of Lord Woolf's inquiry involved asking medical experts for their views on the legal process. This found that the average fee claimed by experts was £400 (Neale *et al*, 1996). There is usually a great deal of work involved in writing a report, and it may be questioned whether busy practitioners would be prepared to spend all their time off working in this way, although the same report notes that one in six experts who responded had produced more than one hundred reports in the preceding five years. One consultant involved in a legal claim noted how being asked to write reports (not always in the role of independent expert) was making inroads into an already crowded schedule:

> *I despair over the frequency with which reports over patients' care are being required of us. I have no doubt that the contract that we arrange with the health authority should probably include one half day to deal with such matters.*

Those accepting the commission to write an expert report also accept that they are prepared, if the claim gets that far, to attend a court hearing and defend their conclusions under cross-examination.

Another potential difficulty concerns the expert's professional motivation, since there are dangers in an expert appearing too often with a particular view. One obstetrician claimed:

> *Oh, there were some names in paediatrics, weren't there, who could be relied on to drop the poor consultant obstetrician in it in view of negligence: 'Because one event followed another, therefore the first one caused* (the second).'

> (Consultant obstetrician 4)

A defence solicitor confirmed that some experts were believed to be partisan:

> *You have to be careful about using experts who appear too often on the one side or the other, and there are some people on the AVMA list* (who) *are really discredited... I would always, for choice, be happy to use an expert who might appear for both sides – it keeps the balance.*

> (Defence solicitor 1)

An awareness that experts have not always been disinterested providers of specialist knowledge has been found at the highest level: Lord Woolf, whose Access to Justice report aims to improve the efficiency of the civil justice system, is reported as saying: 'The wrong culture has grown up whereby experts are essentially being seen as hired guns for each side of advocates of a cause when they should be used as people qualified to give an expert opinion to help the court...' (cited by MacDermott, 1997: 639).

In the American context, Brent (1982) has criticised the 'professional expert' who specialises in providing testimony for litigants. Manuel (1992: 94) reinforces this point: 'We have so-called professional plaintiff's physicians, an exceedingly noxious group of individuals... What we see now is some of our most distinguished professors in the US who are testifying for plaintiff's attorneys not once, not twice, but 10-20-30 times a year.' Confirming the view that some practitioners are indeed partisan, Slovenko (1996: 590) cites one plaintiff who, when asked in court by his counsel 'What kind of physician is Dr J?' replied, 'Well, I'm not sure, but I remember you told me he was a good plaintiff's doctor.'

The out-of-touch expert

In the USA some retired practitioners have apparently joined this band of 'professional experts', a custom criticised by one clinician interviewed here:

> *There should be limits on that. The university puts limits on, for example, professors retiring, where they can only examine students for two years or so after they retire. There should be an absolute limit on that. You're out of touch after that time.*

> (Consultant neonatologist)

While it may be tempting for a plaintiff's solicitor to employ a retired clinician as an expert in the belief that, having retired, (s)he may have fewer competing commitments, this may be a self-defeating strategy. Retired practitioners may not have access to up-to-date clinical information which may be vital to a case. A lack of current involvement also weighed against the expert in a recent court case in which the judge explicitly 'preferred the views of "hands on" experts to academics' (Puxon, 1996b: 265). 'Hands on' experts are those still involved in clinical care. In selecting an expert, AVMA's Medical Accidents Handbook advises plaintiffs to 'make it a rule never to instruct an expert unless he has heard something positive about him from a reliable source' (McNeil, 1998: 273).

An expert's testimony (particularly as to whether or not there has been negligence) must take account of the state of knowledge at the time the relevant events occurred, and this may be years before the case comes to court. However, it can be seen that following retirement, there is a danger of becoming out-of-touch. As there is now greater specialisation in medical litigation among lawyers, an out-of-touch expert may be more of a liability than a help. According to one consumer group representative, even judges have taken to censuring experts:

> *The judges will actually criticise the experts. In the past the judge would say, 'Well, basically they were both very good, but I believe one over the other'. Now they will actually say 'This expert shouldn't have been here, or is past their sell-by-date'. And that's only in the last few years. I remember the first one, that was a particular anaesthetist, and it was a bit of a shock when the judge was actually saying 'This guy keeps coming out, why is he still here? (he's) not even an anaesthetist any more.' That was a bit of a shock. For the judiciary that's a hell of a step.*

> (AVMA official 1)

Experts, as this interviewee indicated, were once accorded considerable respect. This appears to be less the case today. From the USA McElhaney (1989: 98) offers 'Nine ways to cross examine an expert', and in a recent case (not relating to clinical negligence) Brahams (1997: 896) notes that the trial judge had found himself 'unable to accept the opinions of any of the medical witnesses called before him.' She went on to report that the Court of Appeal judge had said that it was unfortunate that the trial had been 'highjacked by the expert witnesses' (*ibid*).

Expertise

The perinatal period covers more than one medical speciality and this can cause difficulties, for not only must an expert have genuine expertise in his or her own field, but the solicitors must ensure that they have identified the correct field. In one case the solicitors stated that their expert (a pathologist) had been critical of the obstetric care. The defence believed he was in no position to make such a judgement, and claimed that he was 'trespassing beyond the boundaries of the speciality'.

Cerebral palsy claims in particular may be difficult to prosecute, for, as MacLennan (1999: 1059) points out, 'No one person is an expert in all the facets of cerebral palsy'. Goldrein and de Haas (1992: 934) point out that in such a claim there will be an 'expert team' which may include 'several, if not all, of the following disciplines: obstetrics, paediatric neurology, neonatology, [paediatric] physiotherapy, [paediatric] speech therapy, [paediatric] occupational therapy, nursing, [paediatric] gastroenterology, clinical psychology, architecture, employment advisory and forensic accountancy [structured settlement advice].'

Even assuming that the plaintiff's solicitors have identified the correct specialty, relying on one expert's opinion may be insufficient. There is high judicial authority (Maynard [1984]) for the view that there is room for disagreement in medical practice, and that a court's preference for one body of opinion over another is no basis for a conclusion of negligence. In one action the plaintiff's solicitors appeared to think that they had a good chance of winning the case because the expert who had produced a report for them concerning an episiotomy repair stated that catgut was 'not the suture material that I would have chosen'. The defence's expert report noted that just because their expert stated that catgut would not have been his choice of suture material does not mean it was negligent to use catgut. This was 'a matter of opinion only.'

It is assumed that the writer of an expert report will be an expert in this field, although Lewis (1996) notes that inexperienced solicitors have been known to instruct individuals whose expertise is questionable. However, it appears that in the past some people tried to pass this on:

> There are experts out there who have made a good living. We know, for example that (some) *weren't actually providing the report, they were getting their junior doctors to do it; and they've come off AVMA's list a long time ago.*
>
> (AVMA official 1)

It was also claimed that some have been prepared to claim an unjustified expertise in medico-legal matters. One solicitor noted:

> *The problem is you get someone – and I have a particular person in mind – who takes a law degree and writes a book on medical negligence, but still offers themselves as an expert... I think that sort of person is useless. It looks terribly good on paper, but actually you don't want that kind of expert at all, and I think people are perhaps misled.*
>
> (Defence solicitor 1)

Expertise in a clinical area usually only comes with a degree of seniority. Being qualified as both a medical and a legal practitioner does not in itself guarantee the expertise needed to adjudicate on another practitioner's conduct.

Efficiency

Those chosen to provide an expert report will usually be senior members of the profession who will often have many other clinical, administrative and academic commitments. Such commitments inevitably mean that writing expert reports is not always the top priority, as noted by a defence organisation to the legal department in one case:

> *I regret to say that* (this expert) *is not known for his speed in the production of his reports.*

While it is quite natural to expect senior practitioners to be busy on occasion they have not been able to be contacted, as in this case concerning cerebral palsy, in which the plaintiff's solicitor wrote to the legal department explaining the delay:

> *Our local agents have attempted to contact Dr H on a number of occasions both in writing and by telephone and he has not responded to them whatsoever.*

In another case concerning an intrauterine death the plaintiff's solicitors noted:

> *We were successful in engaging the services of an independent consultant to consider our client's records. Despite various attempts he seems physically incapable of furnishing an opinion. We are therefore disengaging from him.*

Delays can occur just as easily in the case of the defence expert. In one claim concerning cerebral palsy the medical defence organisation wrote to the legal department:

> *This is becoming most embarrassing! I have written yet again to our expert, this time advising him to let me know if he cannot provide us with an opinion within the next three weeks* (otherwise) *I will go elsewhere.*

Criticism of delays by experts are not always unanswered: in one action an expert wrote to the legal department claiming that delays were often encountered by experts waiting to hear back from solicitors. This is discussed more in *Chapter 15*, which examines the causes of delays in legal actions.

The choice of an expert, quite apart from the potential delays involved, would appear to be fraught with difficulties. The expert must be up-to-date to be credible, and must be seen not to be partisan.

Conclusion

The role of experts is crucial to the course of a legal action, but there are clearly many potential difficulties in this area of the law, a number of these have been highlighted. While it is a mark of respect to be consulted as an expert, it is apparent that such respect has not always been earned. The recently published lists of experts should help to avoid many of the problems examined in this chapter, since those appearing on the list will be deemed to have verified expertise in a subject. Some of the particular problems associated with delays and the use of experts is discussed in *Chapter 15*, and a lack of experience among solicitors in knowing whom to contact is explored in *Chapter 25*.

Chapter 6

F   Finding fault

> *If we had no faults we should not take*
> *so much pleasure in noticing them in others.*
>
> (Duc de la Rochefoucauld)

In terms of securing compensation finding fault is one of the necessary requirements under the current law. However, it is seen in *Chapter 12* that the need to establish causation may be a significant obstacle, even when fault has been admitted or shown. Because of this there has been some debate on the question of whether fault should be an essential feature of the law. This chapter examines some of this debate, firstly from the viewpoint of the debate on fault versus need, and then from the specific viewpoint of no-fault compensation. The second section looks at the experience of no-fault compensation in New Zealand, Sweden and the USA, and considers the possibilities for such a scheme in Britain.

The 'Fault'/'Need' debate

Although research into personal injury litigation has at times criticised its operation and proposed alternatives, the fault-based principle of the law of negligence is unlikely to be changed in any substantial way in the foreseeable future. Investigation into this subject included a Royal Commission (Pearson, 1978), which sat from 1972 to 1978 examining civil liability and personal injury compensation. Despite advocating reforms which included shifting the emphasis away from establishing fault in certain instances (such as road traffic accidents), its findings according to Mansell (1997: 226), 'have been almost completely ignored by the legislature'. Of course, any proposed changes must take into account the political realities of the day, in particular the willingness of the government to confront such a long-standing legal tradition.

The law of negligence, as set out in *Part I*, appears straightforward: if the duty of care is breached and damage results then negligence is established. Atiyah and Cane (1993) note the centrality of the concept of fault to this law, but criticise the need to establish fault in order to obtain compensation. If loss occurs as a result of fault, then compensation may be paid; but if it occurs and fault cannot be proven (as is often the case in medicine), then the victim must bear the burden without such financial help. In New Zealand and Sweden the many apparent injustices of this system, including its administrative costs (Palmer, 1994), led to the introduction of specifically no-fault schemes. These are considered later on in this chapter.

Genn (1987: 163) notes that the theoretical certainties of the law of tort (delict in Scotland) may often be overtaken by other factors: 'this... lack of precision... creates... conditions of uncertainty under which claims are argued and resisted, and... contributes substantially to the pressure on plaintiffs to avoid the risks of trial by compromising their claim.' What might have been seen as a straightforward claim may be affected by several factors: for example a plaintiff's solicitor may lack expertise in personal injury matters (see *Chapter 25*). Although 'neither plaintiff's nor defendant's lawyers, both acting for private parties, have any direct interest in facilitating the administration of civil justice' (*ibid*: 167), the requirements of the civil justice system demand that the vast majority of claims are settled before the court stage. This in turn is used by the insurance companies (who were the defendants in Genn's study) to put pressure on the claimants' solicitors to compromise the extent of the claim. This sort of compromise, according to Mansell (1997: 233) is very unseemly: 'The striking of a bargain between lawyers as to the level of compensation after negotiations... resembles nothing so much as (in a greatly prolonged form) the haggling required before purchase in an Oriental market. The price settled upon in each case often has less to do with the quality of the claim... than with the quality of the bargaining skills of the (lawyers).'

The principle of tort is that, providing fault is established, the injured party is compensated in full: '*restituto in integrum* implies full compensation for losses suffered' (Genn, 1987: 168). However, the 'haggling' process is likely to reduce the eventual level of damages, despite the lack of any contingency fee for the lawyer, given the experience of the defendant in this area of the law. Genn, referring to Galanter (1974), called the insurance companies in her study 'repeat players', a label which could accurately be used to describe hospitals in negligence cases. In addition, as Mansell (1997: 233) points out with reference to a 1994 Law Commission report, 'notwithstanding the principle of full compensation most victims required significant unpaid care by parents, spouses, friends and neighbours.'

However, as Atiyah and Cane (1993) point out, there may be little correlation between a negligent action or omission and its consequences. The theory of 'fault' as a moral principle is further reduced by insurance liability (which almost all practitioners have) and the vicarious liability of the employer. These features, together with the difficulty many plaintiffs have encountered in satisfying the Bolam/*Hunter v Hanley* test, have led to calls for compensation to be payable on the basis of need rather than fault. Advocated principally as a means of ensuring greater fairness for the victims of medical accidents, this would paradoxically sometimes work in favour of practitioners: in a small number of cases, claims have been settled out of court when there was little evidence of any negligence, but when the claim would be more expensive to defend than to concede. When a case is conceded the inference is that the practitioner has been guilty of negligence, but this is not always the case.

Atiyah and Cane (1993) also point out that payment under the law need not be associated with moral culpability; and indeed moral culpability does not always result in compensation. If compensation is to be on the basis of need rather than fault, then the usual provision for this is some form of social security. In Sweden the no-fault compensation is intended to 'top up' already existing social welfare benefits, which are generous by British standards. Finland introduced a drug insurance scheme in 1984, and a statutory patient's insurance scheme in 1987. Based on the Swedish model of no-fault insurance, these measures were intended to reduce the burden on the tort system and ensure a fairer method of compensation: 'The damages are reduced by whatever other benefits the patient can claim from the state or his employer so the scheme "tops up" these benefits...' (Brahams, 1988: 679). To be comparable, benefits in Britain would need to be augmented significantly; an improbable prospect at present. Adopting a top-up mechanism like that in Sweden or Finland would be feasible, however: Atiyah and Cane (1993: 402) note that there are already rules 'which determine when and to what extent no-fault, first-party insurance and social security benefits are to be set off against tort damages.'

Interestingly, the Finnish Bar Association did not oppose the changes, seeing them in the public interest (*ibid*: 678). This is in stark contrast to the view expressed by Mansell (1997) concerning legal opposition to proposed changes to the fault-based system in Britain. In a similar vein Atiyah and Cane (1993: 405) assert that 'the interests of a few hundred barristers cannot, in the long run, be allowed to determine the shape of the law relating to compensation for personal injuries; law is a social service, and in the long run the interests of the consumer and not the administrators must prevail.' In addition, Brahams (1988: 680) notes that in Finland payment is by instalment and not lump sum, so that 'the family of a compensated victim do not gain by his untimely death.' Instalment payments (known as structured settlements) have sometimes been used in Britain, but this is not yet the norm, and the failure to do this has caused problems (eg. in *Calladine v Nottingham AHA*).

If 'need' is to replace 'fault' as the basis for compensation, the argument may then turn to the rationale for distinguishing a disability which is caused by an accident (such as in the New Zealand scheme) from one which is not. Noting that there is a long legal tradition which requires that the victims of negligently-caused accidents be compensated, Mansell (1997: 229) points out that: 'In tort a single tortfeasor is called upon to make good the damage, and clearly the losses of those disabled otherwise are not similarly individually attributable... there is no long tradition of such compensation for those who have become ill.'

No-fault compensation

While there are a number of possible alternatives to and developments in the current legal process, perhaps the most fundamental proposed alternative is no-fault compensation. This possible change gained considerable popularity (and consequently some momentum) in the late 1980s and early 1990s (Gallup, 1989; Smith, 1990; Dyer, 1990). While calls to remove the fault criterion in medical negligence claims have been heard less in recent years, the subject remains pertinent particularly in view of the escalating levels of compensation when negligence claims are successful.

The crux of the fault-based system is the notion that it represents a method of calling people (in this case practitioners) to account. From the criticisms of the current system it is evident that this is a view not shared by everyone. Bolt, the Chairman of the British Medical Association (BMA) Working Party on no-fault compensation, put this very forcefully: '...one of the things that confuses us in this country terribly, is this firm belief that the tort system represents a method of accountability. This is, of course, absolute nonsense' (Bolt,1992: 56).

New Zealand

New Zealand was the first country to introduce a no-fault system under the Accident Compensation Scheme, which was introduced in 1974. It was not designed to deal just with alleged negligence or malpractice in medical matters, but to tackle some of the unfairness and inefficiencies of the tort system. Palmer (1994: 272) claims that 'tort law serves to obscure the real problems and prevent them from being addressed.' Under the new scheme 'the right to sue for compensation for personal injury was abolished in return for the introduction of a system of "no-fault" compensation' (Oliphant 1996: 3).

The Accident Compensation Commission (ACC) and its successors have operated the scheme, which is funded from general taxation, as well as contributions from employers and the self-employed. Payments are 'based on loss of earnings, reasonable medical expenses, and other out of pocket expenses. There is no contribution for pain and suffering' (Symonds, 1992: 11). Brown and Smillie (1991: 249) note that payments based on loss of earnings 'up to a very high salary ceiling' favour the better off disproportionately.

McLean (1988:152, 159) notes that the ACC was gradually given more discretion and therefore the proposed certainty of the scheme became eroded. She goes on to propose that if no-fault compensation is introduced in Britain, the original New Zealand definition of eligibility should not be copied. Oliphant (1996) points out that lessons learned from the New Zealand experience may be valuable if a no-fault scheme is to be introduced in Britain.

Ham *et al* (1988) note that the New Zealand scheme proved to be very expensive, with expenditure rising sharply: between 1975 and 1988 the scheme's expenditure rose by 313% while its income only went up by 122%. Concern about rising costs and the difficulties encountered by the courts in adopting a rigid (and therefore predictable) definition of compensatable personal injury led to a Royal Commission which produced the Accident Rehabilitation and Compensation Insurance (ARCI) Act 1992[1]. The new Act tightened the definition of medical misadventure while maintaining the original division of this concept into medical error (which includes cases of possible negligence) and medical mishap.

Concern had been expressed that the removal of the fault requirement had deprived patients of the means of calling negligent practitioners to account (Oliphant, 1996) although Collins (1993) claims that, despite a substantial increase in disciplinary complaints against doctors, there is no empirical evidence that the scheme had adversely affected the regulation of medical practice. Under the new scheme, possible instances of clinical negligence may be reported by the ARCI Corporation to the relevant disciplinary body.

Sweden

Sweden brought in a 'Patient Insurance Scheme' in 1975 which invokes an investigation of injury and resulting disabilities; this exists alongside the tort system. As Symonds (1992: 11) points out, 'the main concern of patient insurance systems are the relatively low level of compensation and the cost generally to the community.' However, the Swedish system must be seen in relation to the existing comprehensive social security provisions. Social security benefits are already paid to victims, and the patient insurance scheme is intended to help those suffering such injuries by supplementing the benefits paid. To qualify for the scheme, a person must be ill for 30 days or in hospital for 10 days, or must suffer permanent disability, although Simanowitz (1987) notes that the Swedish system strangely does not compensate babies for brain damage which occurs at birth; it is claimed that damages in such cases would be so large as to make the system economically unviable. The Swedish system is funded by capitation payments from the local authorities which administer the health service to 'a consortium of private insurers which then manages the claims and their settlements' (Maclean, 1989: 38).

USA

In *Chapter 4* some features of defensiveness were discussed. Among these was the belief that, thanks largely to the threat or experience of litigation, the provision of obstetric services has been threatened by a 'haemorrhage' of clinical practitioners. Such claims refer principally to the USA (whose experience of litigation is discussed further in *Chapter 21*), where studies (eg. ACOG, 1988; Bredfeldt *et al,* 1989) have identified a significant reduction in the number of doctors prepared to provide obstetric care. To try and redress the causes which have resulted in this state of affairs, limited no-fault schemes have been introduced.

Symonds (1992) reports that in West Virginia and Florida a system of no-fault compensation had to be introduced for claims concerning birth-related injuries as a result of the virtual breakdown of the obstetric services. This seems to confirm the frightening view that many women are at risk of having obstetric services denied them. To try and offset this, an 'obstetrical care incentive program' was introduced in North Carolina, in which certified nurse-midwives were encouraged to practice (Taylor *et al,* 1992).

1　　This was renamed the Accident Compensation in 1981. In 1992 this became the Accident Rehabilitation and Compensation Insurance Corporation.

The Virginia Birth-Related Neurological Injury Compensation Act came about in part due to the work carried out by O'Connell on no-fault insurance (no-fault automobile insurance had been introduced in the 1970s). However, it was an insurance crisis rather than reasoned argument in favour of a more equitable system which proved to be the catalyst for the Act: Fisher (1990) notes that obstetricians in Virginia were left without insurance cover following a large payout by one insurance company. Two other insurance companies restricted their cover, one declining to cover new practitioners and the other restricting itself to groups of ten or more. The Virginia scheme is discussed more fully in *Chapter 21*.

Florida's Neurological Injury Compensation Act (NICA) is an attempt to remove the fault criterion for certain birth-related injury claims. Sloan *et al* (1998) found that, because of the narrow statutory definition of birth injury, many children with birth-related injuries did not qualify for cover. However, comparing claims and payments before and after its introduction in 1989, they noted that some claimants were better off because of the dramatic reduction in the proportion of damages which went to the lawyers. Reviewing the effectiveness of the scheme Whetton-Goldstein *et al* (1999) conclude that medical expenses are adequately covered, but that (compared with the old tort system) income loss is not.

Reviewing the need for no-fault compensation, Manuel (1990: 627) claims that Americans are 'suing themselves into second-class medicine,' but the response is fragmented and dependent on local conditions; only a handful of areas have introduced such schemes to date. A modified version of 'no-fault', based on what they term Accelerated Compensation Events, is examined by Bovbjerg *et al* (1991).

Britain

There is no doubt that there are some persuasive arguments for the introduction of some form of no-fault compensation in Britain. However, while such a move would appear superficially to address some of the inequities of the fault-based system, it would itself not be immune from criticism. Nevertheless, it would seem to be popular among some practitioners:

> *A no-fault scheme for many aspects, I think, would be quite useful. It is terribly difficult for people who are injured or handicapped having to prove negligence just to get money, and so some form of no fault insurance, a no-fault scheme, would save an awful lot of litigation.*

(Consultant obstetrician 4)

In some of the most tragic cases an automatic method of compensation is attractive, not least because it may do away with some of the antagonisms of the current system. One midwife spoke about her involvement in one such case:

> *I delivered someone whose baby, very unexpectedly came out with a low Apgar score... The mother did not realise how sick her baby was.. she feels very angry, and very angry with me, because she thinks I'm to blame, and she's taken the notes around (this city). She's gone to two barristers, I know that, to try and find a case against me...*

(Midwife 2)

There seems little doubt that a natural response to a catastrophe is to try and find someone to blame (this was discussed in *Chapter 2*). While an automatic compensation payment will not remove this, it might take some of the sting out of the situation. Brazier (1987) claims that a no-fault system would increase the number of claimants who would get compensation to help them adapt their lives to their disabilities, and that damage to the practitioner-client relationship through bitter and costly litigation would be removed. Quite apart from the levels of compensation paid in successful claims, the cost of litigation, particularly if the claim gets to the court stage, can be very high. One respondent offered an alternative:

> *If they didn't spend all that money on the court cases but put it into a fund for damaged babies that would make far more sense.*

(Midwife 3)

The cost of the current system is certainly one of the major propellants for change: Rosie Barnes MP, speaking in support of her National Health Service (Compensation) Bill in 1991, claimed that the cost of litigation was thought at that time to amount to £100m. She also noted that the BMA had estimated that by 1996 a total of 13% of all resources available to the average health authority would go towards paying compensation for negligence claims. Tingle (1998) relates that the National Audit Office has reported that expenditure for clinical negligence in the NHS for 1996–97 was put at £235m, and that the total potential liability for clinical negligence could be up to £2.3 billion.

However, problems with the existing schemes in New Zealand and Sweden have indicated difficulties with introducing no-fault compensation in Britain:

> *Causation applies just as much to the no fault scenario as it does to the negligence scenario... there's a common misunderstanding that if we had no fault compensation causation wouldn't be a problem,* (but) *it would be.*

(Defence solicitor 1)

The Pearson Commission (Pearson, 1978), set up in 1972 to investigate civil liability and compensation, condemned the tort system as unpredictable, expensive and unfair, and urged the creation of new disability allowances for all severely handicapped children irrespective of whether their handicap resulted from negligence. However it stopped short of proposing no-fault compensation for medical injuries, although it did so for motor vehicle injuries. Mansell (1997) criticises the Pearson Commission for interpreting its terms of reference too narrowly, and for failing to follow a principled approach to the question of civil litigation:

> *The almost ad hoc approach they favoured with a new no fault scheme for injuries caused by road accidents; with a specific benefit for severely handicapped children; and with a statutory basis for criminal injuries recommended, did not seem to reflect any clear philosophy.*

He argues that the opportunity to mount a comprehensive challenge to the fault based system was thereby lost (*ibid*: 226).

A superficially attractive option, not least because it would solve one of the NHS' most pressing financial headaches, is to introduce no-fault compensation for cases of birth-related handicap. However, this would not address the fact that people with handicap due to other causes would be excluded. Indeed, a significant difficulty for those who would like to challenge the central concept of fault seems to be how to define which accidents or conditions would be eligible for compensation and which would not:

> *Rosie Barnes... and the BMA prepared* (no-fault) *bills, and I looked at both of them, and they really struggled over [a] a definition of medical accident, and eventually they almost got round to a tort type definition, and [b] the problem of causation, because*

they did exclude medical accidents which probably occurred as a result of the condition or the natural reaction to treatment.

(Defence solicitor 1)

Problems with such a definition appear to have stalled calls for this change for the time being. While many obstetricians in the postal survey appeared to favour the introduction of no-fault compensation, criticism of such a proposal in the UK has come from a number of quarters. Simanowitz (1992) claims that it does not address the question of accountability, a point echoed by Beech (1990), and stressed by one respondent:

You have some very cavalier doctors out there, certainly in obstetrics...We're totally opposed to no-fault compensation: if you took away that – albeit not terribly useful – element of accountability, they wouldn't worry at all. You wonder what (particularly consultant) *obstetricians would feel they could get away with.*

(AVMA official 1)

Echoing this point Bowles and Jones (1990) question whether a no-fault system would provide as much of a deterrent as the tort system. As if to answer this Clements claims that 'experience elsewhere suggests that litigation is the best way forward because it's actually the bit that hurts.' However he goes on to note that, 'It's a very poor doctor who only practises well because of the threat of litigation' (cited by Kinnes, 1993). Sloan *et al* (1995) claim that empirical evidence shows that no systematic improvement in birth outcomes can be shown from an increased threat of litigation.

Interestingly, in submissions to the Pearson Commission the BMA strongly opposed the prospect of no-fault compensation, claiming that a fault-based system was a guarantor of individual clinical accountability. The BMA also feared state control of a no-fault system, which it felt would encroach on the profession's autonomy. The BMA subsequently changed its mind and supports a no-fault system, although its 'no-fault' proposals have been criticised (Mildred, 1989) and AVMA and AIMS remain opposed to such a scheme.

Clothier (1989) points out that the right to take a fellow citizen before a judge in order to settle a dispute is a fundamental liberty, and questions why doctors (and by extension other health workers) ought to be made exempt from this: is it for reasons of principle, or simply because the current system is so inefficient? He also claims that the no-fault schemes operating in New Zealand and Sweden, far from providing certainty, merely displace the argument: lawyers now argue about what is admissible as a medical accident. Carson (1988) points out that the concentration on 'cause' (ie. what is an accident?) rather than 'effect' can be very complicated: the arguments about whether a condition has been caused solely by clinical mistake or whether it has deteriorated through natural progression may be interminable. He claims that if social security and social services were adequately funded and so could provide comprehensive benefits, the desire to sue could be reduced and the need for a no-fault system avoided.

Conclusion

The current fault-based system for deciding questions of medical negligence has been much criticised; despite some of the attraction of a no-fault scheme it looks unlikely to be changed in the foreseeable future. Concern about the low rate of compensation for those who have suffered injury or loss has led to changes directed at improving access to justice; these have concentrated on mediation and arbitration, while changes to the way Trusts deal with damages payments aim to ameliorate the financial impact of litigation on the delivery of health care. More openness in dealing with complaints may be a way forward, especially as Trusts struggle to deal with the increase in complaints received.

Chapter 7

G   Grounds for suing

We were not born to sue, but to command.

(Richard I: 1. ii. 196)

This chapter examines the grounds for suing those involved in perinatal care. Most of the data relate to Scotland, but English heads of claim are also discussed. It is important to know the reasons for legal actions: without this knowledge we can not be sure that risk management is being effective in one of its aims, ie. reducing the incidence of litigation. Nevertheless, and despite the distinct lack of published data on this issue, risk management programmes are being implemented. Some of these are discussed in *Chapter 18*.

Limited studies have identified some of the grounds for suing, but these have sometimes been restricted by the nature of the sample. Ennis and Vincent (1990) looked at 64 obstetric cases in which there was either stillbirth, perinatal or neonatal death, central nervous system (CNS) damage to the baby, or a maternal death. They admit that this was 'a highly selected sample that has come to litigation' (*ibid*: 1365). Capstick and Edwards (1990) examined 100 obstetric cases from ten health authorities over a seven-year period, of which 49 related to a brain damaged infant. This illustrates the point that, while cerebral palsy cases may attract the headlines, there are other reasons why people sue. Unfortunately the authors do not explain what these other reasons are. They identified certain allegations about obstetric mismanagement, the most common being inadequate fetal heart rate monitoring.

James (1991) reported a study by the Medical Research Council which analysed 100 obstetric claims made to the Medical Defence Union. This identified six principal heads of claim, with the most common ('Brain damaged baby') accounting for only 31 of the claims. This suggests a broader range of reasons for suing than some appeared to think. James also points out that:

> *When studying patterns of litigation it is important to distinguish between claims notified and claims settled. The former are an indication of the patient's view of compensatable damage, the latter those cases in which independent expert advice agrees that the treatment was negligent.*

> (James, 1991: 36)

It is therefore instructive to examine the accompanying possible causes of the litigation – the motivation. In some cases it is an underlying sense of grievance (which may or may not be well founded) which promotes, and indeed prolongs, the litigation. These features are discussed in *Chapter 10*.

In this chapter it is the heads of claim that are discussed – in James' words, 'the patient's view of compensatable damage'. The charts in this chapter show that there is a low overall success rate in perinatal litigation, although the rate varies according to the specific head of claim. In this research, data from a total of 613 legal files were obtained: 505 from Scotland and 108 from England. The number of heads of claim shown in the charts exceeds the number of legal files, because in several files there was more than one head of claim. This is by no means an unusual phenomenon: in one recent Court of Appeal case (Hallatt [1998]), the judge noted that 'at the trial a large number of allegations of negligence were pursued extending over the whole range of the management of Mrs Hallatt's pregnancy and her labour and the delivery of Thomas. They were all unsuccessful and only one is being pursued on this appeal' (per Hobhouse LJ @ 197).

All open Scottish files, and 172 of the closed Scottish files, were personally examined, as were all the English files. The procedure used by the Central Legal Office (CLO) in Edinburgh for storing closed files changed during the course of the research, which prevented all the files being personally examined. However, essential data from these files were retrieved from the CLO computer database. The files all relate to perinatal events from January 1980 to December 1995, and raised by May 1996; the status of the claim in April 1999 is shown. In order to exclude gynaecology claims from the analysis a cut-off point of 20 weeks gestation was used.

The first two charts relate exclusively to Scottish claims, and so the Scots law terms of 'pursuer' and 'defender' are used.

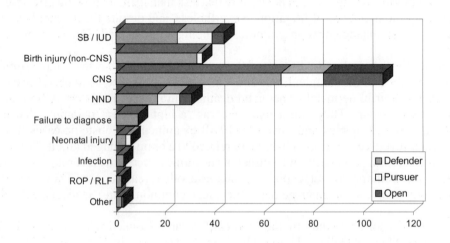

Figure 7.1: Baby claims in Scotland 1980–1995 (status of claim as at April 1999)

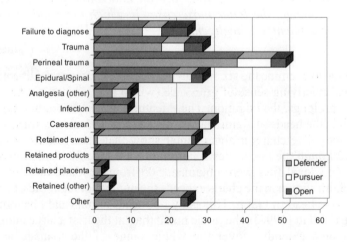

Figure 7.2: Maternal claims in Scotland 1980–1995 (status of claim as at April 1999)

Contrary to the popular myth that perinatal litigation is all about brain damaged baby claims, it can be seen that there is a wide range of grounds for suing. The difference in scale of the two charts should be stressed: in the first the CNS claims (essentially those in which there is some degree of handicap on the part of the baby) are by far the most common reason for suing, and totalled 108. By contrast there is a much more even range in the maternal claims, and no one head of claim dominates in the same way, although it can be seen that perineal trauma is the most common. When all the Scottish heads of claim are added up, the CNS claims represent just 21% of the total.

For comparison the English claims are shown here. It must be considered that they reflect the claims in only two areas, and it is not known how representative these may have been of England as a whole.

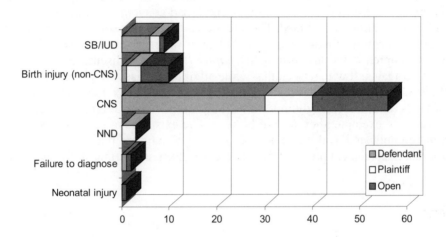

Figure 7.3: Baby claims in two English areas1980–1995 (status of claim as at April 1999)

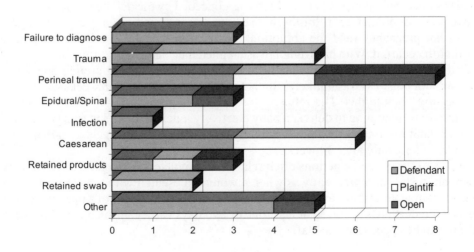

Figure 7.4: Maternal claims in two English areas1980–1995 (status of claim as at April 1999)

Although the heads of claim in the English legal cases were broadly similar to those in Scotland there were some differences, the main one being the proportion of claims relating to CNS damage. Of 117 separate heads of claim in the 108 English files, 56 related to CNS damage. This is a feature which certainly warrants further investigation. At 25%, the rate of success for plaintiffs under this head of claim was higher than the 20% rate for pursuers in Scotland, and in fact contributed to a higher overall rate of success of English claims (34% compared with 25% in Scotland).

The wide range of reasons for suing indicates that the problem is a complex one that cannot be easily described. Perinatal litigation cannot be put down to concerns about brain damaged children alone, and it is important not to focus exclusively on the CNS claims, despite their distinction from other claims, notably in terms of potential damages.

What follows is a very brief description of some of the factors behind each head of claim identified in this research. In this section, given the broad convergence in the heads of claim, both Scottish and English claims are included. The intention is to draw out some of the reasoning behind the decision to sue, although within one chapter only a brief summary can be given. This is by no means intended to be a comprehensive description. In *Chapter 10* there is a discussion of some of the possible motives held by litigants. It will be seen that while all of these cases are perinatal, not all of them are obstetric. While obstetricians might breathe a sigh of relief at being excluded from some of these legal actions, midwives (and, increasingly, nurses working in the neonatal area) are very much involved. Anaesthetists are not exempt either, as will be seen. The existence of several specialities makes this area somewhat complicated, and less amenable to focused targeted improvements, and represents a challenge for risk management programmes. These are discussed further in *Chapter 18*.

Baby claims

Stillbirth/intrauterine death (IUD)

Under this head of claim is usually the rationale that either insufficient surveillance during pregnancy or labour meant that a compromised fetus was not identified, or that signs of compromise were recognised but not acted upon. One case which was conceded by the defence concerned a woman who had had two previous premature stillbirths, both due to placental abruption. Despite being hospitalised for much of her pregnancy (and the abruption occurring in hospital and being diagnosed quickly) another stillbirth occurred. With hindsight it was claimed that elective caesarean section ought to have been carried out as soon as the fetal lungs were thought to be mature, at around 36 weeks (ie. when neonatal respiratory distress was unlikely). In fact induction of labour at 38 weeks was planned, but the abruption occurred before this. The retrospectoscope gives perfect vision with hindsight, but many obstetricians will be unwilling to deliver a baby electively much before 38 weeks gestation because of the risk of neonatal respiratory distress; a study by Morrison *et al* (1995) claimed that such problems were much less likely only after 39 weeks.

Examples of unsuccessful actions often related to completely unexplained IUDs. Very often the first indication to staff of a problem was when a woman presented with a history of feeling no fetal movements for some time; this was three weeks in one instance. Delivery of a macerated stillborn baby indicates that the death has occurred at least one or two days earlier. In such circumstances no blame for the death can be apportioned to staff.

Non-CNS birth injury

Successful actions under this head of claim included fractures to a baby's arm during a breech delivery, and brachial plexus injury in an apparently normal delivery. The fact that the defence conceded this claim appears to indicate an acceptance that excessive force was used at delivery. However, this head of claim has a low success rate as either the injury is thought to be a recognised and frequently unavoidable occurrence after an unforeseen emergency, such as Erb's palsy following shoulder dystocia or, in other cases, the claimed injury was in fact a congenital condition. One example of this related to cutis alopecia, a patchy hairless area on the baby's head which the plaintiffs alleged was due to forceps blades or an incompetently applied fetal scalp electrode.

CNS damage

This is a very emotive subject, and this section gives only a brief snapshot of this head of claim. It was the most common type of claim, and some of the circumstances surrounding it are discussed more fully in *Chapter 13*. The allegation is usually made that a child's cerebral condition (and here 'brain damage' and 'cerebral palsy' are to all intents and purposes interchangeable) is due to staff negligence, either in failing to detect signs of fetal compromise, or in failing to act on such signs. The discussions in *Chapter 13* and *Appendix III* note that there is a poorly understood but complex aetiology to cerebral palsy and that causation is very often difficult to establish.

Even where the brain damage is thought to have originated in the labour period, negligence is not an automatic assumption. In one case a student midwife found that, after the delivery of the baby's head, the cord was tightly around the baby's neck; the cord was clamped and cut, and then shoulder dystocia was diagnosed, and there was a delay in delivering the baby's body. The baby showed signs of neurological damage at 36 hours of age, and subsequently developed cerebral palsy. This case was unsuccessful because it was held that the staff acted appropriately in the circumstances: nothing they did (or failed to do) was construed as negligent.

In another case in which fetal compromise was suspected, a doctor allegedly stated 'The baby would be better out than in.' The plaintiff's solicitors claimed that: 'No action was taken until many hours later.' Although not conclusive proof, this version of events was held to make the defence very vulnerable, and the case was conceded.

Neonatal death

Such actions were very similar to the 'Stillbirth/IUD' and 'CNS damage' heads of claim, in that it was usually asserted that better surveillance would have led to earlier intervention either before or during labour, and that the baby would have survived as a result. Least likely to be successful under this head of claim were those cases concerning very premature infants: one such case concerned a baby born by the breech at 25 weeks, the woman being admitted in advanced labour. The one case concerning a premature infant which did succeed turned on the neonatal management – it was felt that treatment was not aggressive enough when infection was suspected.

More likely to succeed were cases concerning a term baby where the death apparently resulted from mismanagement of labour. In one instance a junior doctor used oxytocic drugs when the woman had already had uterine and cervical surgery and also had epidural anaesthesia in place, and in which there was already evidence of fetal compromise. The uterus ruptured, and the baby was born severely asphyxiated and died several days later.

Failure to diagnose/treat (baby)

Out of eleven cases under this head of claim, six related to a failure to diagnose congenital dislocation of the hips; others related to different congenital conditions such as cataracts or microcephaly. While failing to diagnose something may represent a poor standard of care (a congenital cataract should be picked up on routine neonatal examination by a doctor), the legal requirement that to establish negligence, harm should result from the breach of a duty of care, means such cases do not succeed, the condition being congenital. No cases were successful.

Neonatal injury

Seven claims were noted here: in three cases these related to tissue injuries in the baby caused by venous or arterial lines. In one case the baby lost a lower arm after gangrene set in, but the case was unsuccessful because it was held that this was, however tragic, unavoidable in the circumstances. In another case a relatively minor degree of injury to the baby's arm resulted in damages for the plaintiffs, because it was held that the injury was negligently caused.

Injuries have been allegedly caused by an overdose of drugs; where harm results, such cases are difficult to defend. In one case a baby was given a BCG vaccination, but the dosage was far higher than it should have been.

Baby infection

In three cases the allegation concerned neonatal infection; two of these related to meningitis. In one of these, the family believed that prolonged rupture of membranes (in fact documented at 23 hours) contributed. The third related to septic osteitis, which the parents believed stemmed from an untreated staphylococcal infection of the umbilicus. In this case the consultant paediatrician noted:

> *A high proportion of infants, if not all, have colonisation probably with a staphylococcus in their umbilicus at the time of discharge from hospital... To suggest that they should all be treated with antibiotics would be ludicrous.*

None of these cases succeeded.

Retinopathy of prematurity (Retrolental Fibroplasia)

Two cases (from the early to mid-1980s) concerned this condition, the allegation being that over-oxygenation of the newborn baby caused blindness. This head of claim received a good deal of prominence in a landmark legal case (*Wilsher v Essex AHA* 1986). Babies requiring prolonged oxygen therapy are usually premature, and it is very difficult to establish that giving vital oxygen represents negligent conduct. Neither of the cases examined in this research succeeded.

Other (baby)

These cases related to a baby allegedly born addicted to opiates because his mother had been over-prescribed drugs during her pregnancy, and a baby with a gastro-oesophageal reflux. The first case is still open; the second was unsuccessful.

Maternal claims

Failure to diagnose/treat (mother)

Most of these claims related to a failure to detect conditions during pregnancy, which may be seen as reflecting high expectations in society. The issue of high expectations is discussed in *Chapter 8*. Unusual fetal cerebral or genetic conditions formed the basis of unsuccessful claims, as did the allegedly incorrect diagnosis of Down's syndrome, and (in one case) a failure to detect placenta praevia. Failure to detect spina bifida on ultrasound accounted for three cases, the time in question being after twenty weeks gestation (the cut off point for this research).

Successful actions included parents being told incorrectly that their baby had died in utero, the mistake only being realised 24 hours later; and the failure to detect rhesus antibodies during pregnancy (rhesus negative women ought to be screened routinely throughout pregnancy). A study by Tucker *et al* (1996) found a high prevalence of this failure in women receiving community-led care (given by GPs and midwives) compared with hospital-based care, indicating that moves to reduce routine obstetric surveillance in hospitals must be accompanied by careful anticipation of possible risks.

Non-perineal trauma

Many of the claims in this section related to injury allegedly sustained at delivery; these included damage to bladder or urethra from forceps, or apparent fracture of sacrum or coccyx at normal or instrumental delivery. Few of this type succeeded, it being difficult to prove that the injury was caused by a standard of care amounting to negligence. Certain features, such as coccydynia or symphysis pain, may occur after a straightforward normal delivery. Other unsuccessful actions concerned caesarean scar dehiscence and haemorrhage from gynaecological surgery following subsequent normal delivery.

Examples of successful claims included burns from a hot water bottle given by midwifery staff, chemical burns from improper skin preparation in Theatre, and an allergic reaction from adhesive strapping despite this known allergy being documented prominently in the woman's case notes.

Perineal trauma

This head of claim proved to be the most common of the maternal cases in both Scotland and the English areas accounting for, respectively, 19% and 22%. Several claims included allegations of an over-tight repair which caused unnecessary pain, or a repair which either broke down and required resuturing or became infected; others concerned prolonged postnatal discomfort and eventual refashioning of the perineum. However the success rate in Scotland under this head of claim was not high (19%); it was rather higher in the English areas at 40%, but this was a much smaller sample. Successful claims tended to concern anal sphincter involvement and faecal incontinence, although some concerned simple evidence of poor repair technique. The concern to avoid extensive tearing at delivery underpinned the soaring episiotomy rate in the 1970s (MacFarlane and Mugford, 1984). Less common as a head of claim in the early 1980s, its prevalence peaked at 24% of all maternal claims for 1988–91.

Epidural/spinal

Like some of the neonatal claims noted above, this head of claim concerned obstetricians less directly. Three distinct features were noted:

- analgesia in labour or at instrumental delivery was claimed to be inadequate (this relates to how midwives, obstetricians and anaesthetists respond to the woman's assertion that she is experiencing pain)
- anaesthesia at caesarean section was claimed to be inadequate (which relates to how anaesthetists in particular respond to the same claim)
- after-effects of the epidural or spinal were claimed to be causing pain and suffering.

All of these had a low success rate in terms of litigation. It is clearly difficult to establish that staff were negligent in not ensuring adequate pain relief. One claim which did succeed concerned a caesarean which proceeded with apparently good anaesthesia until just before the baby was born, at which point the mother became very distressed; a 'top-up' of the epidural had no effect and a general anaesthetic was required.

In another case a woman claimed the epidural fractured a small bone in her back; however an antenatal X-Ray pelvimetry (because of breech presentation) was claimed to show the spinal condition which she alleged was caused at delivery. Allegations concerning 'epidural sequelae' have been commented upon (MacArthur *et al,* 1990; MacLeod *et al,* 1995), although there is disagreement on the alleged relationship between epidurals and long-term backache.

Analgesia/anaesthesia (other)

These usually related to claims of inadequate pain relief in either the Labour Ward or Theatre; of the nine closed cases, four succeeded. One concerned a claim made that midwives failed to monitor adequately the woman's pain during labour; another that inadequate supervision contributed to nerve damage from an opiate injection.

One unsuccessful claim concerned an anaesthetic catastrophe, with the woman suffering a cardiac arrest and dying after severe bronchospasm. At post mortem a 'peculiar laryngo-tracheal anatomy' was found, which it is thought contributed to the disaster.

Infection

Seven of the ten cases concerned infection following caesarean section, the other three following vaginal delivery. This head of claim may reflect a lack of acceptance that infections may occur after any procedure, especially surgery. As a recognised complication, particularly post-operatively, the presence of infection is not evidence of negligence and none of these claims succeeded. This is not to say that a claim of this nature could never succeed, only that, in the circumstances investigated here, staff were not found to have been negligent.

Caesarean section

A number of different reasons lie behind this head of claim. Few of the Scottish claims succeeded, usually because it was held that certain eventualities may occur especially during an emergency operation. These included damage to ureter, fallopian tubes and bladder. In one case in which alleged damage to a fallopian tube led to secondary infertility, the employer wrote:

(The Consultant) *does not consider it normal practice in an acute obstetric emergency to counsel patients in detail on all the possible difficulties that might, very infrequently, arise.*

In another there was a concealed abruption and intra-uterine death; although labour was induced, it was felt that the abruption was causing disseminated intravascular coagulation and an emergency caesarean was performed. In order to control haemorrhage a hysterectomy was required and while this represented a very unfortunate outcome for the woman, there was no evidence that negligence had occurred.

An example of a successful claim involved a concealed post-operative haemorrhage, which necessitated a lengthy laparotomy. The woman's solicitors claimed:

As a result of the treatment which our client considers to have been negligent, she has suffered a permanent cosmetic defect in the form of a longitudinal scar 20 inches from above the navel, and our client will no longer be able to wear a two piece swim suit.

In another the solicitors stated:

Our client advises us that the sight of the operating marks has an adverse effect on her sex life and would actively deter any relationship with another man if she and her husband were to separate and be divorced.

Despite such a fervent description, this claim (as with most under this head of claim) did not succeed.

Retained products

Allegations of retained products of conception were fairly common, accounting for more than 10% of all maternal claims in Scotland. However, they had a low success rate (14%). These cases often related to the belief that a failure to ensure that all of the placenta and membranes had been delivered following the baby's birth constituted negligence. In many cases the claim seemed to arise out of a belief that any postpartum haemorrhage (PPH) must be due to retained products. This was not the case: at dilatation and curettage (performed for PPH) frequently the only finding was of endometrial tissue, and even where there was evidence of placental or membranous tissue, negligence has not necessarily occurred.

Of the six cases which concerned caesarean section delivery, five failed; in the one which succeeded 'considerable quantities of placental tissues and membranes' were found at dilatation and curettage. Although the placenta was thought to be complete at the time of delivery, the surgeon clearly had not checked the uterine cavity thoroughly before closing.

Retained placenta

Two cases concerned a retained placenta (a recognised occurrence after vaginal delivery). In one case an initial attempt to remove it proved unsuccessful, and a considerable wait then ensued because both on-call anaesthetists were occupied elsewhere. It was removed almost five hours after the delivery under a general anaesthetic. No negligence was established in either claim.

Retained swabs

By contrast, this head of claim was almost universally successful. This type of case is often cited as an example of the legal doctrine 'res ipsa loquitur' – the thing speaks for itself – the inference being that only through negligence could a swab be left inside a patient. In fact, of the 26 closed cases studied here one did fail: towards the end of a caesarean section the obstetrician was informed by Theatre staff that the swab count was incorrect. Apparently he then released a suture which he had almost finished inserting, quickly retrieved the swab, and closed up. Although this was the allegation it was held that the swab had not been truly 'retained', and so no harm had been caused. In other cases, however, swabs were found inside patients even when the Theatre swab count was apparently correct; such cases were indefensible and usually settled quickly.

Retained (other)

Three cases concerned part of a stitching needle which broke and was retained at perineal repair; one was successfully defended (no harm was found to have resulted), and the other two were won by the plaintiff. In one case she developed serious complications and received a large sum in settlement. A fourth case concerned a needle which broke during caesarean section and was retained. This case was unsuccessful: the situation was explained to the woman, fortnightly X-Rays kept track of the needle fragment and it was successfully retrieved ten weeks later; staff were held to have responded appropriately to a known possible complication.

Other (maternal)

This term covered a wide range of heads of claim, from assertions that the wrong drug had been given in pregnancy or labour, to complaints about the attitudes of staff and of being prematurely discharged from hospital. Staff 'failures' figured prominently: a failure to send an ambulance, leading to the baby being born at home; failing to remove an intra-uterine contraceptive device following childbirth; and failing to diagnose a cerebro-vascular accident in a mother, leading to delay in remedial treatment. None of these cases were successful. Two maternal deaths were also included here (neither was successful).

Another head of claim was psychological trauma, which can concern the mother, the father, or the child. In one case it was claimed that the mother was traumatised by being given the wrong baby to feed during the night; as a result she developed a severe anxiety reaction with associated guilt at not recognising that the baby was not hers. In another (which concerned a retained swab which presented as a lump) psychological trauma was claimed to have been caused because of a family history of cancer. The solicitors involved here wrote that:

> The only evidence that we will be able to lead in such a matter would be that of the client and her husband and family, which we can assure you will be most graphic.

A legal department official noted:

> What I am finding more and more, and particularly if certain firms of plaintiff solicitors are used, is 'psychological injury' thrown in... particularly with anything 'obs and gynae'... Sometimes (it) is thrown in as an additional claim, or is the main ground of claim.

A perhaps tongue-in-cheek court discussion relating to this is described by Slovenko (1999: 589):

> Plaintiff's lawyer: *Is that your conclusion, that this man is a malingerer?*
>
> Psychiatrist: *I wouldn't be testifying if I didn't think so, unless I was on the other side, then it would be a post-traumatic condition.*

There is certainly a perception that this head of claim has become more frequently used, and this has been attributed in part to media publicity about its existence. By describing the symptoms of post-traumatic stress disorder (PTSD), such publicity, according to Bradley (1998: 225) makes 'evaluation of the symptoms difficult for psychiatric experts.' Field (1999) is scornful of the trivial nature of many injuries which are claimed to have caused PTSD, and also notes that 'on-going litigation acts as an artificial reinforcing factor for unpleasant memories and their accompanying affect' (*ibid*: 36).

In one case in which obstetric events subsequently led to sterilisation, damages were claimed for the psychological distress of not being able to have more children. Whether or not one believes in a universal right to have children, this case poses interesting questions on how the degree of harm is assessed: in this case the debate turned on whether suffering in this way was affected by certain religious or cultural beliefs. The question of how such damage can be quantified in financial terms is examined in *Chapter 17*.

In cases where a delivery was traumatic, psychological distress may be caused by the thought of further pregnancies: in one case in which a woman suffered a third degree perineal tear she subsequently had a termination of pregnancy because she was terrified of the thought of another delivery.

Claims about psychological damage in the father of the child were more rare, but did occur. In one case in which both parents claimed for psychological distress related to a traumatic delivery, the defence retorted that the patient's husband was not in fact present at the time and so his claims to 'wake up at night sweating with the memory of the trauma' were false. In another similar case concerning a traumatic delivery the husband claimed damages for psychiatric illness/depression induced by the trauma of the delivery, and in this he succeeded.

Psychological damage relating to the child usually referred to a condition (such as cutis alopecia) which might give rise to the child being teased or bullied; such cases were covered in the 'non-CNS injury' head of claim above.

Conclusion

The grounds for suing are many and various. Popularised as a crisis about 'brain damaged babies', perinatal litigation is a far more complex phenomenon. While it is true that the cerebral palsy claims were the single most common reason for suing, they represented just over one fifth of the Scottish claims. They were a much more significant feature of the English claims, and this difference is difficult to explain. The area in which most of the English research took place provided comprehensive data covering the entire period in question, and it is unlikely that 'non-CNS claims' (whether baby or maternal) were under-represented.

An understanding of the wide range of grounds for litigation will, it is hoped, contribute to a more informed risk management process (discussed further in *Chapter 18*). The variation in the reasons for litigation emphasise the range over which patient dissatisfaction is evident. This relates to the concept of expectations which is taken up in the next chapter.

Chapter 8

H High expectations

Blessed is the man who expects nothing,
for he shall never be disappointed.

(Pope [letter to Fortescue, 1725])

Introduction

There is a common belief that expectations within society have increased, and that this has contributed to a 'blaming culture' (discussed in *Chapter 2*), in which complaints and litigation are common. The forces which fuel expectations are difficult to define precisely. The media and antenatal education each have an important role to play, and while health service practitioners have little control over the former, there is considerable scope to furnish realistic expectations through tailored antenatal teaching. This chapter explores some prevailing attitudes towards expectations and then examines views concerning choice and consent.

Expectations

Within the health service there appears to be a belief that women's expectations concerning pregnancy and childbirth have risen and are very high. The rapid expansion of available information, both in the popular media and now through on-line services (Shepperd *et al*, 1999), has ushered in a generation of mothers-to-be who must surely be more informed than their predecessors. The growth of 'market forces' in the health service in the early 1990s created a situation in which the 'consumer' was held to have considerable power. Indeed, there has been a call to introduce specific 'market research to identify consumer expectations and explore areas of both satisfaction and dissatisfaction' in maternity care (Crowly-Murphy, 1996: 219).

While the traditional comparison of experience of care with prior expectations in determining satisfaction levels is criticised by Avis *et al* (1997) as being too narrow, this may still appear the most obvious method and has been used in recent 'birth review' initiatives. With reference to such initiatives Beaton and Gupton (1990: 138) note that 'inherent in the development of birth plans is the danger that women may be encouraged to think that planning the "perfect" birth is possible.' One midwife commented:

> *I've often thought the longer the birth plan the more complicated the labour... people come in with such expectations, it's Murphy's law that it won't go quite so well, and then these people feel even more let down because they've had such high expectations.*

(Midwife 4)

A rather parodied version of this alleged anticipation of perfection was noted by one interviewee, who talked of:

> *Playing the NCT video. You're shown this video... they sit on a bean bag, it's all nice and they're burning joss sticks, and this baby comes out, and that's great.*

(AVMA official 1)

O'Meara (1993) and Hallgren *et al* (1995) stress the need to identify each individual's expectations when planning childbirth education; perhaps an optimistic prescription given pressures on the health service. Nevertheless, the likelihood of disappointment when things do not go as people would wish (or expect) is well documented: Creasy (1997) found a strong potential for disappointment when the development of complications required transfer from community to consultant care, but also noted that the situation could be improved by giving adequate explanations and encouraging continuity of care.

In this study's postal survey an increase in awareness and expectations was held to be largely responsible for a perceived increase in litigation. Indeed, not only is clinical excellence expected, but – according to the legal department in one claim – the ability to forecast the weather:

> *A part of the claim relates to the adverse weather conditions and the assertion that these should have been predicted. This is an unusual area in which to allege medical negligence.*

Significant proportions of both midwives and obstetricians have blamed this increase in expectation on 'the media'. It is of course only fair to note that the health service is not unique in experiencing litigation (also discussed in *Chapter 2*). Ham *et al* (1988: 15) claim that, 'the most likely explanation is the awareness among victims of the possibility of legal redress and their readiness to pursue this route'. This claim is echoed by Dworkin (1989: 1340) who states that, 'the American people have become increasingly aware of the power of law as a force for good, largely as a result of the civil rights movement of the 1950s and 1960s.'

The perception that society will not accept an outcome that does not match their expectations appears to be wide-spread: Herczeg (1997: 181) claims that, 'only 100% healthy babies are accepted. Pregnancy is regarded as a "success story" and if the baby is born with neurological defects (cerebral palsy) the parents and their advisors feel, that someone responsible for the defect should be found in the chain of management.'

Few would doubt that the media have a significant role to play in educating pregnant women. There is, however, a danger that the reporting of a handful of probably atypical legal cases (eg. McKain, 1991; Robertson, 1991, 1992) may promote the belief that litigation is the usual route taken when an outcome is poor, and that large amounts of money are there for the taking. The amount of damages can be very newsworthy (in 1998 Dyer reported one case which received £3.3m), but such reports do not explain that these very large amounts are among the highest awards: the average (and median) for damages awards are a fraction of such figures. Further data on compensation can be found in *Chapter 17*.

There is no doubt that certain parts of the media are believed to present a very 'rosy' view of pregnancy:

> *I got Parenting magazine quite recently... What is being written? It's like: 'Oh it's rather nice, it's a little outing, go and have a scan, get a little picture; another little outing, go and have your induction, and out pops baby.' It's painted in a very surreal way. It's quite worrying.*

(Labour ward manager)

Of course, high expectations do not relate solely to the area of having babies. Referring to the other end of life's spectrum one obstetrician noted:

> *Some GP was telling me that he or a colleague were being sued... they had an eighty-four year old guy who had got a chest infection and they prescribed antibiotics, and they are now being sued because the patient wasn't sent to hospital...*
>
> (Consultant obstetrician 2)

Another obstetrician believed that the media were to blame:

> *The patients know more, they see things on television, they read them in magazines and their expectations are high.*
>
> (Obstetric registrar)

A midwife claimed the health service has had to comply with this level of expectation:

> *They're trying to provide a service that the patients want, which is much more than just delivering the baby or giving the antenatal care. It's all the rest of it, the social part of it. It's the social part that takes the time, it's not the taking somebody's blood pressure. or testing the wee. But they want it with all-singing, all-dancing midwives...*
>
> (Midwife 12)

While some may want to blame sections of the media or other societal forces for increasing the expectations of the public, health service practitioners as a group cannot claim immunity from such accusations. Shaw (1946: 12) makes the cynical claim that 'when the doctor is... the defendant in an action for malpractice, he has to struggle against the inevitable result of his former pretences to infinite knowledge and unerring skill.' Whether by fault or design, today's practitioners may also be charged with promoting an idealistic image of pregnancy and childbirth. Another midwife asserted that antenatal scans in particular represent a form of propaganda which begins early on:

> *With the women going for scans and so on, there is this subtle implicit kind of promise that everything's going OK.*
>
> (Labour ward manager)

One view is that practitioners ought to be highlighting the limitations of such technology. If a congenital defect is not detected despite ultrasound scanning, it may be thought that the person carrying out the scan was somehow negligent. It is possible that, having shown the parents an active baby on the screen and giving (or selling) them a print-out of the screen picture ('Baby's first portrait'), practitioners are inadvertently implying that nothing will go wrong and that all the parents have to do is decorate the nursery and wait for the happy day. How is the health service to counter this? Antenatal clinics/classes seem the obvious starting point, but even here midwives are apparently dealing with pre-conceived ideas:

> *Expectations are much much higher... In my antenatal classes I would say 'What is a normal healthy baby?' And everybody's view is 100%, and that is what everybody expects nowadays.*
>
> (Midwife 14)

Another midwife summed up her view of such expectations:

> *It's very humbling, childbirth, there's no way you can guarantee 100%.*
>
> (Labour ward manager)

However, there is a strong perception that many people will not put up with anything falling short of perfection:

> *My general impression is that everyone expects to have an entirely normal pregnancy, an entirely normal labour. If there's anything which detracts from that there must be someone found to blame... I suppose that the general public are encouraged to feel that, unless things are absolutely perfect, that they have a right to a rebate...*
>
> (Consultant obstetrician 1)

This use of market language is particularly appropriate when considering the potential for litigation. Another midwife commented:

> *It still bothers me that expectations of the public are that every pregnancy will end up with a live healthy normal baby, when that just isn't the case. I think people think it's like buying something, faulty goods almost, that they can take it back and complain.*
>
> (Midwife 4)

Not everyone bemoans this increase in expectations, however:

> *I think people's expectations should be high... I think people... are quite rightly questioning things, and I don't think that's a bad thing... because then it makes us look at our practice and adjust it, you know. If we're not meeting the requirements of the client group, why are we not meeting it?*
>
> (Midwife 6)

Midwives of course must tread a fine line in promoting the essential normality of pregnancy and labour, while not falling into the trap of implying that nothing ever goes wrong. One midwife claimed that:

> *It's easier to ignore it totally, but that's letting the women down. Even talking about forceps delivery or caesarean section, they don't really want to think about it, because 'These things don't happen to me'... Who wants realism when at that stage they want to be optimistic about it all?*
>
> (Midwife 4)

She went on to say:

> *It's a terribly difficult situation and scenario to bring up in parenthood education that something might go wrong, and that nothing they can do and nothing we can do can stop that... I found it very difficult to bring up in the classes... It's so sensitive, because the class are all sitting there so happy and so looking forward to the birth of their live healthy normal baby, and that might just not happen.*

In earlier research (Symon, 1994) one midwife claimed that the media were to blame for this, since they were:

> *... creating a very false impression, and we deal with it every day in here... they're reading these flowery articles... They would just like it to be all natural, no pain, no need for analgesia: the baby just comes out and that's it. It's not a realistic picture at all... coming to labour there's no question of pain. There's six to six thousand women deliver here each year, and I've yet to meet one that said it wasn't sore.*

Trying to counter this perception in the antenatal period is not easy. One midwife in the postal survey wrote:

> *I know of one colleague who was censured for telling a Preparation for Parenthood class at a labour talk that they would experience excruciating pain.*

These comments suggest that the antenatal focus is almost totally on the positive and upbeat aspects of childbirth, and that there is a failure even to mention that things might not go according to plan. Advertisers are well aware that happy gurgling babies can be used to sell almost anything. However the use of such idealistic pictures may contribute to the societal expectation that everything will be as it is in the advertisement – happy, healthy, and clean. While some may condemn formula milk companies for using 'smiling baby' pictures to promote their products, such pictures are also used in parentcraft classes and antenatal clinics to promote breast feeding. How can this idealistic presentation be made more realistic? One midwife reflected Hallgren *et al's* view (supra) that parenthood education must be tailored individually:

> *The perception of the general public is that they don't anticipate any problems, but I still don't know how we would get over communicating that to our client group... On a one to one* (basis) *it might be easier... I don't know how you make it more realistic without terrifying the life out of people. That's the big problem we have.*

(Midwife 6)

How risk is explained to pregnant women is discussed further in *Chapter 18*. The apparent balancing act was commented on by one consumer group representative (specifically with regard to the notion of informed consent): 'There seems to be a difficulty between giving advice and coercing people...' (Consumer group representative).

As with so many aspects of modern health care, communication appears to be the key. The tone adopted in establishing a relationship with a pregnant woman is crucial, but again there is a balancing act between being the woman's advocate (ie. representing her best interests) and being a professional (with all its overtones of hierarchy and control). An aspect of paternalism was commented on by a senior lecturer:

> *I think the Scots have particularly a feeling of duty of care... They feel responsible for their client. They find it difficult to recognise that the client has something to do with the whole situation...*

(Midwifery lecturer)

Whether or not this view accurately reflects a Scottish approach, and whether such an approach is also typically found in other parts of Britain, may be questioned. If the midwife-woman relationship is paternalistic, it runs counter to the spirit of *Changing Childbirth* (DoH, 1993a) and the Scottish Policy Review (Scottish Office, 1993). Communication and rapport between service users and providers are critical if women are to be involved on a more equal footing in the planning of maternity care (discussed further in *Chapter 20*). Whether or not providers are getting better at this is also disputed:

> *Well, they say they are. I think the mechanisms are beginning to be in place, but it is very difficult, I think it's going to take a long time. I think it is very difficult for the consumer to have a voice within these large institutions... In rural areas it can be very difficult, particularly when people know each other. I think there's a huge reluctance to get involved in complaints.*

(Consumer group representative)

Providing sufficient information so that women can make informed decisions based on realistic expectations, and tailoring this on an individual basis, may seem a tall order. In busy antenatal clinics staff may feel that there is not the time both to evaluate individual requirements and furnish the right amount of information in a palatable format. The promotion of team midwifery and the encouragement of continuity of carer strive to make this goal attainable.

There is considerable scope for research into women's expectations and subsequent experiences. Given that many expectations with regard to pregnancy and childbirth appear to originate before any contact with health professionals, the importance of the media and other sources of information must be taken into account. As well as massive media coverage of pregnancy and childbirth, there have been high profile legal cases in recent years which have affected the debate about a woman's right to choose a particular course of action. Such an exercise of choice is bound up with the debate over the right to decline treatment. When expectations are not met, the ensuing dissatisfaction may eventually lead to legal activity.

Conclusion

High expectations represent a significant challenge to the health service, particularly in maternity care. Positive images of family and children are widely used by the media, and these seem to have contributed to a belief among some people that anything less than 100% is unacceptable. In *Chapter 11* some of the discrepancies between expectation and outcome are discussed in relation to known complications. Expectations also relate to matters of expressing choice; these are discussed in *Chapter 3*, along with the notion of informed consent.

Chapter 9

▌ Involvement in litigation

This chapter examines a critical feature of perinatal litigation: the emotional effects it has on those practitioners against whom an allegation of negligence is made.

Much of the debate about litigation has turned on the widespread perception that it is both commonplace and increasing rapidly. However, there has been very little published evidence for claims about the incidence of litigation in this or any other field. Without adequate publicly-available knowledge, the debate about the extent of litigation, the consequent use of public funds, and about what constitutes a justified response to the prospect of litigation, is at best ill-informed. Despite this, claims of a progressive increase continue to be made (Tharmaratnam and Gillmer, 1995; Easterbrook, 1996), a claim echoed by one of the interviewees:

> I suspect that if in obstetrics and gynaecology there was any other illness which cropped up with the same frequency, and increasing frequency, (as) litigation, that one would have an epidemiological assessment of it, and you would carry out research in a big way to see what this new disease is...

(Consultant obstetrician 4)

Similarly there has been anecdotal evidence about the apparent effects of litigation, both in terms of defensive clinical responses (some of these were discussed in *Chapter 4*), and emotional effects. Comprehensive quantitative data on the incidence of Scottish litigation are included in *Appendix I*. This chapter concentrates on a qualitative evaluation of the effects of litigation.

Involvement in litigation: the emotional responses

Becoming involved in litigation is said to be many practitioners' worst nightmare. The thought that you may have to stand up in a witness box and defend your actions, perhaps years after the events in question, is daunting, if not terrifying. Compared with obstetricians few midwives have been required to endure this ordeal, but the possibility exists that anyone who is, or has been, involved in clinical care may be the subject of allegations of negligence.

The emotional responses involved do not apply only to cases which become formally legal. Little is widely known about either the scale or nature of litigation, or of why some people sue and others do not, and so it is possible to view any poor outcome as a potential prelude to legal proceedings. The emotional reactions of family physicians to making mistakes have been described by Newman (1996). These include emotional adversity, needing someone to talk to, and needing professional reaffirmation and personal reassurance. A very personal account of such involvement is given by Sacks (1997). This section examines the responses of several practitioners who have become involved in poor outcomes and subsequent litigation. The following headings describe some of the apparent responses of the interviewees to an involvement in litigation. It is not claimed that this represents the complete picture: while some of the responses are fairly easily categorised, there is no simple descriptive form which can encapsulate the emotional responses of those caught up in litigation.

Shock

Shock is an understandable first reaction. In one case this was related to the time taken to initiate the action:

> *They actually didn't take any legal action after the birth of the baby. So it was a terrible shock: nothing happened, and then suddenly out of the blue I was informed that they were taking legal action. It must have been 18 months or so after... I know it was quite a long time.*

(Midwife 16)

In fact 18 months is the average period between a perinatal event which does not concern cerebral palsy and subsequent legal notification. Cases involving cerebral palsy often take much longer: while three years is the average, some have been initiated more than ten years after the birth in question (Symon, 1999a). Perhaps surprisingly, one interviewee who had been involved in a legal case expressed the view that litigation is seen as more or less inevitable:

> *We all kind of feel the longer you're there, it will happen to you at some point, maybe not to the same degree but it will happen. You will be involved with something, you know, because you can't eliminate it.*

(Midwife 1)

This appears a rather sanguine response. If an outcome (usually of a birth) is known immediately to be poor, then staff may display signs of stress much more quickly. All staff who have been involved in such an outcome will know of the worry involved:

> *I remember waking up in the morning, and I remember having this awful sense that nothing was going to be the same again. I hadn't quite realised what was going to happen, but I just felt in such a state of shock and distress. And then having to come back to work that morning. It's like you want to pretend that everything's going to be all right... I was in such a state of shock...*

(Midwife 16)

While it may seem trite to say, clearly nothing can prepare someone for the first notification that an allegation against them has been made:

> *The morning that I got the letter through the post saying that it was coming up, nobody warned me that was coming although* (the hospital) *knew about it... the first I knew of it was when it came in the post. I looked at it and thought 'Well, what will I do?'*

(Midwife 7)

The anguish of being involved was even more apparent in the case of another midwife:

> *It was months and months afterwards that a letter came to me from a lawyer, alleging medical negligence. It didn't go to the hospital, it came direct to me. I was really quite shocked. They weren't aiming for an explanation from the hospital; they hadn't gone through official channels to my supervisor of midwives or to the Labour Ward manager or to the consultant. It was actually personally directed at me.*

(Midwife 11)

Allegations of negligence, while they usually concern the actions of one or more individual practitioners, ought to be sent to the hospital or the relevant health service legal department. In this instance, an apparent lack of appropriate experience on the part of the solicitor – in sending the initial letter to the midwife personally – caused quite unnecessary distress, particularly as there was in fact no evidence of negligence in this case. This midwife described a sense of unreality when informed that litigation was pending:

> *I think there's a period when you don't believe this has happened to you. You worry about every word you say...*

(Midwife 11)

For many of those involved, the emotional reaction seems to turn in on the person concerned, and after the initial shock, there are other feelings.

Fear, worry and guilt

The frequent, long gap between an event and subsequent legal action has been mentioned, and by way of example Halle (1997) reports one obstetric case which took 27 years to originate. One obstetrician commented:

> *What worries you is that, if that's 27 years ago that that case came up, how many more years of misery in retirement are you going to have with all these cases coming forward?*

(Consultant obstetrician 2)

The thought that even retirement is no protection against legal involvement is discouraging to say the least. An important point to bear in mind is that many legal cases are unanticipated: when the mother and baby are discharged from care by the midwives/obstetricians there is sometimes no inclination that the outcome has not been good – this is particularly so in some cases concerning cerebral palsy.

Fear of possible future litigation is one aspect; another is the fear of a repetition, as this interviewee noted:

> *It takes a long time to get over this fear that it's not going to happen again. You've still got this fear about it happening again, and how would you cope with it?*

(Midwife 16)

It is acknowledged that many aspects of perinatal care are very stressful, but little would surpass the stress of being involved in a poor outcome and subsequent litigation:

> *The stress of going through that was quite incredible... it took two and a half years from me getting the letter...*

(Midwife 11)

For some the response is turned inwards and is displayed as guilt:

> *I felt this terrible burden of guilt about the whole thing for a couple of years after. I used to think about it so much; and particularly when she had another baby.*

(Midwife 16)

Another noted:

> *I felt really guilty, you know... as you do... You think 'Well, what could you do?' You mull it over a million times 'What can I do? What ..?'*

(Midwife 1)

A thorough investigation determined that this midwife had done nothing wrong. Her expressions of self-doubt, however, were a recurring theme. Another midwife, who said that she was not worried about the ramifications of a birth whose outcome was known to be bad (and which resulted in litigation), said of another birth two weeks later (at which the baby was discovered to have a congenital condition):

> *I felt more guilty about that incident. Does that make sense? It was actually from that second incident that my confidence went completely and I didn't want anything to do with Labour Ward for a very long time, for three to six months.*

(Midwife 3)

Other defensive clinical responses were discussed in *Chapter 4*, but the effect for one midwife was a general dampening of confidence rather than a specific change in practice:

> *It did very much do a lot of harm to my confidence, there's no doubt about it, and I basically was asking for advice and reassurance a lot of the time when I wouldn't normally have done from my peers and from the Labour Ward sisters and things, until I began to feel a bit more confident again. It's taken a long time...*

(Midwife 6)

As this midwife notes, an individual's response will change over time. For some, after the initial shock (and sometimes guilt), there is a turning outwards in terms of emotional response.

Anger and resentment

It is acknowledged that an allegation of negligence can be both hurtful and damaging to a professional. There are concerns about being impugned and, perhaps especially for very senior practitioners, there may be a reputation to protect. In such cases it is understandable that the emotional response turns outwards. One midwife spoke of her feelings after the strain of appearing in court:

> *After the court case I felt very angry with the* (litigant), *I really felt very angry with her...* (the lawyer) *was shouting at me, and I didn't feel intimidated by him, I just felt really angry. I thought, 'What do you know about it?'... I thought I'm not going to be persuaded that I did something that I didn't do...*

(Midwife 7)

This emotional reaction allowed for some outflow of feelings. For some professionals accused of negligence, there is certainly a sense of wounding, and resentment is felt, but this is not expressed outwardly:

> *There will be few people in* (obstetrics) *who haven't had some flurry with lawyers. Most of them will never have been in court... most people who try to do a decent job are very pained professionally that they should be accused of negligence...*

(Medical director)

Another noted:

> *I am deeply hurt if any patient complains or has a poor outcome under my care, and I don't think it needs litigation to make me feel awful about a situation that doesn't work out very well.*

> (Consultant obstetrician 4)

It is one thing to feel a sense of hurt; for some there is a redirecting of feelings towards others, as in this claim in which the registrar noted to the consultant:

> *While I have no doubt that the trying circumstances surrounding this patient's admission are clouding her memory I find the tone of the solicitor's letter insulting and practically libellous.*

It does appear that some people in this situation have attempted to turn such feelings into action against the litigants. Among lawyers there seems to be an awareness that the resentment felt by practitioners sometimes tries to find such an outlet:

> *The reaction among certain doctors has been very high-handed: 'Can I sue this person for defamation? How dare they impugn my reputation?' I just say 'Well, sorry, but you don't really have a case. If you do, then you should consult your own individual lawyer about it, but I'm sure he'll tell you the same. I don't think you would get it off the ground.'*

> (Defence solicitor 2)

> *I'm aware that sometimes doctors are extremely upset by what is alleged to have been said and they do ask whether they should pursue it, and they are gently told 'Don't worry', because often the patients will not have any assets to speak of anyway, and it simply stirs up the whole problem again.*

> (Defence solicitor 1)

While some of those involved seem to turn their emotional response outwards (in some cases by wanting to target the litigants themselves), for others the response remains inward-looking. Sadly, this response is sometimes quite severe.

Depression

The term 'depression' is used here in what may be termed a 'lay' sense; in other words a reaction in which there is a mood disorder, or a protracted or disproportionate melancholy. In one case the relevant midwife had retired and left Britain. Upon being notified that a legal action had been initiated and that she was involved, she responded:

> (Your letter) *had a dire effect. A dark cloud descended which I'm finding hard to shake off. Each time I try to telephone you my voice disappears, hence this letter.*

Another midwife wrote:

> *I do not really wish to be involved in any legal problems now that I have retired, but I was on duty when Mrs L was delivered, therefore I will have to make a statement I suppose.*

The lengthy period leading up to the court case and eventual judgement caused another midwife to react in other ways:

> *The other way I coped was by putting on 2½ stone. I ate in the wee hours. Withdrawing from the world, crawling into a corner and watching rubbish on the telly, which I never do normally. But I felt upset, I would just think 'I can't cope with that, I'm not going to think about it, I'll go and watch some rubbish on the telly.'*

> (Midwife 7)

Thankfully she is now able to look back on this period without obvious bitterness, and in fact managed to turn her own traumatic ordeal into a learning experience which has benefited others. A colleague who was subsequently involved in a legal case said:

> (She) *has been the most wonderful support... she was the one that basically said 'Let's get finished and get things written down' the very next day, and basically made me sit down and do it while it was all fresh in my mind... she was a wonderful support.*

> (Midwife 6)

The capacity of individuals to open up under such circumstances will vary. One respondent felt that female staff were more likely to be able to do so:

> *I think there's a gender element to this, dare I say it... if a woman is upset about something she has to talk it through. It's an unusual woman that doesn't really want to talk it through – this is a generalisation again. Some chaps, at least in my experience, have wanted to shut off when the mistake is made, and they'll maybe talk it through with a best friend, but then it's switch off.*

> (Labour ward manager)

The need for support systems may seem obvious, but sadly this does not always materialise. In the postal survey one midwife made this comment after becoming involved in a legal case:

> *Afterwards I wanted to form a support group for midwives who had been in that position. I wanted to be there for them, because I felt no one was there for me.*

This feeling of being alone was confirmed by one interviewee who said that colleagues simply 'stood back' when news of the litigation became known. A possible explanation for this lack of support was given by the midwife whose traumatic experiences in court have already been mentioned:

> *It's almost as if they fear they will catch something. If it can happen to you it can happen to them. That's what it is. A lot of people – apart from not knowing what to say – it makes them very frightened, because they think 'If that can happen to her, it can happen to me.'*

> (Midwife 7)

In theory there are support mechanisms for staff involved in any procedure (for instance disciplinary or legal) which is inherently stressful. Membership of a professional body or trade union brings certain rights of representation, but for the college/union officer this period can also be stressful:

> *I was involved with one case of litigation. I was the* (RCM) *steward at the time... They really put pressure on* (the midwife). *I was trying to get hold of Personnel, to say*

> *'Hang on, this isn't right. You can't just go straight into that depth of the disciplinary* (process) *before you've done any investigation.'*

(Midwife 12)

Initiatives such as Birth Afterthoughts (Charles and Curtis, 1994) have been set up to allow women who feel that they have suffered a poor outcome to voice their concerns and discuss the details of the case with the relevant staff. While such moves have attracted criticism (Robinson, 1998; Northcott, 1998), there may be scope for similar moves to enable practitioners to deal more effectively with the strain and stress of either poor outcomes or actual litigation. Some risk management programmes attempt this, but these do not appear to be widely implemented as yet.

This discussion of emotional responses can only portray some of the experience of involvement in litigation. In trying to depict these emotions a level of generalisation has been necessary. Reactions will of course vary according to the circumstances and individuals involved. Many of the interviewees whose comments are reported here are very experienced practitioners, and yet their years of experience did not prepare them for the emotional trauma of a poor outcome and the litigation that followed.

Conclusion

There would seem to be a great deal of scope for improving the support given to those practitioners involved in litigation. The stress and distress caused may impact not only in a practitioner's working life, but also in his/her private life. While a person's affairs outside the workplace may be largely invisible to the health service, there seems little doubt that they may affect how effectively that person functions while at work. Support through counselling and debriefing have been suggested as part of risk management (examined further in *Chapter 18*), but it would appear that there is room for improvement here. This is not to deny a plaintiff her right to initiate litigation, only to comment on the detrimental effect such allegations may have, whether or not they are well founded. Practitioners have sometimes been critical of a plaintiff's decision to sue, such views are now considered in *Chapter 10*.

Chapter 10

J Justification: the perceived motives behind litigation

The grounds for suing were discussed in *Chapter 7*, and while these tell us something of the nature of litigation they cannot paint the whole picture. They cannot, for example, explain why some people sue and yet others, in comparable circumstances, do not. Discussing the justification for initiating litigation is necessarily speculative: no plaintiffs (or potential plaintiffs) were surveyed, although consumer group representatives were able to tell some of the story. This chapter examines some of the possible underlying justification for initiating litigation.

In *Appendix II* it is noted that the incidence of litigation is not routinely published. Data concerning the rate of occurrence of accidents and errors are rare, and as a consequence comparatively little is known about why people complain or sue. Of particular note are the conclusions drawn by Brennan *et al* (1991) concerning the apparently low rate of litigation compared to the rate of negligence.

It seems to be the case that many people who could sue in fact do not. Felstiner *et al* (1981: 633) maintain that reasons for not suing include, 'a failure to perceive that one has been injured; such failures may be self-induced or externally manipulated.' This introduces an apparently haphazard element into the process, so much so that it has been claimed that 'physicians in high risk specialties live with the fear (that) they are as likely to be sued by chance as for their conduct' (Akazaki, 1999:9). In trying to identify the factors which predispose towards litigation, May and Stengal (1990) compared the characteristics of those who sued with those who did not. They found that those who did sue typically sought advice from friends and relatives; had less knowledge about the intricacies of health care or law; and had less status and power than those who did not sue. Examining other possible reasons for suing, Kraus (1990: 309) notes that a study by a malpractice insurance company in Tennessee found that 35% of malpractice lawsuits 'had been filed because of the physician's attitude.'

Beckman *et al* (1994) analysed plaintiff depositions (testimony made under oath which may be used when the case comes to trial) and found that there were four main perceptions underlying the decision to sue. These were that there had been a poor understanding by the defendant of the patient/family perspective; dysfunctional delivery of information; a devaluing of patient/family views; or desertion of the patient. They also found that, in a significant number of cases, it was a health professional who had triggered the decision to sue by suggesting maloccurrence.

In the case of *O'Driscoll v Dudley HA* it was claimed that the impetus to sue had come from a television programme which had apparently suggested that cerebral palsy might be related to negligence at birth. The child was born in 1960, and the programme shown in 1975. The family evidently thought that because it was open for them to sue when the person was 21 years old, they had to wait until that time, and they duly initiated litigation in 1981. There is certainly a range of opinion as to the justification behind litigation. This chapter now examines some of these views.

Impressions of the justification

Lord Woolf notes that in researching his Access to Justice report (Woolf, 1996), many claimants expressed the view that litigation was initiated because of a failure on the part of practitioners to explain: 'For what it is worth, during my inquiry litigants repeatedly told me that all they sought was an explanation or apology that was never forthcoming. All too often patients have been forced into litigation by lack of communication from those representing the medical profession' (Woolf, 1997: 365). Such research has been rare, and in this study's interviews several acknowledged that their beliefs about litigation and its underlying causes stemmed from general impressions rather than knowledge of actual data.

> *I would have supposed that people are more ready to make claims because of the publicity about legal claims.*

(Queen's Counsel)

> *It's a general impression, mainly from the press... probably the national press more than anything... I just feel that (*the legal profession*) are probably looking for business – (*although*) that's probably unjust.*

(Midwife 14)

Certainly there is a belief that a proportion of solicitors may be encouraging litigation. One midwife respondent in the postal survey explained her belief in a rise in litigation this way:

> *Potentially a rise in cases in this area due to a firm of lawyers who are representing clients for a proportion of any settlement – no other fees.*

It should be noted that contingency fees, whereby a solicitor negotiates in advance of accepting a case a percentage of any damages which might be won, are not in fact permitted. Conditional fees, on the other hand, a 'no win no fee' arrangement, are allowed.

Not all comments concerning justification for suing were derogatory:

> *I think probably the main reason for litigation is that couples don't understand what happened to them, and it's to get information. I think the quality of information has been concealed, and people are not very good at communicating if there's been a difficulty.*

(Independent midwife)

Another midwife commented that it was often very difficult to predict which incidents would end up becoming the subject of litigation:

> *The people who really have grounds for litigation often don't sue, and often the things that you get are petty.*

(Midwife 11)

There may be many factors involved in the decision to sue. To begin with, there must be some sense of grievance (cf. Felstiner *et al*, supra), or at least a feeling that things have not been explained sufficiently. However, there have been times when the apparent motivation is difficult to understand. In one legal claim, in which a woman alleged that she was not given analgesia during perineal repair despite 'begging' for this, the junior doctor who performed the repair was indignant at the allegation. He had dictated a letter to the GP immediately after suturing the perineum, because of a piece of tissue being sent for histology, and, citing this letter, commented:

> *'This delightful lady...' I would not have spoken in these terms had there occurred in the room the kind of conflict that Mrs H alleges. I recall her as a woman who at the time was very happy at the way she had been treated.*

Within the legal file there was a copy of a 'Thank You' card sent by this woman upon her discharge from hospital, written to:

> ... *all the doctors, midwives and staff who brought our miracle* (baby) *into the world.*

This evidently does not indicate a significant degree of dissatisfaction, and yet the woman subsequently (in fact more than five years after the events in question) made an allegation of negligence. The time between an event and subsequent legal notification may be important in interpreting someone's sense of justification: in one of the legal claims examined the solicitor's letter arrived just seven days after the incident, when the woman was in fact still in hospital. In other cases there has been considerable delay.

Dissatisfied complainants?

One possibility for examining why people bring legal claims is to look at those claims which start out as complaints. In one instance in which a baby's cheek was cut during an emergency caesarean section (a recognised complication), the father alleged that both parents went to the consultant to complain. However, in the father's words they felt:

> ... *angry at the flippant manner in which the case was treated.*

They subsequently went to solicitors, and the matter was settled for almost £10,000 plus costs – an expensive way for the hospital to find out that staff appear unsympathetic. It might be argued that sensitive and appropriate handling of complaints would prevent legal involvement. In another case that did not concern any allegations of clinical negligence, the first letter of claim came after the pursuer had her complaint upheld by the Health Service Commissioner (Ombudsman). Despite there being no allegation of negligence, because of the Ombudsman's findings the defence were prepared to make an ex gratia payment of £500.

In a case concerning a retained gauze swab, the woman wrote first to the consultant who admitted that 'there can be no excuse' (this is invariably true in such cases). About a month later she contacted a solicitor: a formal admission was quickly made and the case was settled. In another case a patient claimed that she had had an inefficient epidural anaesthetic. Her initial complaint went to the hospital, and an explanation and apology was given. At the time she appeared to accept this, but later decided to go to a solicitor.

Other more critical cases have also started out as complaints: one, in which the baby developed cerebral palsy, also involved the Ombudsman before the patient sought formal legal advice. In another, in which the baby was stillborn, formal investigations of the midwife's actions by the Chief Area Nursing Officer and the relevant National Board were carried out; although no action was taken against the midwife the formal and very senior level of investigation appeared to fuel the patient's sense that the midwife had indeed been at fault.

Some of these cases succeeded, others did not. There does not appear to be any consistent background to legal cases which originate as complaints made to the hospital. However, the insensitive handling of complaints or requests for information may in fact promote litigation (the need to furnish people with satisfactory explanations is explored further in *Chapter 20*). One midwife commented:

> *There is no counselling unless the couple ask for it. So the majority of people who sue, sue to get more information, to find out what actually happened.*

> (Independent midwife)

That formal legal action is required to get this may be seen either as a criticism of the health service and its apparent inability to furnish sufficient explanations, or as an indictment of some people's alleged propensity to sue.

One of the themes to emerge from the debate surrounding *Changing Childbirth* (and the equivalent Scottish Policy Review) was the importance of trust between service users and providers. In theory a trusting relationship will act as a bulwark against legal involvement; by the same measure, when trust is absent, litigation is more likely:

> *Often in maternity services there isn't a relationship between the professional and the woman. I think that a lot of these cases wouldn't even arise if there was a trusting relationship to begin with.*

> (Consumer group representative)

> *(Patients) are slowly being dragged into litigation because of the attitude of people, and because of that trust being broken down, so you get to the point where you don't believe a word that the medical profession will say, or* (anything) *that's coming out in any shape or form from the Trust.*

> (AVMA official 1)

A trusting relationship can only be built when communication is effective. This relates to the expectations that people have before they have any formal dealings with the maternity services and, of course, these are largely beyond the control of health professionals. There is though scope to educate people so that unrealistic expectations can be modified and made more reasonable. Such a skill is not possessed by all practitioners, however, and certain clinical circumstances will make such explanations difficult:

> *Sometimes it's the failure to accept. And it might be failure to accept the explanation for simple things... You know that in Intensive Care things are always going wrong – that's the nature of the business. If they're not accepting of those sort of things, then I go on High Alert because they may well not be accepting the overall care of their child.*

> (Consultant neonatologist)

Although practitioners may feel that they now provide more comprehensive (and hopefully empathetic) explanations, what certainly seems to have become more recognised in recent years is the reduced likelihood of people accepting explanations at face value. This relates to the question of trust mentioned by the AVMA official above: if trust is completely absent, then no amount of explanation will satisfy those with a sense of grievance. Whether publicity about the right to complain has contributed to an increase in complaints and claims is a moot point. What is not in serious doubt is that people believe they have a right to adequate explanations:

> *People always ask us* (why) *complaints and claims are going up... In the maternity services as much as anything else people now come out there and think 'Well, that was a pretty traumatic experience'; or 'Something is badly wrong: perhaps we should investigate this.' In the past people just didn't do anything about it Things were left.*

> (AVMA official 1)

Again, this should not be seen as unreasonable. We all cherish our right to complain if we think a product is faulty or a service has been substandard:

> *My personal experience – although I've been involved in a case recently – people just want to know what's happening. I personally think we should be doing more* (explaining).
>
> (Midwife 2)

In a responsive health service such explanations are imperative. Quite apart from acting to defuse potential litigation (many legal actions stem from misunderstandings rather than actual negligence), honest discussions and explanations are essential in creating and maintaining a trusting relationship with service users. However satisfaction levels are measured (and there is some debate about this), the nurturing of trust is an obvious requirement if practitioners are to take the health service successfully forward. Simply put, an absence of such trust will militate against effective communication and will predispose towards litigation.

Other motivations

In one case which concerned a child who suffered an Erb's palsy, the solicitors wrote:

> *...Our clients, who are not litigation minded, requested us not to take any legal steps, particularly because of the high standard of care which appears to have been devoted to the child since birth.*

If the plaintiffs were not litigation minded, it does beg the question as to what they felt they would achieve by contacting solicitors. One very plausible reason for initiating litigation is that it is an outlet for anger. In one case in which a baby developed cerebral palsy subsequent to meningitis (this not being detected, it was alleged, due to staff error), the consultant neonatologist noted that:

> *Both* (parents) *were very angry indeed at the time of the illness. Even at that time they were trying to find someone to blame...*

The sense of wanting to blame someone for such a tragedy can perhaps be imagined. People react to stress in very different ways, and while some (it is claimed) seek explanation and apology, others may want to exact retribution. This was put very forcefully in one of the claims examined here. The woman concerned wrote:

> *I have never suffered such torture as was inflicted on me at that moment... this so-called doctor... I will not rest until this woman faces retribution...*

Clearly there is much more than a desire for explanation and apology in this case, but this was certainly an unusual example.

A critical aspect concerning motivation to sue is the length of time it takes pursuers to raise their legal action. From the legal files studied here it was seen that there is a considerable range: the shortest period was one week, while other claims have taken many years to arise; Halle (1997) notes one which took 27 years. One factor would be the length of time it takes someone to become aware that they might have a reason to sue: in most cases the reason, if not apparent almost immediately, becomes so in the first year after delivery. Injury to the mother will usually be evident straight away; damage to the child may take longer to become apparent, but in either case a delay of several years before seeking legal advice cannot be easily explained. In one case in which it was alleged that products of conception were retained, the first complaint was made by the woman concerned; then, almost three years later, a solicitor's letter arrived. In another case, excluded from the main study because the child was born in 1969, the action was not raised until 1990. The solicitors claimed:

> *As regards limitation, it is open to Miss P to raise an action up to three years following her eighteenth birthday. This period will expire* (in six weeks) *and accordingly this is a matter of extreme urgency.*

There appears to have been little sense of urgency for 21 years. It is possible that the family had only become aware that litigation was an option – there was considerable publicity in 1990 about this, with changes to the Legal Aid requirements effectively making certain cases much easier to raise.

In another case concerning a child born in 1982, the mother went to see her GP in 1987 and complained about the care she had received; however, it was another five years before she consulted a solicitor. In a separate case in which the baby developed cerebral palsy, the first complaint was made to the hospital, and a full explanation was given by the consultants. Three and a half years later, solicitors were contacted. Again, such delays are hard to explain.

It ought not to be thought that practitioners routinely resist the notion of patients and their families obtaining compensation:

> *Many people... will go to litigation predominantly if they are left with a handicapped child, which will put an unbearable burden on their purses or on their marriages... that number of complaints, basically, will not go down.*

(Midwifery manager)

> *A lot of what I call the more serious complaints, the ones that people perhaps should have some form of compensation for, can be anybody, but you wonder about some of the other complaints, about the motivation, which presumably is money... As far as the other cases, the cerebral cases, I think that there should be some form of compensation that really doesn't necessitate... proving negligence.*

(Consultant obstetrician 2)

No-fault compensation, whether restricted to cases involving cerebral palsy or on a more comprehensive basis is a separate issue (see *Chapter 6*). A 'fast-track' method of arranging financial awards in the most serious cases, particularly when a baby has suffered a degree of handicap (whether negligently caused or not), is an attractive proposition, but can be criticised on practical grounds.

Serial litigants

There have been allegations made in the USA that some people are 'serial litigants', and it would appear that some US obstetricians have refused to treat any patient who has already been involved in allegations of negligence, the fear apparently being that such patients are likely to sue again (Hengstler, 1986; Black, 1990). From this research there was little evidence of plaintiffs being involved in litigation more than once. One, referred to above, was only included once in the doctoral research because her original legal complaint was not clinically based. Another litigant to pursue more than one action sued initially on behalf of a child who had cerebral palsy. Having formally dropped this claim, she then sued concerning a retained swab. When this action was repudiated, the original action was resurrected, and it is possible – although this is only conjecture – that doing this was a means of increasing pressure on the defence to settle the second action. Although claims involving a retained swab are usually conceded quickly, an initial repudiation may be made simply to allow the hospital time to investigate the claim. If the facts are then found to be as alleged by the plaintiffs, the claim will be settled.

In a similar case a mother sued over the birth of her second child, who developed an Erb's palsy. When the hospital announced their intention to defend this action the mother contacted the hospital to say how angry she was at this. As she and her solicitors moved to serve a writ on this action, she initiated another action concerning the delivery of her first child. Whether the hospital's decision to defend the original action influenced this is again a matter of conjecture.

A more unusual case saw a mother sue over alleged negligence at a forceps delivery. Her child developed cerebral palsy, but it was established that the child's condition at birth was good, and that the child's brain damage was more likely to have been caused by the father picking the baby up at one week of age, and allegedly hitting the mother with it. The mother subsequently sued over alleged negligence at a subsequent operation at that hospital, and over the caesarean delivery of another child at a different hospital, claiming severe pain during the operation. At one stage she contacted the legal department and said that:

> A mate of hers had received £12,000 for a whiplash injury and she reckoned she ought to get a lot more for a handicapped child.

While this unfortunate woman does not have her troubles to seek, as the law currently stands compensation can only be paid when negligence on the part of the defendant is established or admitted. There is a separate debate about no-fault compensation, particularly for brain damaged infants. Another patient to sue more than once did so concerning the same incident: she dropped the original action (concerning a caesarean delivery), but then raised it again almost eight years later. She claimed that, due to subsequent medical treatment, she had 'been led to believe that there had indeed possibly been negligence at the time of delivery.' The consultant concerned agreed to her notes being released again, but stated 'I am sorry she was not able to accept the recommendations of (the original expert).' Once again she subsequently dropped this claim.

Although these are examples of patients who have sued more than once, these are not representative of litigants as a whole. The vast majority appear to become involved in such legal matters only once.

The obdurate litigant

A considerable degree of tenacity on the part of the plaintiff is required if a claim is to be pursued successfully. In all but the most open-and-shut cases (such as those concerning retained swabs) the course of the legal action takes many months and even years. While those who endure the emotional (and financial) strain of pursuing a claim evidently possess such tenacity, obduracy goes at least one step further. The reluctance to accept that a claim has been unsuccessful is understandable, but some plaintiffs appear unable to let the matter drop.

It was commonplace, having got nowhere, for plaintiffs to instruct a new firm of solicitors. Given that not all solicitors have expertise or experience in medical legal matters, this may be sound common sense, but it can be taken to extremes: some of the legal cases examined here took a long time to conclude because the plaintiff had gone onto her third or even fourth firm of solicitors. In one case, where the plaintiff was on her third firm and requested that her case notes be sent to a third expert, the legal department noted wearily in a letter to the employer:

> *I appreciate this is becoming a little ridiculous, but hopefully this should be the last referral, particularly* (since) *any claim... should be time barred* (within a few months).

Usually when the plaintiff's nominated expert supplies a report which is unfavourable to her case, the matter is dropped. One firm of apparently inexperienced solicitors (they had already written to the legal department asking them to 'Advise us of the appropriate body in London to write to to obtain the names and addresses of doctors who may be willing to assist') seemed unwilling to do this:

> *We have already taken an opinion from Dr F... in his opinion there was no medical negligence involved. In these circumstances surely a second opinion is desirable from everyone's point of view to clear up this matter once and for all.*

This made it sound as if they might go on requesting further opinions until they got one which was favourable to their client's claim.

Conclusion

People evidently sue for a number of different reasons, and once again there is ample scope for further research to help establish why some patients become litigants and others do not. It cannot be linked automatically to the clinical outcome: many who suffer a poor outcome do not pursue the matter, even sometimes where there may be evidence of negligence. Equally, some patients pursue litigation tenaciously, even after explanations by clinicians and advice by experts that they have no case to pursue.

Most sympathetic practitioners, I believe, are prepared to support specific cases of litigation. Without disparaging the stress experienced by those who bring a legal action, it is important – as *Chapter 9* demonstrated – to acknowledge that the process of litigation has a detrimental effect on practitioners as well as on the delivery of health care.

Chapter 11

K Known complications

The question of apparently high societal expectations was discussed in *Chapter 8*, and within that chapter some of the difficulties with obtaining informed consent were mentioned. Trying to give detailed information in an emergency situation is unlikely to be very effective. This chapter explores the problematic question of how much information can reasonably be given in the clinical setting. It discusses the influence of known clinical complications and rare occurrences in determining the outcome of a legal claim, and suggests ways of trying to pre-empt litigation by improving communication in the antenatal period. The question of foreseeability is crucial in medical negligence litigation, as Powers and Branthwaite (1996: 85) note: 'An action in medical negligence will only succeed if the plaintiff can establish that foreseeable harm has resulted from breach of a duty of care.' Clearly practitioners must tread a fine line between trying to provide information and dealing with a clinical situation. From an examination of legal files this chapter now examines how staff appear to have provided information about known difficulties.

Known complications

The need for women to be given accurate and sensitively-presented information is widely recognised. The amount of information available to pregnant women and new mothers, in the form of booklets and leaflets, appears to have grown exponentially in recent years, but despite this there is still doubt about how much information actually gets across. The *Changing Childbirth* report noted that 'all too often it is left to the patient to ask about a service' (DoH, 1993b: 45), and even then it appears that many health professionals are not in a position to provide answers (*ibid*: 32).

The practical difficulties in providing information about known complications was acknowledged in a leading Scots case concerning consent:

> *The risks inherent in a particular operation or procedure, the manner in which the operation may affect or damage a particular patient, the medical need for the operation and the ability of the patient to absorb information about his situation without adding damage to his health are all matters where the doctor with his own clinical experience and the benefit of the experience of other practitioners is best able to form a judgement as to what the patient can safely be told in the exercise of medical care. Nor is it practical or necessary that the patient should be told of every risk...*
>
> (*Moyes v Lothian Health Board* 1990, per Lord Caplan @ 449)

There are significant difficulties in deciding how much detail about possible complications ought reasonably to be given in advance. Such advance explanations may provide a defence in cases where negligence is alleged, but describing comprehensively those complications which may arise in any labour, for example, can be criticised as a scare tactic, and as a means of promoting high levels of technological monitoring. As with so much else in maternity care, there is a delicate balance between providing sufficient information at a level that can be absorbed, and overwhelming a pregnant woman with facts and figures. In acute situations the scope for giving information will of course be limited. In one case in which there was apparently some damage to a fallopian tube during an emergency caesarean section, the employer wrote to the solicitors:

> (The Consultant) *does not consider it normal practice in an acute obstetric emergency to counsel patients in detail on all the possible difficulties that might, very infrequently, arise.*

To say that complications are 'known' refers of course to the knowledge which practitioners ought to have. The difficult question is how much of this information ought to be passed to the pregnant woman, and when. This debate is related to the notion of obtaining a woman's consent (*Chapter 3*), and of predicting and dealing with risk (*Chapter 18*).

One case concerned the allegation that an intrauterine death ought to have been somehow prevented. The defence rested on the fact that the patient was diabetic, and that intrauterine death is a known complication of this condition. Providing adequate steps are taken to monitor the pregnancy, and the timing of delivery is consistent with good practice, then clinicians are unlikely to be guilty of negligence. Nevertheless, it is still necessary to keep the woman informed of the plan of management.

Retaining the placenta (or part of it) after delivery of the baby is another well known complication, and it does seem that some women have a predisposition to this:

> **Case**: The woman claimed staff were negligent in not ensuring that all of the placenta was expelled; the retained products became infected. Piecemeal removal of adherent fundal placental tissue was carried out.
> She had delivered three children previously, and twice before retained her placenta.

This woman would seem to be predisposed to retaining placental products after delivery. In the subsequent investigation staff were believed to have dealt with the situation in an exemplary fashion, although it might be questioned – given the woman's history – whether adequate antenatal warning of the possibility of such a recurrence was given. Had this been done, it may be surmised that she would not have felt the need to make an allegation of negligence.

Caesarean sections featured prominently in the legal cases under review. While any surgical procedure carries inherent risks, there was a strong perception among some respondents in the postal survey that certain members of the lay public believe such operations to be both straightforward and risk-free, and therefore an option which happily precludes the need to go through labour (Symon, 1998). There is also a belief that caesarean sections may be given more readily to those who are more articulate, and possibly more likely to sue (*ibid*). From a study in Los Angeles in the early 1980s, Gould *et al* (1989) point out that there is a clear socio-economic distinction seen in a woman's likelihood of receiving a caesarean, so much so that it may be termed an operation of affluence. While the North American situation is not directly replicable here, it may be that similar considerations occasionally occur. However, it seems unlikely that most practitioners would support the notion of an elective caesarean in the absence of any clinical indication.

Even an elective caesarean carries potential risks, and nor is this operation a guarantee that the child will not be handicapped: in this research two children who developed cerebral palsy were born by elective caesarean. While it is true that complications and poor outcomes are more likely to occur when the operation is performed as an emergency, unforeseen occurrences can arise even in elective cases. When the caesarean is unplanned, there is clearly limited opportunity to explore and discuss all the possible complications before the operation begins. Allegations concerning caesarean sections were a prominent feature of this research (see *Chapter 7*).

> **Case**: A ureteric fistula developed after caesarean. The woman had been in labour for a long time, and tissues were oedematous and friable.

This case relates to a complication which can cause considerable distress. Nevertheless, while the development of fistulae is a known complication of long labours, there is little that staff could do to prevent it occurring, short of having decided to operate sooner. Such a decision could be criticised by those who wish to minimise obstetric intervention in labour. In trying to promote a normal outcome staff may choose not to mention possible complications, but when the outcome is poor, as in this case, the woman can complain that she was not kept adequately informed.

Allegations about maternal injury at caesarean section were complemented by similar claims that the baby has suffered injury during the operation. In one case a cut to the baby's head occurred during an emergency caesarean for fetal distress (the lower uterine segment was noted to be very vascular). The cut was closed with steristrips. The consultant obstetrician noted:

> *It seems to me that Mrs G is very fortunate to have a live baby, and although one regrets the mark on the baby's scalp, the difficulties in determining the depth of a very vascular lower segment can be considerable...*

Such claims rarely succeeded, particularly if the operation was an emergency and there had been some concern to deliver the baby rapidly. As long as the surgeon can show that he or she proceeded with due care such relatively minor injuries, while undoubtedly distressing to the family concerned, do not usually provide evidence of negligence. One case which did succeed concerned a cut to a baby's cheek at caesarean section, although the decision to sue (and possibly the success of the claim) had much to do with the apparently unsympathetic attitude of the consultant when approached by the parents for an explanation.

Providing patients with information on known complications is a vital component of the doctrine of informed consent. However, this can be taken to extremes, and there have been suggestions that the law move from a requirement of informed consent to one of 'rational consent' (Mason and McCall Smith, 1999). However, determining what a 'rational' person would want or need to know in certain circumstances is a particularly subjective matter.

It is very easy to be critical when an outcome is known. One of the most difficult approaches to counter is the assertion that a different course of action ought to have been adopted at the relevant time in order to avoid certain known complications. This being wise after the event can be termed 'retrospectoscopy'. Divers (1994) used the term 'retrospectoscope' to describe the instrument by which perfect vision can be acquired with hindsight; a fairly common feature of legal claims. In one case the solicitors argued that an elective episiotomy would have avoided the perineal problems which their client subsequently developed. Episiotomy is an area which has seen demands for a drastic reduction in intervention: episiotomy rates are now far lower than they were in the 1970s largely due to 'consumer' demand, and a realisation by practitioners of the limited need for this procedure.

Staff, as in the case above, may be criticised for not deciding earlier in the labour to deliver by caesarean section. In addition, a fairly common claim is that a caesarean ought to have been carried out electively. Roberts (1993) points out that in today's litigious climate, such a contention should not go unchallenged. In one case in which a baby developed Erb's palsy, the solicitors wrote:

> *Our client considers that* (the Erb's palsy) *resulted from lack of care by her medical attendants in failing to adopt the alternative caesarean method of delivery...*

This was the woman's first pregnancy, and the baby was large (over 4 kg), but to assert that in any situation in which a large baby is anticipated the woman ought to have a caesarean section is absurd.

Quite apart from the subjectivity (and inaccuracy) of assessing fetal weight (the term 'guestimate' seems appropriate) there are implications for the promotion of pregnancy and labour as essentially normal physiological events. Where the line is drawn between promoting this concept and providing adequate information about possible complications is a skill, depending on the practitioner being aware of a woman's clinical risk factors, as well as her ability to impart information which may be complex and even frightening.

Rare occurrences

While known complications have been seen to provide grounds for a successful defence, rare occurrences are more problematic. By their very nature they will be topics which are unlikely to be discussed in the antenatal period, and so when they materialise, in addition to causing distress, they may also cause resentment. One such occurrence is the onset of coccydynia – pain in the region of the coccyx aggravated by movement or pressure. In several cases it was alleged that the condition occurred as a result of negligent performance of forceps delivery. However the condition may develop spontaneously after a normal delivery, and so the assumed causative element – the use of forceps – may be incidental. Either way it is very difficult to prove that the forceps did in fact cause the damage.

Another case saw the solicitors claiming that their client ought to have had a caesarean section because the pregnancy had gone past forty weeks; in this case an abruption led to a fresh stillbirth. Such attempts to claim greater wisdom find little favour with practitioners who have to deal with such issues without the benefit of hindsight. To advertise the possibility of placental abruption (or any other sudden catastrophe), at whatever gestation, can be seen as an attempt to scare women into accepting monitoring procedures and even operations which might not be necessary.

One case concerning a rare occurrence related to a very serious development after a caesarean:

> **Case**: The plaintiffs claimed that anuria resulted from negligence at caesarean section. The defence asserted that she developed postpartum haemolytic uraemic syndrome, which was quickly diagnosed and treated. Unfortunately some cortical necrosis occurred, and the woman required renal dialysis. A urologist stated that this woman had the smallest arteries he'd seen in either adult or child, and it may be supposed that this predisposed to acute cortical ischaemia.

Although the result for the woman is tragic, it appears that staff coped adequately with this unexpected complication, and so the case was unsuccessful. The following extremely rare (and, once again, tragic) occurrence demonstrates the limitations of a fault based legal system:

> **Case**: The plaintiff's solicitors claimed their client was 'permanently paralysed' as a result of an epidural anaesthetic. Delivery had been by forceps, following which either amniotic fluid embolus (AFE) or pulmonary embolus appears to have occurred. An epidural haematoma was diagnosed, and evacuated. Stocking anaesthesia and paralysis of lower limbs was then noted.
>
> The neurological discharge note stated that the working assumption was that the haematoma was caused by the removal of the epidural catheter in the presence of anticoagulation (for the AFE). The haematoma is thought to have caused the paralysis.

This tragic case resulted in no compensation being awarded since there was not apparently any evidence of negligence. Such cases may provide ammunition for those who advocate a no-fault compensation scheme for medical accidents.

Another unusual case concerned the discovery of a swab which was passed vaginally 53 weeks after a caesarean section:

> **Case**: The theatre register claimed a complete swab count. The theatre midwife who wrote a report stated she was sure the count was complete because she'd signed the register to say so.
>
> The swab passed vaginally, however, was the same as the swabs used only in Theatre. It was assumed that it was left in the uterine cavity, and then slowly worked its way out through the cervix.

Since this case was indefensible, the amount of damages had to be assessed. A depressive illness related to these events was claimed, and so a psychiatric opinion was obtained.The psychiatrist, apparently without knowing the full details of the case, agreed that the woman was suffering from a depressive illness related to her delivery, but stated:

> *The fact that she believes that the swab had been working its way through from her uterus to her vagina is in keeping with her poor intelligence...*

The psychiatrist's incorrect assumption about this woman's ability to understand events led to an unfortunate conclusion that she was imagining things. It seems however that her version of events was correct, and she succeeded in her legal action and was awarded damages.

The onset of a rare complication demands that staff react in an appropriate manner; if they do so, then it is unlikely that negligence will be established. By their very definition, rare occurrences will test staff abilities, but it is the ability to deal both with the routine and the unexpected which distinguishes the skilled from the merely competent practitioner.

Conclusion

There is great difficulty in deciding how much information ought to be given to pregnant women about things that might go wrong. Clinical risks must be weighed up, and in the antenatal period there is usually time to do this. It is impossible to prescribe exactly how much detail about possible complications ought to be given when discussing birth plans. Difficulties with conveying different levels of risk are discussed in *Chapter 18*. As *Chapter 8* noted, there is a common belief among practitioners that the general public have high, sometimes unrealistically high, expectations concerning pregnancy and labour. This suggests that at both an individual and organisational level there is greater scope for advertising the fact that things do not always go according to plan. To achieve this without inducing fear and panic, while still stressing that most pregnancies and labours will be concluded without mishap, is a tall order. In today's litigious climate, however, it is something which individual practitioners and organisations must address.

Chapter 12

L   Litigants and the legal process

The law of negligence is part of the civil legal process, and a plaintiff may bring an action if she[1] believes that she has suffered damage because of the negligence of a practitioner. The test for medical (and midwifery) negligence is covered in detail in standard texts (eg. Dimond, 1994a; Montgomery, 1997). Briefly put, a plaintiff must show that the practitioner owed a duty of care (this is not usually in doubt); that this duty was breached; and that damage resulted from the breach (the causation issue is discussed later in this chapter, *p.109*). If these three criteria are met, then compensation can be awarded.

There are many reasons for dissatisfaction with the legal process, not least because of delays (these are discussed further in *Chapter 15*). However, there have been many more reproaches of the law other than that it is not a speedy process. This chapter explores some of these other criticisms. Because this research focused on the views of clinical practitioners rather than on those initiating litigation, the discussion necessarily leans towards this side of the argument.

Litigants

There is a view which holds that some litigants enter legal actions with little regard for the effects their allegations of negligence may make. Such a view ought not to tempt us to think that people should be restricted in their freedom to initiate litigation, for this is a fundamental freedom in a civil society. While it can be assumed that the plaintiff will believe that either she or her baby has suffered in some way, some legal actions appeared to be based on no more than a misunderstanding, and there is little doubt that improved explanations would have prevented some actions; the need for effective communication is considered in *Chapter 20*. One senior midwife noted how perceptions of such matters can differ:

> *There are a lot of complaints that are trivial to people who are working in the service all the time, but are not trivial to the patient.*

> (Midwifery lecturer)

This relates to the question of people's expectations, and whether they may at times be too high (a topic examined in *Chapter 8*). The perception that certain people are more likely to sue is an interesting feature of the current debate, and usually takes one of two forms. On the one hand there is the assertion that litigants are typically found in the professional classes. A respondent in the postal survey claimed that members of the legal profession may be treated preferentially:

> *I do think that if the woman is in the legal profession, or her partner is, it can sometimes affect the way she receives care. I know of one obstetrician who wishes to see such women personally. He also wrote in the antenatal comments section*

---

1   For the purposes of this chapter the plaintiff will be assumed to be a woman, although occasionally it is her partner.

'Lawyer!' Another senior doctor later added the comment 'So what?', which infuriated the (first) *obstetrician, who blamed midwifery staff.*

(Midwife)

A consumer group representative contradicted the belief that only the articulate middle classes make complaints:

My experience of working in women's health in other fields is not that women are not articulate, the problem is that only some women are prepared to articulate their feelings to other people... I don't subscribe to this view that there are these few articulate women who are complaining all the time...

(Consumer group representative)

On the other hand there is also a belief (partly due to recent restrictions in eligibility to Legal Aid) that litigants are from a very different stratum of society. One midwife noted that an apparent increase in litigation in her area was due to those from 'poor but militant backgrounds who see it as a way to make money quickly'. Asked about this a senior clinician commented:

A lot of (them are) *just poorly educated. I don't think they're even militant. I think they're isolated often... The very young often just don't know where they are. But as long as there's a family round about them, and you can speak to Granny. If Granny understands what you're saying, she will spend her time telling these younger 16 and 17 year olds what the situation is. But if you're dealing with poorly educated young people on their own with a lack of family support, then they can often be very difficult.*

(Consultant neonatologist)

A study by Burstin *et al* (1993) which asked 'Do the poor sue more?' concluded that, contrary to popular opinion, they do not. There is also the belief that publicity about legal cases (eg. Henderson, 1997) creates a certain momentum, and encourages people to take action on flimsy grounds:

It's more people jumping on the bandwagon when something has – or hasn't – gone wrong, and heading to complain, and then heading towards solicitors.

(Consultant obstetrician 3)

A senior lawyer also noted how publicity could encourage litigation:

My perception isn't just from professional circles, as somebody who reads the papers, (it's) *all the newspaper reporting. There's all sorts of medical claims, and I'm sure – again this is just amateur supposition – I'm sure that must encourage people to go to solicitors, and also encourage solicitors who may not know anything, or very much, about it to pursue the matter.*

(Queen's Counsel)

There is certainly a feeling that within society there is generally a greater propensity to complain, and indeed increasing litigation appears to be a factor for many different occupations (Dingwall, 1994). This appears to reflect a reduction in the perceived status of certain groups, perhaps especially professional groups. One experienced educationalist noted that at times this has almost become a form of vindictiveness:

> *I think we're in a society where people want compensation much more than before. They want to be able to point the finger of blame, and they want to be able to say 'I got that person.'*

> (Midwifery lecturer)

This view was reaffirmed by another midwife:

> *I think generally society is just too conscious of 'Somebody has done wrong, let's get them back'.*

> (Midwife 14)

Another (recently retired) midwife noted wistfully:

> *Society has changed. People just used to be grateful to have a live baby.*

> (Midwife 12)

Another midwife noted:

> *Only two generations ago people accepted that babies died, or that even mothers died... It maybe helps in the grieving process to find someone to blame...*

> (Midwife 4)

Underlying these comments is the belief that litigation is often not warranted; in comparatively few cases – compared with other personal injury litigation – was the action successful. Initiating litigation which has only a slim chance of success can be criticised on a number of fronts: litigation comes at an emotional cost to all concerned (see *Chapter 9*); financially there are few winners; it requires significant administrative resources, usually over a long period of time; and its adversarial nature does little to promote understanding between the two parties.

Despite criticisms of an apparently increased propensity to sue on the part of the general public it should not be thought that people take this course of action lightly. The perceived need to invoke the law, after all, comes only when someone feels sufficiently aggrieved. However, there are critical views of other aspects of litigation, and some of these are now discussed.

Criticisms of the legal process

That there are many reasons for dissatisfaction within the legal process comes as no surprise. There have been many criticisms of different aspects of the legal process; two of these (delays and the role of solicitors) are discussed more fully in later chapters (*15* and *25* respectively). In this section several other aspects are singled out for criticism.

While the pressures of pursuing a legal action are not in question, there is no doubt that the experience of being named in a legal action is stressful for practitioners; such a reaction is not eased by a feeling of helplessness. A senior lawyer acknowledged that part of his job was to provide support in such circumstances:

> *If you take a case all the way through, it's a major hand-holding exercise very often for the (practitioner) under attack... some of them by the time they reach that stage are retired, and here they are, first time they're involved in something like this, I feel very sorry and sympathetic for them. As you approach the (court hearing) stage you're on*

the 'phone to them, you're writing to them regularly, you're reassuring them, you're with them in court.

(Defence solicitor 2)

However, two midwives involved in separate claims noted how they did not feel they had been kept sufficiently informed:

It went to independent medical experts... I didn't know what happened after that, which is one of the things as a midwife that I felt most bitter about.

(Midwife 11)

It was a long long time before I heard what happened. All I got was a 'phone message... saying 'The case has been settled reasonably economically out of court' – whatever that means!

(Midwife 16)

Those involved have to accept that few claims will proceed at a quick pace, but there is a general belief that they will eventually result in the correct judgement. Inherent in any standard discussion of medical litigation is the notion that deserving claims will succeed, and undeserving ones will not. This basic principle underpins the rationale of litigation.

There are nevertheless occasions when the theory is not matched by practice. Genn (1987: 163) in a large study of civil litigation, claimed that a lack of precision and predictability 'creates... conditions of uncertainty under which claims are argued and resisted, and... contributes substantially to the pressure on plaintiffs to avoid the risks of trial by compromising their claim.' The level of experience of the plaintiff solicitors may be a significant factor in determining whether the plaintiff receives adequate compensation, or indeed any compensation at all (see *Chapter 25*). Moves to restrict medical claims to those lawyers with the requisite knowledge and skill may help to improve this state of affairs.

Some of the respondents with experience of litigation confirmed that considerations other than the merits of the claim could affect the outcome. In one case the defence solicitors wrote:

I am not convinced that the other side have a particularly good case on the issue of causation, as I have a feeling that the child would have been stillborn anyhow, but nonetheless I agree with you that it would be worth negotiating the cheapest possible out-of-Court settlement as early as possible in order to save costs all round.

Asked about this, a defence solicitor conceded the point:

It's pragmatism, I suppose. Economic settlements have come on board more since Trusts came into the picture. Prior to that economic settlements were never seriously considered. Trusts are much more prepared to look at the cost.

(Defence solicitor 2)

That financial considerations must be taken into account is unlikely to shock anyone who is currently employed in today's (comparatively) cash-constrained health service. The devolution of budgets to local level has restricted the scope (previously enjoyed by large health authorities/health boards) for hospital Trusts to absorb legal costs and damages awards. However, what might loosely be called the justice argument does demand that practitioners are not implicitly acknowledged to have been at fault when this is not in fact the case. Equally, justice demands that when a practitioner has been at fault, this is acknowledged. Just as some claims of dubious legal merit were settled when the likely level of compensation was low, so in one case the opposite happened. The employer wrote to the defence organisation:

> *This sounds like a tragic case, and I regret that concern for the financial impact of a large settlement on the* (Trust) *and its Obstetrics and Gynaecology service militates against any immediate concession of liability.*

Thankfully in this case the defence quickly acknowledged that the claim could not be defended and a negotiated settlement resulted. This case does, however, highlight the considerations which those responsible for the financial aspects of claims must make. No employer will be thrilled at the prospect of having to pay out a large sum in damages. Because of such a consideration in one claim the employer wrote to the legal department:

> *I feel that any straws that might be clutched at should be investigated for clutchworthiness.*

Quite where economic considerations leave the 'justice' argument in a claim is a moot point. There may also be logistical difficulties in defending a claim:

> *We had a very supportive expert report... in all his 900 cases he'd only had one anything like* (this)*... and it was eminently defensible. On the other hand the registrar who had done it was then in Australia, and the thought of flying him in for a County Court trial with shaky dates – our solicitors say that County Court trial dates are very often not solid, they get shuffled – was not a very alluring prospect. We thought we could probably buy it off for two and a half thousand, although the claim was for much more, and we did.*
>
> (Legal department official)

Several apparently defensible claims were settled because the relevant staff were in far-flung corners of the world. It might be thought that practitioners would object to such a decision, since their professional reputation is impugned (Brazier, 1987). While some have done so, it appears that such a response may be changing:

> *The doctors, from being in a situation where they would feel they were being sold down the river, now seem to be a little more pragmatic as well. They can see the hassle of being tied up in court for a week or two...*
>
> (Defence solicitor 2)

Even when it is believed that there has been no negligence it is quite understandable that practitioners would want to avoid a court appearance, given the extreme stress of such a situation. Uncertainty about the outcome (confidence in one's own version of events notwithstanding) and the sheer inconvenience of having to be in or near the court for one or more days may both encourage a negotiated settlement. Another consideration was noted by one respondent:

> *Some judges are known as pursuer's judges, and some judges are known as defender's judges. Once you know which judge you're getting that could just tilt the balance and make you settle.*
>
> (Defence solicitor 2)

In theory court personnel are dispassionate about a case: they have no vested interest in its outcome. However, it has been suggested that within legal circles certain people tend to lean to one side or other of an argument. The same has been alleged about those who act as expert witnesses for defendants or plaintiffs, as discussed in *Chapter 5*.

Problems with causation

Some of the longest and most bitter legal battles have been fought over the question of causation regarding cerebral palsy, partly because the financial stakes are at their highest with regard to this condition. Its association with premature delivery is discussed in *Appendix III*. Nevertheless, it is the perceived link between cerebral palsy and the intrapartum period which attracts most attention In one case an educational psychologist apparently attributed a baby's cerebral palsy to birth asphyxia, a claim which was indignantly rebutted by the consultant paediatrician, who stated:

> *I do not think she is in a position to make this judgement.*

This case was successfully defended. Causation may also be an issue when perineal refashioning ('perineoplasty' or 'perineotomy') is required: in one case the plaintiff's solicitors argued that the need for this represented prima facie evidence of negligence on the part of the midwife who stitched the woman's perineum. Usually it can be quickly established that the woman's current condition and the perineal trauma from the delivery are linked, but this is sometimes disputed:

> **Case**: At delivery the woman's perineum remained intact, but there were vaginal lacerations which required suturing. The plaintiff claimed there was a delay before suturing, and pain during the repair, which had to be refashioned later.
> Although this woman had longstanding gynaecological problems, including dyspareunia for many years before this pregnancy and admitted loss of libido, these factors all formed part of her claim.

Causation may be more difficult to establish if a long time is taken in initiating a complaint. In one case it was alleged that a crush injury to pelvic nerves occurred during a forceps delivery. While the solicitors claimed that the injury was immediately apparent, it was almost three years before the claim was made: a writ claiming £50,000 in damages was moved just before the expiry of the triennium. The obstetric staff were adamant that the delivery was not traumatic, and queried how the woman came to make a diagnosis of 'displaced bladder and bowel' and 'fractured coccyx'. Coccydynia may of course occur after a normal delivery: the use of forceps may be incidental and not causal.

A common complaint is that practitioners have not ensured that the placenta and membranes are delivered in their entirety, and that this has resulted in either haemorrhage or uterine infection in the postnatal period. The matter of causation here is not as straightforward as a lay person might think: the presence of haemorrhage at this time is not necessarily due to retained products of conception, but this does appear to be a common belief.

> **Case**: The plaintiff claimed that products must have been retained because she had to have two 'D+C's'. Histology showed no placental or membranous tissue, and it appears she had a uterine infection which caused decidual/endometrial bleeding.

This case was dropped after an expert report was obtained. Even where it is shown that some placental or membranous tissue has been retained, the matter of negligence cannot be assumed, as in this similarly unsuccessful case:

> **Case**: After delivery the midwife recorded the placenta as complete, and the membranes as ragged.
>
> The expert report stated: 'Throughout Britain, in one year, hundreds of women will be admitted for evacuation of the uterus a few weeks after delivery because of retention of small pieces of placenta. Such is a normal complication of normal delivery. To allege negligence over this is ludicrous.'

A dead baby is a tragic outcome and it is perfectly natural that parents in this situation should look for explanation, and even perhaps someone to blame. While midwifery and obstetric medicine strive to identify 'at risk' situations which may predispose to this terrible outcome, and then intervene to prevent the tragedy, such attempts are unlikely to prove completely successful. The trauma suffered by parents in these circumstances can only be imagined. Whether the initiation of a legal action helps to accelerate and conclude the grieving process, or whether the adversarial legal system generates more antagonism and prevents supportive counselling by health care workers, is a matter of some debate. In *Chapter 9* it is shown that some legal actions are based on the fact that a child has been either stillborn or has died soon after birth.

In some ways such cases are related to many of those concerning cerebral palsy, the charge against staff being that the delay in delivering the child was so significant that the child did not survive at all (rather than survived but is handicapped). There are certain situations or conditions which are associated with an increased risk of intrauterine death, one being diabetes. When the extra monitoring advised in such cases is made difficult by conditions such as obesity, the possibility of a poor or tragic outcome is higher. In one case the woman weighed well over 100kg by the end of her pregnancy; ultrasound scanning and electronic fetal monitoring were felt to be difficult. The expert report stated:

> *If Mrs D had been less obese at the start of her pregnancy, and if she had maintained good diabetic control throughout, the outcome might well have been different.*

This case was unsuccessful. In another case, a diabetic pregnant woman failed to attend her antenatal clinic appointment; when she next attended, she said she had felt no fetal movements for three weeks. An intrauterine death was confirmed on scan. Unsurprisingly this action did not succeed either.

Certain other conditions may be the subject of debate concerning causation. In one case a baby was born with a midline skin defect over the sagittal suture – an area of alopecia was present. While the maternal grandmother was adamant that this was due to the forceps delivery, in this case a condition known as cutis alopecia – a congenital patchy absence of hair – appeared the most likely explanation. Several legal cases have been initiated in this manner, the lay assumption being that a bald patch must be due to either forceps, fetal scalp electrode, or amniotomy hook. Some of these cases succeed (one did where it was held that a midwife had dislodged a piece of scalp when removing a fetal scalp electrode; damages of £750 were awarded), but many fail. It can be argued that insufficient explanation of such congenital conditions will fuel legal claims. The question of explanations is examined further in *Chapter 20*.

The cause of an injury may be admitted, but the defendants may claim that the mere presence of a condition is not itself evidence of negligence. One such condition is Erb's palsy, in which the roots of the brachial plexus are damaged. This is a recognised complication following shoulder dystocia, since forceful traction is required in order to accomplish delivery. Without showing that the defendants negligently failed antenatally to identify a baby so large that shoulder dystocia was probable, or that they used excessive force, such cases are unlikely to succeed. Predictions of birthweight – and consequently of possible shoulder dystocia – are known to be inaccurate (Gonen *et al*, 1996). However, the failure to document difficulties encountered with delivering the shoulders can lead to an inference that unnecessary force was used if an Erb's palsy does result. In one case the lack of either case records or consistent staff recollections describing such difficulties weighed heavily against the midwives concerned.

Plaintiffs may claim that deficiencies in a child's eyesight are attributable to events surrounding birth or the newborn period. One of the most notable medico-legal cases in recent years concerned allegations of negligent monitoring of blood oxygen levels in a neonate which resulted in blindness (*Wilsher v Essex HA*). Another case with a similar outcome concerned allegations that midwifery staff had not identified eye infections at birth, resulting in the baby going blind in one eye. This case failed. The action was only raised when the child was eight years old, although the blindness had been diagnosed eight months after delivery; and it was shown that eye swabs taken at birth and after discharge home showed there was no infection present. In fact the child had a congenital cataract (which in theory ought to have been diagnosed on routine detailed examination in the newborn period). An ophthalmologist commented:

> *Even if* (the) *cataract had been detected at birth I do not think this would have changed our management as the prognosis for unilateral cataracts is extremely poor...*

Conclusion

The civil legal process is rarely a speedy creature, but the detrimental effects of long delays may be eased if practitioners are kept informed on a regular basis. However, some of those with experience of the law have claimed that they felt insufficiently supported. The legal process may also throw up anomalous results which bring into doubt its suitability for attaining justice. Some meritorious claims do not succeed (and for a variety of reasons), while other less worthy claims have been conceded on economic or pragmatic grounds. Causation is a central feature of a fault-based legal system, but is often problematic, and its existence can not be automatically assumed in clinical terms. Poor outcomes may not be the result of substandard care, even when poor care is admitted. As noted in *Appendix III*, intrapartum events are thought to have a causal relationship with the appearance of cerebral palsy in only a minority of cases.

Root and branch changes in the law are not likely in the near future, although Lord Woolf's reforms aim to ameliorate some of the more antagonistic elements of the adversarial process. There is an inherent component of confrontation in the current system which might be improved by better standards of communication before there is a perceived need to involve solicitors. The importance of good communication is discussed in *Chapter 20*.

Chapter 13

M   Monitoring

It was seen in *Chapter 7* that claims alleging negligence leading to cerebral palsy were the single most common reason for suing in this field of health care. In *Appendix III* there is a brief description of the condition, and a discussion of some the markers which have been associated with fetal or neonatal compromise. Some have claimed that these markers are predictors of cerebral palsy. This chapter concentrates on an examination of several claims concerning allegations of inadequate monitoring, since this is the usual stance adopted in allegations regarding cerebral palsy. It is well recognised that interpretation of CTG traces varies, even when 'experts' are involved (Ayres-de-Campos *et al*, 1999). Perhaps more worryingly, even experienced practitioners can, after a short gap, interpret the same trace differently (Nielsen *et al*, 1987).

The importance of monitoring

The relationship between cerebral palsy and intrapartum events is a problematic one. This section discusses a number of legal actions which have concerned allegations about monitoring.

One of the dangers of 'false positives' (ie. the diagnosis of fetal compromise from apparent fetal heart rate abnormalities when there is no other corroborating evidence) is not only that they may lead to unnecessary interventions, but that they provide supporting 'evidence' for a plaintiff if no immediate action is taken and the outcome, for whatever reason, is poor. One expert report noted:

> *If we are to accept that any obstetrician is to be the subject of litigation if he delivers an infant that is abnormal after an abnormal CTG, then it would be better not to perform antenatal CTGs because it can always be argued that delivery was too late if the child is cerebrally damaged.*

The whole topic of CTG is one which divides many practitioners and patients. Its importance in legal terms is hard to overstate, since it often provides a continuous record of one aspect of intrapartum fetal well being, despite its poor predictive value for cerebral palsy. The following cases illustrate how practitioners may become involved in legal arguments.

In one case, the midwives were criticised when a fetal scalp electrode (FSE) became disconnected some 5–10 minutes before delivery. There was meconium staining, and the woman was transferred from the midwife-led unit to the consultant unit. A fetal scalp electrode fell off, but auscultation of the fetal heart was carried out between that time and delivery, and this was recorded as satisfactory throughout. The parents seized on the few minutes when the FSE was unattached to explain the child's subsequent condition (cerebral palsy). The writ stated:

> *The hint of meconium staining... ought to have alerted the... midwifery staff and registrar to the risk of fetal distress occurring. Accordingly continuous FHR recording ought to have commenced at that time.*

It would appear from the various reports that the midwives did all they could have been expected to do, continuous fetal heart rate recording using an abdominal transducer may be very difficult immediately before delivery, and in this case the scalp electrode was unattached. As the midwives continued to monitor the fetal heart rate using intermittent auscultation and recorded that this was satisfactory, their actions appeared to be defensible.

At times it may be difficult to use the CTG to record the fetal heart rate, and in such instances good documentation is essential. In one case a baby was very asphyxiated at birth. The plaintiffs claimed that monitoring should not have been discontinued. It was documented that it was very difficult to listen to the fetal heart rate as the woman moved about the bed a lot. The midwife looking after her noted frequent 'loss of contact' with the fetal heart rate on the CTG trace, and stated:

> *I made the decision to stop the print out from the monitor but kept the transducer and belt in situ, and I was continually listening to the fetal heart.*

The midwives' reports indicated that the fetal heart rate was satisfactory at all times, and in this case the expert report backed up the midwives' actions. In other cases reports have criticised midwifery actions:

> **Case**: The plaintiff's solicitors claimed that instead of diagnosing fetal distress in labour, staff assumed the 'heart rate coming and going' was due to a defective CTG machine. They asserted that only when the third machine was showing the same sort of trace was the woman sent for caesarean section.

In Theatre a placental abruption was discovered. There was nothing documented to say the CTG machine was replaced at all. When eventually the CTG traces were found, they revealed one change of machine, from an old to a newer model. There was a gap of 2½ hours when the CTG was not used, and in this time there were six written recordings of a fetal heart rate, at half-hourly intervals. The medical expert felt that the midwives could be criticised for not having a more comprehensive record of the fetal heart rate.

Another claim concerned apparent abnormalities (persistent early fetal heart rate decelerations) which were not acted upon. Despite there being reduced variability and meconium staining the staff appeared to think these were benign, and CTG monitoring was discontinued for a while. The expert report stated:

> *There is a period of 90 minutes...when there was no CTG recording. This is an unacceptable situation where the patient has had a previous section, at 42 weeks with meconium staining, and with CTG abnormalities which are persistent and who was on Oxytocin.*

This catalogue of 'at risk' factors does not appear to have alerted midwives to the need for extra vigilance. An interesting point is noted in a separate case where the question of whether the midwife could insist on carrying out such monitoring was raised. It was clearly documented in the notes that the woman's preference was not to have CTG monitoring if possible. Criticising the midwives' acquiescence in this request, her solicitors wrote:

> *Continuous fetal monitoring when the decision was made to give a syntocinon infusion should have been insisted upon...*

When the question of being able to insist was put to midwives and obstetricians in the postal survey, it produced considerable differences of opinion. Continuous monitoring when syntocinon is used is felt by many to be mandatory, and yet there were other examples of poor monitoring in such circumstances. In one case there was no continuous monitoring despite one record entry stating:

> *Uterus rock hard between contractions.*

The dangers of over-stimulating the uterus with syntocinon, so causing acute fetal hypoxia (and usually intense pain for the mother) are well known, but appear to have been forgotten in this case. In another case a lack of action over many hours by midwives was criticised. The plaintiff's solicitors claimed:

> *It would appear that a fetal monitor was incorrectly adjusted and, accordingly, the readings which it gave were not properly interpreted and significant abnormalities were disregarded.*

The CTG had 'wrong speed' written on it, and it seems that different speeds for the print out were used at different times in labour. The machine was an old model and did not automatically record the date and time on the trace; unfortunately neither did the staff. The expert report noted:

> *I do not recall having ever seen a trace with such a smooth line and almost complete lack of beat to beat variation... The nursing* (sic) *staff faithfully recorded the events but apparently failed to appreciate the significance of the flat trace and therefore did not report it to the medical staff.*

This action was conceded by the defence shortly before the court hearing was due. There were other cases in which the CTG showed abnormalities which were ignored by staff. In one instance the expert reported:

> *It is difficult to see the point of fetal monitoring if no action is to be taken when there are obvious abnormalities in the recording.*

In another case there was a similar damning lack of awareness on the midwife's part about the CTG. The defence solicitor stated:

> (The midwife) *admitted quite freely that she spent many hours in watching a fetal heart monitor which she was insufficiently trained to interpret or understand at the time. She has since been better trained and, looking back at the fetal heart traces during the period she was on duty, she sees them as being abnormal. In my opinion, quite a bit of liability must therefore attach to a system which asked midwives to watch a monitor which they are insufficiently trained to understand.*

CTGs will remain a critical part of intrapartum care in many units. The need to ensure that staff are properly trained in CTG interpretation is one step which employers can address, but it should be remembered that the UKCC *Code of Professional Conduct* 'encourages (practitioners) to declare their incompetence in certain procedures rather than to try to undertake them' (UKCC, 1992a:1). Individual midwives also have a responsibility to ensure that they are adequately prepared for the duties entrusted to them.

Storage of CTG traces so that they survive and are readable is also a matter of concern to hospitals. The possibility for electronic storage has been mooted, since paper and ink quality can deteriorate over the years. In one case the CTG trace from the delivery survived, but was presented at a medical meeting: a registrar used a thick black felt tip pen to illustrate points he was making, effectively obscuring the trace. In another teaching hospital case the CTG trace could not be found at all. Many people were doing research, and it appears that the trace was borrowed for this reason. A central hospital register of research studies may be required so that records can be more easily found,

Conclusion

It is hard to over-emphasise the importance of CTGs in this area of the law, despite the many misgivings about its use. Adequate training of all staff members in its interpretation, together with efficient storage (and retrieval when required) are the minimum which hospitals must guarantee. Educating the public, as well as staff, about the limitations of the technology will help to establish a more realistic understanding of its applicability.

As with every other sphere of practice, good documentation in this area is essential and may well provide the practitioner with his/her best defence. As McRae (1999: 318) notes, documentation should include observations rather than judgements such as 'Good baseline'. This is considered further in the next chapter. What these cases have shown is how a legal case may be decided by the actions of staff concerning the CTG. While its widespread application remains controversial, the CTG is not going to disappear, and those who work in units where it is employed must be competent in its use.

Chapter 14

N Notes and records

The notes are few!

(Blake, to the Muses)

This chapter discusses the importance of case notes. Every practitioner can cite the reasons for maintaining good case records and most, I believe, think that they are themselves competent in this respect. Nevertheless, inadequate case records have been cited in many reports into suboptimal outcomes (MCHRC, 1997) and litigation (James, 1991), and they are a crucial area in defending allegations of negligence (Cetrulo and Cetrulo, 1989; MCHRC, 1999). Detailed and contemporaneous accounts may be a vital feature in helping a practitioner to remember a particular woman/family or sequence of events (*Chapter 22* highlights problems of memory recall). Equally, a case record with sparse, illegible or unsigned entries may prove to be as much a hindrance as a help when a retrospective investigation is necessary.

It should be remembered that patients have a statutory right of access to their case notes under the Data Protection Act 1984 (which applies to computerised records), the Access to Health Records Act 1990 (which relates to hand-written records), and the Access to Medical Reports Act 1988. Access may only be withheld if it is established that 'serious harm would be caused to the mental or physical health of the patient or any other individual; (or) where the identity of a third person would be made known and this person has not consented to access' (Dimond, 1994a: 95). Given such comparative ease of access, practitioners must be careful to include only factual information in the notes.

While it cannot be assumed that something is true merely because it is written down, in practice great reliance will be laid on the version of events held within the notes. In one case a consultant noted angrily:

> *The statement in the lawyer's letter that she was treated in a variety of ways which 'did not aid recovery and in fact caused her condition to deteriorate' is absolute rubbish, and does not take cognisance of the written facts in the case notes.*

Despite concerns about the veracity of case note entries, the notes will often provide the best evidence available, particularly if – as is often the case – there is a long delay between events and subsequent legal notification (see *Chapter 15*). The following discussion, divided into four sections, is intended as a guide to certain aspects of the role of case records in legal actions. The first three discuss cases in which notes are missing, inadequate, and inaccurate or confusing. The last examines some claims about changes in the standard of record keeping.

Missing notes

It is of course a requirement for an employer to provide suitable storage for case notes. Inefficiencies in the storage and retrieval system are considered in the next chapter from the point of view of delay in the legal process. The discussion here relates to the difficulties in investigating and determining the course of events when notes 'go missing'.

In most cases the principal documentation will be the case notes, but it is not just missing case notes that may hinder an investigation. There are many other items of documentation that may be required, including staff duty sheets and shift summaries, as in this case, in which the expert noted:

> *Information about the total number of patients in labour and the number of staff on duty during the night in question is not available, neither is it known if the midwife in charge of the Labour Ward reported any such problems if it was appropriate for her to do so.*

In one published legal case the judge noted: 'The paediatric notes held at (the) hospital have gone missing. It is not suggested for one moment that there is anything sinister in this. But the lack of notes covering the first days of the plaintiff's life is unfortunate to say the least' (De Martell [1995] per Simpson J @ 242).

Not everyone is prepared to give the defence the benefit of the doubt in such matters: Beech (1990: 3) is very sceptical about such 'loss of evidence', claiming that this is often a defence ploy. However, contrary to this claim, missing notes do little to bolster the defence's case since they will usually provide the most evidence in rebutting an allegation of negligence. Even missing parts of the documentary evidence can hinder the defence, as in one case in which the employer noted to the defence organisation:

> *From our point of view the combination of sparse notes and the absence of the fetal heart trace is unfortunate.*

Missing CTG traces have been a particular problem, since many hospitals have not devised a secure method of storage. Practitioners are mistaken if they believe that having a 'hard copy' of a CTG trace precludes the need to write regular entries regarding the fetal heart rate. It is indeed when entries in the notes are inadequate that difficulty is encountered.

Inadequate notes

Detailed entries must be made in the notes, especially when a decision has been taken with regard to management. In one case a registrar was unable to recollect any of the events in question, and admitted:

> *I would not necessarily make any comments in the notes if correct management was being followed.*

A lack of documentation in such 'wait and see' decisions can make it appear as if no decision has been taken. In another case a student midwife admitted that her entries were poor:

> *As I was anxious to get a better quality CTG, I didn't take my hands off the transducer and was aware that I wasn't recording this in the case notes.*

In a similar situation the midwife noted:

> *FH* (fetal heart) *listened with sonicaid – satisfactory – I did not record it as the notes were in the other corner of the room and Mrs K needed me next to her all the time.*

These situations are readily imaginable: in cases where fetal compromise is suspected, the need to ensure that the fetal heart rate is heard as clearly as possible may mean that the attending staff member has no hand free with which to write entries in the notes.

The need to be able to trace staff from their entries in the notes requires that they sign their name legibly. In one case concerning a child with cerebral palsy there was the following unsigned entry in the Labour Ward notes: 'Tonic uterine contractions. Syntocinon reduced'.

Even with apparent identification, some signatures (and indeed printed names) are little more than squiggles on the page: in one case a legal staff member described one such (north European) signature as an 'Arabic hieroglyphic' in appearance. Without identification it is extremely difficult to clarify who did what and when. James (1991) advises staff to print their name as well as giving a signature, and some units now supply junior medical staff with their own name stamp.

It is not always the case that having the case notes will assist the defence. In one case in which there had been a failure to monitor a woman's haemoglobin levels during her pregnancy the expert noted:

> *We are often dealing with good medical practice which is difficult to prove because of lack of good documentation. In this case unfortunately the documentation is excellent and makes the bad medical practice very evident.*

However, it is usually when there are missing notes or long gaps in the case notes that the defence is presented with problems. One midwife, who had herself been involved in a legal action, and who said she had subsequently improved her own documentation, noted that her colleagues were not always as careful:

> *I see colleagues now... there are whole episodes, there are hours and hours of care that are just missed.*

> (Midwife 11)

In one case, there were no notes made between the following two entries:

> 08.00 'Vertex visible, pushing commenced.'
> 08.40 'SVD, live boy with aid of episiotiomy.'

In this case the CTG trace was missing, and so there was no record of the fetal condition for the entire active second stage of labour. When the outcome is poor and there is not the documentation to state that care was adequate, it can appear as if the standard of care was on a par with the standard of record keeping. Cohn (1984) notes that a court will conclude, notwithstanding a practitioner's assertions to the contrary, that if something is not recorded, it was not done.

Cases have been lost partly because staff have failed to make appropriate entries, and sometimes any entries at all. In one case the failure to note any difficulty with a delivery led to the inference that excessive force had been used when Erb's palsy was diagnosed. Another case highlighted the failure of community midwives to record what they said or did despite making several home visits. The lack of any description of further monitoring, given a history of reduced fetal movements, weighed very heavily against them.

In another case an obstetrician failed to make any entries regarding an episiotomy and forceps delivery. The case centred on the material used for the repair of the episiotomy; the labour ward summary written by the midwife said catgut was used, and the section relating to the repair had the entry 'pp Dr Y'. The doctor thought he had used Vicryl sutures, which self-absorb; in fact it transpired from laboratory examination that the sutures were made of silk, and so should have been removed in due course. The failure to do this caused problems: the plaintiff's Writ claimed for loss of her sex life and an inability to enjoy her daughter for nine months. The plaintiff was successful in this case and obtained several thousand pounds in damages.

Inaccurate or confusing notes

It seems obvious that what is written in the notes should be clear and accurate. Needless to say this is not always so. In one case a midwife included what were apparently two mutually exclusive statements in her admission note:

> *No SRM... black substance in the vagina.*

The expert report concluded that the midwife's actions were not those of a competent professional, the black substance evidently being meconium. In the same case there was a discrepancy of twenty minutes between the recorded timings of the midwife and the doctor, which may have been crucial.

In another case there was further confusion over the entry 'SR informed'. It was not clear whether this referred to the labour ward sister (abbreviation 'Sr'), or the senior registrar (abbreviation 'SR'). Abbreviations are commonly used as a time saving measure, but can cause confusion, and there have been calls to minimise and standardise their use (Dimond, 1998b).

Entries in the case notes or other records may be relied upon heavily, but will not necessarily be taken as proof of what happened. Entries may be quite erroneous: in more than one case the Theatre records have shown a complete swab count, but a retained swab has subsequently been found, making the case indefensible. Equally, contradictory entries do little to convey a sense of competence:

> **Case**: The baby transfer form stated 'Cord round neck x 1'. The infant summary form had 'cord around neck' by one staff member, with someone else adding 'x 3, tight'.

Which of these was correct could be crucial in determining whether staff actions were appropriate. In another case there were three different versions of the baby's Apgar scores at one and five minutes: one entry recorded them as one and five, another as three and four, while the third claimed they were two and four. While the Apgar score has been criticised (Marlow, 1992), it remains the almost universal method of assessing the condition of the newborn baby, and is in theory an objective scoring method. That it is not always so was demonstrated in one case in which there was some discrepancy as to the condition at birth of a second twin: one report said 'live baby boy', another stated 'A/S (presumed to be the Apgar score) 0/10.' The plaintiff's expert was dismissive, claiming that the staff:

> *...were incapable of differentiating between a dead baby and a live baby.*

Poor writing can cause further problems with interpretation of records:

> **Case**: From reading the case notes the plaintiff's solicitors claimed that an obstetrician cut the bladder during a caesarean section, and so ought to have called for a more senior colleague to assist in the repair. The expert nominated by the legal department retorted that the plaintiff's expert had misread the notes: what the surgeon wrote was 'left angle bleeder caught', not bladder, although it later transpired that there was in fact bladder involvement.

Most people find their own writing legible. However, in one neonatal case, the defence conceded the action because the midwife concerned had only a poor recollection of the events, and could not make sense of one or two of her own entries. There is a particular problem with entries which are made when tired or rushed.

Confusion may be caused inadvertently because of the terminology used. In one case concerning alleged retained products a midwife had written in the labour ward summary that the placenta was complete but the membranes were ragged. This caused disagreement as to whether negligence had occurred in not ensuring that all the products of conception were expelled. In another case an attempt to get round this conundrum caused more problems. The midwife in question had written, following her usual practice, that the placenta 'appears complete' in the delivery notes. The expert stated:

> (I) *checked a random sample of case sheets within* (my) *unit to check on practice; one member of staff uses the term 'appears complete' and in her interpretation she has no doubt that the placenta, to all appearances, is complete and personally I would agree that unless the placenta or membranes are recorded as incomplete, I would conclude that they are complete.*

It is clear how such entries could give the impression to plaintiffs that they may have a case. Given this, it may be wiser for staff to be more assertive and record the placenta and membranes as complete if they appear to be so, rather than try to cover oneself in case a small piece of either placental tissue or membrane has been retained and subsequently causes problems such as haemorrhage or infection.

Changes in record keeping

Because of some of the problems identified in this chapter, many practitioners have altered their own conduct with regard to record keeping. In the postal survey by far the most common example cited by midwives of a personal change in practice due to the fear of litigation was an increase in documentation.

As stated earlier, documentation is not confined to the case notes. One midwife who had been involved in a legal claim said:

> *I notice that I now write down everything on the CTG. I never had problems writing my notes.*

(Midwife 2)

However, some practitioners perceive significant changes in their own record keeping:

> *If it's a high risk area, and there's a baby who's been asphyxiated, then there's no doubt about it, we are documenting those extremely carefully.*

(Consultant neonatologist)

> *It's quite interesting: if somebody comes back to have a subsequent baby and you've looked after them previously, and you see your level of documentation five or ten years ago... you cringe. And now I think we document something at every document point of contact with the client, whereas before there'd be huge gaps if everything was OK...*

(Midwife 4)

Responses in the postal survey included the following with regard to increased levels of documentation:

Ensuring that I write everything down regardless of how trivial it may be.

Improved (in fact almost paranoid) record keeping.

If documentation is almost paranoid, then it's unlikely to constitute an improvement. What seems clear is the desire of midwives to produce a good account of events. This desire to produce a good standard of case notes was also stressed by one consumer representative:

You get these beautifully documented notes where (the midwives) *write everything down beautifully in longhand, and essentially what they're doing is writing down that the baby died, but they're not actually doing anything about it.*

(AVMA official 2)

This may be seen as the midwifery equivalent of the Nero syndrome: scribbling away while Rome burns. Where such practices originate is a matter of contention. One senior lecturer stated:

I did a seminar and said 'What is the reason for record keeping?' And the response was 'Fear of litigation'. Their thoughts were 'We only keep records because we might be called to account.' Litigation should be at the bottom of the list; something to remember, but not the prime reason.

(Midwifery lecturer)

This lecturer was adamant that these senior students had not been taught this in the classroom, and that this appeared to be a habit which had been learnt from watching qualified staff.

Conclusion

Case records will be relied upon heavily in a legal investigation. Given the unexpected nature of many legal claims, staff who fail to keep clear contemporaneous records, particularly in the Labour ward, may be putting their heads in a noose. It may be difficult to maintain a good standard of record keeping when the unit is extremely busy or when emergencies occur, but there is a clear duty to make adequate entries in the case notes as soon as is practicable. This will assist any retrospective enquiry, in particular by helping the relevant staff members to recall particular sequences of events.

Chapter 15

O   Overlong

Delays have dangerous ends.

(Henry VI, Part 1)

Anyone who has been involved in a legal action will know that the legal process is rarely speedy: one of the least edifying features of litigation is the fact that delays are commonplace. These occur for a number of reasons, and this chapter examines some of the possible reasons for delays. The chapter is divided into sections which examine delays in initiating litigation; delays in tracing case records and staff; delays which may be attributed to plaintiffs, their solicitors, the bureaucracy of the legal process, or the need to involve experts; and delays in closing the legal claim.

Delays in the legal process

Initiating litigation

The 'lag time' – the time between an event and subsequent legal notification – is a conspicuous feature of medical litigation (Dingwall *et al*, 1991). From the cases examined here there is some evidence that this is reducing (Symon, 1999a), but any delay is likely to cause problems. Difficulties with trying to remember events which occurred months or years earlier are discussed in *Chapter 22*. This section briefly describes some examples in which significant delays in initiating litigation have been noted.

The statute of limitations aims to ensure that most personal injury actions are brought within three years; this is known as the triennium. This, however, does not apply in the case of babies (for whom the triennium only commences when they reach adulthood), and so in perinatal litigation there is often a lengthy period before the legal action is raised. In one case in which the baby was born in 1969, the plaintiff's solicitors wrote in 1990:

> *As regards limitation, it is open to Miss P to raise an action up to three years following her eighteenth birthday. This period will expire* (in six weeks) *and accordingly this is a matter of extreme urgency.*

There had evidently not been much urgency about seeking legal help for many years. In another case there was allegedly damage to the baby's scalp during a forceps delivery. Although the claim was not received until the child was twelve years old, the problem had been recognised much earlier: corrective surgery had been tried when the child was six.

There is a great variation in the length of time it takes people to initiate litigation. The extremes of length noted above (and Halle [1997] cites one case which took 27 years to be brought) are only one end of the spectrum. At the other end of the spectrum some people evidently contact a solicitor very quickly, the shortest 'lag time' noted in this research being seven days. For a legal action to be initiated the relevant people must be aware that there is a problem, and this is not always immediately apparent, especially in the case of babies. If a woman suffers some morbidity following childbirth this may not be evident straightaway. However, in one case in which it was alleged that the problems were apparent immediately after delivery, the first intimation of a complaint or claim took two and a half years to arrive. Such ostensible discrepancies are difficult to explain.

Tracing records

Once an allegation of negligence has been made, the employing authority will conduct an investigation into the circumstances surrounding the allegation. The initial step is to locate the clinical case records in the hope that these will provide an account of the relevant events, as well as identifying the staff involved. The variable quality of such documentation (as noted in the previous chapter) means that this may not always be possible even when the case notes have been found. However, there were times when tracing the case notes was itself a problem.

In some cases the delay in identifying the case notes was due to a plaintiff having changed her name after the period in question; that solicitors give her current name will be of little use to the hospital records department. Other delays were due to the solicitors requesting only the baby's notes, or only the mother's notes, when in fact they needed both. Occasionally there was delay because the case notes relating to the child were still in use. This was most likely if the child had a chronic condition and required regular treatment – cerebral palsy is a case in point.

Frequently delays were due to organisational difficulties. These can cause serious problems: in one case there was no action over the first four years because the original case notes were lost somewhere between three hospitals and the legal department. There have been suggestions that such delays are a stalling tactic on the part of the defence (Beech, 1990). This claim was specifically rebutted in one case, in which the consultant paediatrician noted:

> *I am afraid that the notes were lost somewhere in the bowels of the hospital and only a very determined effort enabled us to unearth them. My delay in responding was not because there was something we wished to hide but rather simply 'technical'.*

Other delays occurred because staff had obtained the notes from the records department for their own use: in one instance a research doctor obtained the notes two years before the action was raised, since when they had apparently gone missing. Since no legal action was anticipated at the time, it would be wrong to ascribe sinister motives to this disappearance.

However, there were times when the hospital records system left much to be desired. In one case the employer wrote to the consultant:

> *It is now over a year since I originally wrote to you.*

This brought the reply:

> *I have repeatedly asked for the case notes over the last year and have been consistently told by the records officer that it was impossible to obtain these records because the records department* (at that hospital) *was undergoing reorganisation.*

This sort of excuse will do little to persuade those distrustful of bureaucracies that the health service is 'user-friendly'. However, any large organisation may suffer from such difficulties, as in this case in which the health board wrote to the legal department:

> *This has been one of those investigations which has been dogged by some of those things which occasionally cause delay. The records were not immediately available when I requested them, and later there was a misunderstanding about where they could be perused by the doctors.*

Although these obstacles may at times be unavoidable, there is no doubt that they are frustrating. In one case in which there was a long delay in releasing the notes the plaintiff's solicitor wrote:

It is fortunate that I am a well controlled man. Somebody less patient would by now have done something drastic.

A legal department solicitor replied:

I am glad that I am dealing with 'a well controlled man' and I am delighted to confirm that your patience has borne fruit.

In another case the legal department had trouble arranging a defence, because the hospital had released the case notes to the plaintiff's solicitors. The department wrote indignantly:

This is not a very satisfactory position. As you will be aware, principal medical records should only be released in response to a court order. I would be obliged if you could advise the medical records officers (at the hospital) *of this.*

This case occurred some years ago; release of case notes is covered by statute (under the Access to Personal Files Act 1987; the Access to Medical Reports Act 1988; and the Access to Health Records Act 1990) and is now much speedier and more straightforward.

At times only parts of the case notes were available. In cases concerning cerebral palsy this may be critical, since one of the parts of the notes most easily lost is the CTG trace. These come in a variety of sizes of paper, and for many years no satisfactory storage system was available, the traces typically being tucked into the inside back cover of the maternal case notes. It should be remembered that in many cases which retrospectively allege negligence at birth, there is no hint at the time that the baby has suffered any kind of asphyxial insult, and particular care in storing the traces may not be anticipated.

In one case a doctor had presented a CTG trace at a medical meeting and had used a thick black pen to illustrate the points he was making, effectively obscuring the trace. For the CTG trace to be unavailable is as much an obstacle to the defence as to the plaintiff. There is an argument that in the absence of a trace which shows unequivocally that no fetal heart rate abnormalities were present, it is open to the plaintiff to claim that the child's condition is directly related to intrapartum asphyxia which was not recognised and acted upon.

The attraction of CTG traces for researchers has at times meant that vital traces have been unobtainable, as noted by the legal department in one case:

A lot of the research into CTG traces locally was done by a junior research doctor... who is now working in (country). *Contact with* (this doctor) *has led to a large number of cardboard boxes containing CTG traces being returned to the records department..*

There is now a general acceptance of the need to keep medical records relating to childbirth for at least 21 years, given the effective lack of a statute of limitations for cases concerning brain damaged children (25 years appears now to be favoured by many units). This was not always the case, and in some cases all or parts of the records have been destroyed. In one reported case the judge noted:

The length and complexity of this litigation has been significantly increased as a result of the defendant's... apparent destruction of the plaintiff's records in the ICU at a time when objectively the obligation to retain those records should have been obvious.
(*Le Page v Kingston & Richmond HA*, per Samuels J @ 242)

In another case the solicitors enquired why the X-rays had been destroyed. The hospital's reply was that:

> *X-rays are kept for six years; there was nothing untoward seen on these films, so there*
> *was no reason to keep them.*

As they were pertinent to a legal claim it would have been prudent to keep them, although clearly the line must be drawn somewhere: no hospital has infinite storage space, or the facilities or finance to convert all records into electronic form.

The ownership of case notes is a topic which has caused some heated debate. In one case, in which the midwifery notes could not be traced for some time, it transpired that the plaintiff had taken them home with her, and her husband refused to return them to the hospital, stating they belonged to the family.

Delays in legal actions sometimes occurred because the plaintiff's solicitors did not request that they be sent a copy of the case notes so that they could nominate an expert who would then produce an opinion. Sadly this was not an uncommon occurrence: cases examined in this research have revealed delays of up to three years in requesting the case notes.

Inexperience in the procedures of medical litigation militate against speedy resolution, and may significantly hinder the plaintiff's chances of success. Accredited lists of solicitors have recently become available and these should increase the chances of finding a suitably experienced solicitor. This is discussed further in *Chapter 25*.

Tracing staff

Once the case notes are collated, the process of piecing together the relevant events begins, and one of the first tasks is to trace the staff concerned. In cases which take several years to come to light, this may pose significant problems. There is a high degree of job mobility among health service staff with many clinicians trained in Britain moving around as the job market or personal circumstances dictate. Either of these may include going to work abroad for a while. Equally many clinicians trained outside Britain may work for a few years in a series of hospitals in order to gain experience and membership of professional bodies. Given the high turnover of clinicians, particularly among junior medical staff, and especially among 'locums' who may work in one hospital for no more than a weekend, tracing those involved in an incident even one or two years previously may be problematic. It certainly will be if, as can happen, the events in question occurred some ten or more years ago.

Due to the increased awareness of the needs to maintain good records of all kinds from a medico-legal standpoint, hospitals are now much more careful to keep track of their employees. That this was not always so is illustrated by the following comment from one hospital services manager:

> *Medical staffing and the personnel department did not keep records of medical staff*
> *employed by this authority at the time in question* (1985). *It was only by examining the*
> *records in detail that I was able to elucidate even the names.*

For clinicians who go to work abroad for a while there is the possibility that they have maintained their membership of their medical defence organisation (MDO), and so a contact address may be found. In one case, however, the relevant registrar moved abroad and resigned from her defence organisation as well. In another, the defence organisation records were less than helpful in tracing a particular obstetrician. The MDO wrote to legal department:

> *Unfortunately the Dr R which we identified turned out to be a dentist and an elderly*
> *one at that.*

In another case the MDO was described by the legal department as being 'less than helpful' in tracing one of their members, since they had demanded a search fee of £100 + VAT. A difficulty may arise if entries in the notes are not legible, and the absence of a countersigning signature may make identification extremely difficult. In one case the consultant obstetrician wrote to the legal department:

> *... midwives and doctors are writing in the same part of the clinical outpatient record in the maternity case sheet. On looking at that* (particular) *case sheet we found it essentially impossible to work out when an entry was made by a midwife and when an entry was made by an obstetrician. This whole issue might further complicate the detective work required when an obstetric case is being looked at years later.*

Regarding the identity of the (north European) author of a particular entry the legal department noted:

> *It usually requires a great deal of detective work by comparing clinical notes with the correspondence of the same date so that you can work out whether the Arabic hieroglyphic is actually* (a name).

Occasionally this detective work is faulty: in one case an obstetrician was identified and the case notes sent to him for comment. He was rather puzzled by this and wrote back saying that at the relevant time he was working in an Ear, Nose and Throat department. It has been known for a graphologist to be consulted in order to identify the author of an entry in the case notes, a needless use of public money considering the ease with which such identification ought to be made.

Having identified the relevant staff there may be problems in obtaining useful reports. This problem is compounded if the staff in question now work in another country. In one case one of the midwives involved was found to be on an 'International Friendship' hospital ship, whose next port of call was somewhere in Australia, before sailing on to Papua New Guinea. Another case concerning a birth injury was thought to be quite defensible, but was conceded since the quantum was likely to be small, and one of the probable witnesses was believed to be in either Hong Kong or Australia.

Particular difficulties are encountered when a case takes many years to come to light, since certain members of staff are likely to have retired. Of course the ultimate cul de sac in tracing relevant staff occurs when the clinicians concerned have died; in *Kelly v Bastible* the writ was served twenty years after the death of the doctor in question. Delays can only be overcome by hospitals insisting on clear (signed) entries in the case notes and maintaining accurate records of current and past staff.

Plaintiffs

The first section in this chapter detailed some of the instances in which a plaintiff had delayed initiating litigation. While it might be assumed that the plaintiff has least to gain from delaying the subsequent course of the legal action, at times this has happened. In one action concerning haemorrhage at caesarean section, the plaintiff changed solicitors, then said she didn't want to pursue the action, but did not put this in writing. She then failed to keep an appointment with her new solicitors and was unable to be contacted. Another plaintiff changed her firm of solicitors and resurrected her legal action a year after the legal department had last heard from her original solicitors. However, after this she apparently failed to give the new firm any instructions. Repeated requests from the legal department brought no response and so the legal department, who were about to close their file, were left not knowing whether they could do so. In a similar case, and in response to requests from the legal department for clarification about the state of the claim, the solicitors replied:

> *It is many months since we had instructions from our clients and while the matter would therefore seem to be inactive, we are certainly not closing our file...*

Other examples are seen in the following quotes from plaintiff solicitors when writing to the legal department. One firm wrote that they were experiencing

> *A difficulty... in taking our client's instructions.*

Another stated:

> *We apologise for the delay in replying, but would advise that we have only now obtained our client's instructions.*

The reasons behind such inaction are difficult to discern, but it is clear that such delays may have a detrimental effect on the staff concerned. Some of these aspects were discussed in *Chapter 9*.

Plaintiff solicitors

As noted earlier, there are now accredited lists of plaintiff solicitors to which a potential litigant can refer. However, for many years (and for the duration of almost all the research reported here) this was not the case, and many claims have been unnecessarily protracted through a lack of experience on the part of the plaintiff's solicitors. While this is considered at more length in *Chapter 25*, this section examines this feature from the point of view of delays.

Very often the reason for the delay was not immediately clear. Letters would be sent requesting updates on the state of affairs, but for one reason or another no answer was forthcoming. One cause for such delays was that the plaintiffs were seeking a second expert report. In one, a firm of solicitors, having obtained one unfavourable report, claimed that:

> *Surely a second opinion is desirable from everyone's point of view to clear up this matter once and for all.*

While they may have believed this to represent their client's interests, it could be argued that it was only prolonging their agony and increasing their expenses. The solicitors were, however, honest enough to admit that this is what they wanted to do. More often it would appear that plaintiff's solicitors kept quiet if the report they had received was unfavourable, perhaps trying to find another expert who might produce a more favourable opinion. One case concerning cerebral palsy saw the following:

> February 1992: the plaintiff's solicitors informed the legal department that they were hopeful of getting a supportive opinion.

> October 1993: the legal department reminded them of this.

> April 1994: a further letter from the legal department asked if they were any further on. The plaintiff's solicitors said at that time they had instructed another expert.

> September 1995: the legal department wrote again. The reply brought the news that the plaintiffs had changed their firm of solicitors.

The new firm tried a different tack, writing: 'How about a nice ex gratia payment to settle it all?'

Such a delay seems to serve no one's interests. Since the claim concerned a child with cerebral palsy it would not become time-barred by the statute of limitations, but the plaintiff can not receive any compensation until negligence is established. A factor which plaintiffs may not take into account is that, having made such an allegation against doctors and/or midwives, the staff are left with these accusations hanging over them. Until the case is decided one way or the other they are left with this uncertainty and the fear that they may have caused or contributed to a tragic outcome.

A frequent cause for delay was that the plaintiffs had, as in the last mentioned case, changed solicitors. In effect this puts the case back to square one for the new solicitors have to go through exactly the same procedures as their predecessors. In one case delay was caused through the first firm of solicitors losing their client's file. In another (which concerned cerebral palsy) the second firm nominated the same expert who had produced an opinion for the first firm.

In one case some delay was caused by a rather puzzling name on the writ served by the plaintiff's solicitor, as explained by the legal department to the relevant hospital:

> *You will note that an anonymous second defender, Dr X, has been added in the heading and frankly I am not sure what the implications of this may be. I have never come across anything of the sort before... I am only guessing, but I suspect that the Statement of Claim was settled by the Counsel some time ago and that he put Dr X in his draft expecting* (the plaintiff's solicitor) *to find out who this was and fill in the name...*

This particular solicitor caused some anguish for the defendants, since he appeared to be doing little to advance the cause of his clients. The legal department wrote to the hospital manager:

> *As usual I am having no luck in getting* (him) *on the telephone. He is never there, and my messages are never answered...* (He) *seems to be quite unversed in medical litigation;* (he) *has just issued a summons asking for copies of the relevant medical records. We actually released these to his medical adviser* (seven years ago)*!*

One case concerning a retained swab could have been settled much more quickly than it was: the defence conceded that negligence had occurred straightaway, and a financial offer was made within two months. The swab was removed on the fourth day, was not infected, and appeared to have caused little long term harm, but the plaintiffs held out for another thirty months for more money before accepting the amount offered.

Slowness/bureaucracy

The section above discussing attempts to trace the case records noted that delays sometimes occur because of organisational difficulties. Such difficulties can occur at any time during the course of an action, and are more likely when several different parties are involved. Until the introduction of NHS indemnity for hospital doctors in 1990 the interests of such doctors were the concern of the relevant medical defence organisation (MDO). The MDO for each doctor involved in the case had to be contacted separately, and these would liaise with their member before allowing him or her to produce a report for the legal department. While this procedure is not now essential (it no longer being mandatory for a hospital doctor to be a member of an MDO), most doctors are members and will consult their defence organisation before agreeing to produce a report. However, NHS indemnity means that the financial responsibility of any conceded claim rests with the employer, and there is no doubt that this has helped to expedite some settlements.

Delays could occur due to the MDO's bureaucracy or lack of efficiency. In one case from the 1980s the following occurred:

> June. Legal department, in response to plaintiff's solicitors enquiring about the delay:
> 'We regret the delay. Hope to hear from the MDO soon.'

August. Legal department: the relevant MDO will discuss their member's liability at the September meeting.

October. Legal department: an expert instructed in this case did not return the notes in time for the September meeting.

MDO to legal department: 'We did not have an October Council meeting owing to a lack of cases.'

October again. Legal department: the MDO will discuss this case in November.

This delay was very unedifying and did not impress the plaintiffs. In another case concerning a failure to diagnose spina bifida, the plaintiff's solicitors wrote in exasperation:

> *We think we have been extremely patient until now. However we are disappointed with the lack of progress from your end. We have instructed Edinburgh agents to proceed with all haste with a court action...*

In this case the delay seemed to be because three MDOs were concerned and they were deciding on the division of their respective liabilities.

The issue of job mobility was mentioned in the section on tracing staff, and it was noted that staff trained outside Britain make up part of the workforce. While there are three principal MDOs in Britain, those trained elsewhere may retain membership of another organisation and this can cause delays. In one case one of the doctors involved had gone to Australia, his MDO also being based there. The two MDOs agreed to fund the compensation equally, but arranging this took some time, as the legal department noted to the employer:

> *The* (MDO) *is based in Australia and correspondence is difficult and slow.*

Experts

For a plaintiff to establish negligence and causation, the testimony of an expert is an essential requirement. It is usual for the plaintiffs to request that a nominated expert produces an opinion and in many cases examined here, the case notes were only released to the expert. Delay can occur as those chosen to act as the providers of expert opinion tend to be the very senior members of the profession who generally have many other clinical, administrative and academic commitments. Delays in securing the services of experts from certain specialties because of competing demands were noted in *Chapter 5*. A solicitor explained some of the difficulties of such experts:

> *Well, I think there are real problems because Trusts are making their consultants much more accountable for their time, as you know, and that's impinging upon writing reports and reading papers, and it's leading to delays. Lawyers are berated always for the terrible delays, but as you know, we have to work with the system, and if you wait six months for a report, it's not your fault.*

(Defence solicitor 1)

One expert wrote to the legal department claiming that the delay may equally be encountered because of legal inaction:

> *My experience as an expert witness is that our legal colleagues demand expert opinions at short notice, we then hear nothing from them, often for years.*

At times the delay in this part of the legal action has not been the expert's fault. In one case the plaintiff's solicitors wrote:

> *These records were unintelligible to us and we have passed them to our expert who has returned them to us indicating that the records forwarded by you to us exclusively relate to a throat condition in childhood and not concerning her delivery of her child.*

However it was not uncommon for a delay of several months to occur waiting for the expert report. In one case this was because the plaintiff's solicitors had instructed a professor whose interest was gynaecological oncology, when the case concerned neonatology. In another concerning a child with cerebral palsy the solicitors asked for the case notes to be sent to a consultant neurosurgeon. They were, but he apparently did not take any action for eighteen months.

In yet another case the legal department wrote to the nominated expert care of the employer to see why he hadn't returned the case notes. It then transpired that he had died some months earlier. It was not known if he had produced a report, but as the plaintiff's solicitors were silent it was assumed that he had done so and the solicitors did not wish to pursue the matter further.

A number of instances in which delays occurred due to an inability to obtain a report from (or even to make contact with) a nominated expert were cited in *Chapter 5*.

Closing the claim

A number of reasons for delays in the course of legal actions have been examined; sadly there were also cases in which there was some delay in closing the legal file. In some the plaintiff's solicitors did not inform the legal department that their client was no longer pursuing the action. The legal department will not usually close the file until a lengthy period of time has elapsed, knowing that the delay may be due to other reasons. In one case the following occurred:

> June 1990. Three files of case notes were sent to the plaintiff's expert.
>
> April 1992. The legal department wrote to him asking if he still had them.
>
> July 1992. They wrote again asking for an answer to the first letter. He replied saying he'd lost the first letter, and couldn't remember what had been asked.

It transpired that he had returned the notes to the medical records office once he'd completed his report instead of to the legal department.

In this instance the action might have been closed two years earlier than it actually was because of this failure to inform. The plaintiff knew her case had not been successful, but the staff involved were unaware of this. In another action which concerned allegations about an episiotomy repair, it eventually transpired that the plaintiff 'had simply forgotten about the action because she did not want it to go any further'.

Delays can occur even when they appear to be proceeding towards the court stage. Court timetables are busy and in order to give sufficient warning to all witnesses a date well into the future is usually agreed. In some cases witnesses have to be flown back from distant parts of the world, and this often cannot be organised quickly.

The court process being somewhat unpredictable, the length of court time anticipated may have to be reviewed: one case saw a hearing fixed for a date in February, then postponed until May because the one day booked for court was thought to be inadequate. The plaintiffs then wrote to say their expert could not make the new agreed date, and so further delay occurred. While matters drag out in this way, both plaintiff and practitioners are left with an open-ended worry. Some of these concerns were raised in *Chapter 12*. However, one midwife involved in a legal action seemed to accept that the process was likely to be lengthy:

> *Well, now, I'm actually quite unsure about what's happening because that's... oh, a couple of years or so since I've heard anything, and I had anticipated that you're talking about five years for it to go to the court.*

(Midwife 1)

Whether other practitioners would accept a long delay with such apparent equanimity is a moot point. Some practitioners' reactions to the experience of litigation are discussed in *Chapter 9*.

Conclusion

All delays will be frustrating for the plaintiff and for the staff concerned. Moves to speed up the procedures, perhaps by making them less adversarial, have been suggested (Woolf, 1996). It is possible that instead of each side nominating an expert, both sides could agree on one expert who would furnish a report on which the case could perhaps be decided; this would also reduce costs. Instead of each side instructing solicitors, it may be that the case can be heard by an arbitration panel with both medical and legal representatives. This would certainly reduce delays caused by different solicitors pursuing essentially similar courses of action. Some of these possibilities are discussed in *Chapter 23*.

Chapter 16

P   Protocols and guidelines

Within health care there has allegedly been a rapid increase in the number of protocols, policies and guidelines in recent years. This certainly appears to be the case in maternity care. This chapter examines some of the background to the growth of these now seemingly indispensable elements of clinical care, and then discusses the views of a number of people who have experience of dealing with them in practice.

The terminology used may be significant: a protocol may carry considerably more weight than a policy, which in turn may be relied upon more than a guideline. Whereas it may be difficult to justify deviating from a prescribed protocol, a guideline is not as significant: it is not a rule. Unfortunately there is no unanimity about the use of the various terms, and in some units they appear to be used almost interchangeably. In this chapter I try to draw out the distinctions between them, although the general discussion refers to them all.

There is clearly a tension inherent in the notion of unit protocols and policies: on the one hand some advocate offering a service which reflects individual choice; on the other the interests of equality of provision demand a relatively standardised level of care although, as Drife (1995) points out, absolute consensus on what constitutes best care would be all but impossible to achieve.

Protocols serve several purposes: in addition to advocating a theoretical equality of treatment, they aim to ensure that the standard of care given to patients does not fall below a defined minimum standard, and in so doing provide a defence against an allegation of negligence. Providing the protocol is devised with best practice and evidence-based care in mind, and providing practitioners follow this protocol, a plaintiff could not show that the practitioner's acts amounted to clinical negligence. Although it may be assumed that protocols are there to be followed, it has been suggested that compliance may in fact be very low (Yoong et al, 1992).

While it would be wrong to characterise the development of protocols as being purely defensive (ie. devised solely with the prospect of litigation in mind), there is no doubt that employers, faced with a growing threat to their budgets from the costs of litigation, are keen to minimise their chances of an expensive payout. Whether the imposition of protocols represents an improvement in terms of the standard of care is debatable. Portrayed by some as a means of reining in the autonomy of practitioners, it has been claimed that they may also implicitly represent a managerial control of patients (Charlton, 1999).

In the preceding postal survey a majority of both obstetricians (76%) and midwives (64%) said that they had known of a woman refusing a routine policy. For the doctors the most common examples were caesarean section, CTG, artificial rupture of the membranes (ARM), administration of syntometrine, and induction of labour. For the midwives CTG, syntometrine, venepuncture, and ARM were the most common. A few midwives claimed that there was no such thing as a routine policy in their unit, all care being individually tailored. The dangers of unit protocols being too prescriptive was demonstrated in a notorious water birth case a few years ago (Anderson, 1994).

The development of protocols and guidelines

The development of clinical guidelines stems partly from the growth in audit and research. In maternity care there is certainly no shortage of outlets for research and audit findings, with several obstetric and midwifery journals. There are also research conferences, on-line services such as

Medline, CINAHL and the Cochrane database, and now the on-line National Research Register.

There are many groups which have examined clinical practice relevant to obstetricians and midwives, usually with a view to establishing practice guidelines. For example, there is the Clinical Resource Audit Group (CRAG), which funded the Scottish Caesarean Section Audit; this looked at the feasibility of developing clinical practice guidelines with a view to reducing the rate of caesarean sections. However, recent evidence suggests that this has not been achieved. There is also the Scottish Intercollegiate Guidelines Network (SIGN), established in 1993, which has produced almost 40 sets of guidelines for clinical practice.

There are a number of other such groups, including the Scottish Programme for Clinical Effectiveness in Reproductive Health (SPCERH); Promoting Action on Clinical Effectiveness (PACE); the Scottish Practice-Based Accreditation in Clinical Effectiveness (SPACE); the (English) National Pathways Association (NPA) and, not to be outdone, the Scottish Pathways Association (SPA).

The National Institute for Clinical Excellence (NICE) has recently been established in England, and this will produce guidelines for clinical practice. It is acknowledged that NICE will take account of affordability, so the guidelines it produces will not be wish-lists. Coulson (1999: 16) notes that 'NICE guidance disseminated to hospitals and primary care groups will not have legal force, but ministers will make it clear they expect it to be adhered to.' The Commission for Health Improvement (CHI [or CHIMP]) will have the task of enforcing NICE recommendations. The Health Secretary has the power to act on CHIMP's reports by insisting that a hospital take certain action. As a last resort (s)he 'can remove the chairman and the board of any health authority or trust and issue directives to NHS bodies on action they must take' (Weaver, 1999: 22).

Specifically within maternity care there has been the comprehensive work of Iain Chalmers and his colleagues in the Cochrane Database upon which to draw. 'Effective Care in Pregnancy and Childbirth' was published in 1989, which demonstrates that the concern to implement effective policies is not something particularly new.

The Scottish Obstetric Guidelines and Audit Project (SOGAP) has produced four guidelines (on preterm delivery, haemorrhage, epilepsy, hypertension). Although its title is 'Obstetric', and the principal driving force behind them came from the Scottish Executive of the RCOG, the development of these guidelines was very much a multi-disciplinary affair. This also relates to the Scottish Intercollegiate Guidelines Network (SIGN) too. It may be that Scotland, due to its smaller size, and the fact that the majority of the population is contained within the central belt, is more amenable to such changes. Certainly the Scottish Office (1997) document *Designed to Care* claimed that 'Scotland, at present, leads the UK in its work on clinical effectiveness.'

It seems that there is no shortage of groups looking at how to improve standards. The implicit understanding is that improving standards will reduce the likelihood of being criticised or even sued.

Given that specific guidelines are being produced, it is possible to ask several questions: Will the drive to implement them work? Are they necessarily a good thing? Will they help to defend practitioners against allegations of negligence, or might they even be used against staff?

Regarding their implementation, Page (1997: 13) talks of the 'domination of the ineffective', and claims that: 'It will be easy to get locked into the virtual reality of the rhetoric of evidence-based maternity care, because the actual reality, of challenging an enormously powerful status quo, is very uncomfortable.'

A sense of ownership regarding the guidelines will probably accrue if the person (or, more usually, the group) which produces them allows the various professional groups to make a contribution. A wide consultation process – including 'consumer' input (see Duff *et al*, 1996) – will probably work best. For this practitioners must be open to debating the merits of research.

A 'top-down' approach, in which protocols are not produced locally, runs the risk of not gaining widespread acceptance. Taylor-Adams and Lyons (1998: 3) claim that, 'many protocols in use in hospitals today are large documents composed of excessive amounts of paperwork, with wording which is incomprehensible or ambiguous. Therefore staff avoid reading and using them.' They go on to recommend 'a condensed pocket-sized protocol which outlines the main elements of the guidelines' (*ibid*).

Possible benefits of protocols and guidelines

There is repeated evidence from the Confidential Enquiries into Stillbirths and Deaths in Infancy which indicates that a common feature in poor outcomes is the failure on the part of staff to follow accepted good practice. Added to this there are reports of legal actions which demonstrate the same thing: the monthly Medical Law Reports give an idea of how often clinical staff are accused of negligence. An allegation of negligence essentially claims that a practitioner has failed to provide competent care, and in some cases the failure on the part of a practitioner to follow a local protocol is held to constitute a breach of the required standard of care.

Faced with evidence of this nature, it seems inevitable that there will be a drive – on the part of managers and employers – to ensure that staff act in certain ways, especially in the light of claims that 'explicit guidelines do improve clinical practice' (Grimshaw and Russell, 1993: 1322). Litigation is, after all, a very expensive business for the health service. It is also costly in terms of the emotional trauma caused to all involved. An awareness that poor outcomes (and litigation) affect many different people suggests that those seeking to determine practice must consult widely. One interviewee claimed:

> *The policies that exist need more consumer input. I feel there's very little consumer input to these policies and guidelines; and that even when it's requested it's often a token consumer, and it's often very difficult to get views actually taken on board. There's the assumption that the consumer knows less than the professional.*

(Consumer group representative)

Practitioners of many years' standing may feel that they do know more than many consumers. Obstetricians and midwives have a continuing professional duty to be up-to-date with current best practice; no such requirement exists for those who use the health service. This level of professionalism aims to ensure the standards of care are optimised, in particular for certain clinical conditions:

> *I think every maternity hospital should have clearly defined protocols for management of pre-eclampsia, management of hypertension, management of 'small-for-dates', when to induce patients, management of breech, what to do in the event of twins, exactly a step by step breakdown, and I don't think it really should be left to individual consultants.*

(Consultant obstetrician 4)

Management of 'high risk' pregnancy or labour requires a degree of consensus, not least from the perspective of equality of treatment. This senior obstetrician claimed that wide differences in obstetric practice used to be commonplace:

> *Whereas paediatricians might let each other know what's on at the weekend, I'll bet you that... 40 years ago the* (obstetric) *consultants wouldn't even tell each other when they were inducing, why, what the problems were...*

(Consultant obstetrician 4)

Because of the organisation of obstetric cover in British maternity units, women requiring other than 'low risk' midwifery care in labour may be monitored by obstetricians from a team other than that under which they booked. For this consultant the need for agreed protocols is clear:

> *I feel fairly strongly that we muddy the waters by having strong views ourselves... because the people who are going to work things in the end of the day are the midwives, and the junior staff... the people applying the régimes were often using drugs with which they weren't familiar because they were allocated by different doctors, whereas if they had had single protocols it would have been easier.*

> (Consultant obstetrician 4)

He went on to note that different approaches need to be 'ironed out':

> *There's the consultant who says he will not allow any of his patients to deliver a breech, or the colleague who says he will insist that they be given a trial of breech. What we need is a protocol across the board so that we can get these things right.*

There are clearly benefits to be gained from standardising certain aspects of care. To a degree such requirements reduce the scope for autonomy both of the pregnant woman and the practitioner. Nevertheless they do so in an attempt to ensure that care is optimal. One midwife, who was herself involved in litigation, explained how this represented an improvement:

> *Quite often... you were just in the room and you were left, and you got on with it until something arose and you contacted them. You buzzed or you shouted 'Can somebody come in', whereas now they* (Labour ward sisters) *have to come in. They come in at the start of the shift, review the women and come back...*

> (Midwife 1)

Some midwives may see this as interfering with their autonomous practice. However, in a maternity unit care is multi-disciplinary, and true autonomy is constrained. There is a delicate balance to be drawn in deciding when and how often to review; some practitioners will need more supervision than others. That such a practice has now become a policy indicates a degree of cautiousness in this unit, in that it appears to be required that a senior midwife is happy with the progress of each woman's labour. This can be seen as promoting best practice, or inhibiting the autonomy of both the midwife and the pregnant woman.

There is a degree of overlap between the moves of employers to dictate what practitioners do and the defensive reactions of practitioners themselves. In *Chapter 4* it was noted that many doctors and midwives are now ensuring that they maintain more detailed records. One midwife claimed that this response was determined in part by the unit:

> (The hospital) *had a very strict policy of documentation. Even if labour had gone on normally, you had to update your documentation at least every hour, just to say where that woman was, what her contractions were like, was she comfortable, had you given anything for pain, the baby's heart rate – not just to say 'good variability' but the specific ranges of the baby's heart rate.*

> (Midwife 11)

Again, this may be seen as too deterministic but, as was noted in *Chapter 14*, poor documentation represents a significant obstacle to a thorough investigation of events.

Possible dangers of protocols and guidelines

It may seem obvious that a unit protocol is based on sound research evidence, but it is claimed that this is not always the case:

> *My main concern, and it concerns some of the other midwives here, is that not a lot of the policies are actually research based. Some of them definitely aren't, and I'm talking specifically on length of second stage and things like that...*
>
> (Midwife 6)

Poorly grounded protocols may give a false sense of security, in that they lend a dubious legitimacy to questionable practices. Another interviewee claimed that:

> *One of the problems is that it can end up at the lowest common denominator.*
>
> (Consumer group representative)

A basic minimum is a more positive way of looking at this but there is a danger that a protocol, while trying to ensure safe practice, inhibits best practice. Symonds (1987: 848) expressed the fear that the extensive use of protocols and guidelines may mean that we may all be 'constrained to a straightjacket of clinical conformity'.

One midwife said that in one hospital:

> *... it was totally dictated, for everything you did there was a protocol or a procedure.*
>
> (Midwife 11)

The enjoyment of one interviewee who was not so constrained was obvious:

> *I don't have any specific protocols as such I have to follow. I can take each case individually and deal with situations as they arise – arise on an individual basis. I don't have any stipulations of 'Well, in this case you have to do X, Y or Z.'*
>
> (Independent midwife)

For most hospital-based practitioners, however, protocols and guidelines will be in use. A senior midwife pointed out how they could diminish the woman's individuality:

> *The care givers approach a situation not on an individualistic basis. I think they look at the situation in a kind of blurred way, what I would call a narrow way. To implement A, B and C is not necessarily the best care.*
>
> (Labour ward manager)

The lack of thought inherent in the approach which follows a protocol or guideline uncritically was censured by one interviewee:

> *Experienced staff can actually be gagged by policies or protocols which don't allow them to use their clinical judgement and don't allow them to enter into a closer relationship with the parent... It's a confusion between policies, protocols, professional advice, etc. and the woman's right to make a choice. It seems to be that professionals sometimes get these confused, that they think that policies and protocols override women's rights.*
>
> (Consumer group representative)

There is a possibility that nationally determined protocols, devised with certain criteria in mind, may be imposed upon local areas where a different situation exists. How much scope will there be for local hospital or community trusts to deviate from such centrally-determined policies? There are dangers in following the 'evidence', when the 'evidence' is not strictly relevant: for example, a slightly different population being studied, or the circumstances not being quite the same. Grimley Evans (1995) warns us not to confuse 'evidence-based' practice with 'evidence-biased' practice.

It is, therefore, important that protocols/policies/guidelines are acceptable to those who have to use them. One midwife claimed with regard to protocols that:

> *Everybody has pride in their own work, but everything is now written down to the point of being ridiculous, and unnecessary.*

> (Midwife 8)

It is easy to imagine that many midwives will be unhappy about having their every action determined by protocols, especially if such protocols have more than a whiff of medical dominance about them. For example, a senior lecturer told me that one of the students in her class had written in an essay:

> *The women had two-hourly vaginal examinations as per hospital policy.*

> (Midwifery lecturer)

This led to an enlightening conversation. The lecturer said:

> *I'm really surprised that this still goes on. Is this the policy of the hospital, or are you just interpreting it?*
> *Oh no, that's the policy.*
> *What if the women don't want it?*
> *Oh, but they get it.*

The fear of litigation is sometimes used as the excuse for such an approach. One midwife claimed:

> *(Litigation) probably means you're practising more defensively, where before you could treat people as individuals and adapt your practice to suit the individual... Now there maybe is a tendency to control from a policy document.*

> (Midwife 8)

A rather chilling phrase, and an approach which does little to promote the notion of autonomy mentioned in *Chapter 3*. The danger of limiting the critical thinking of a practitioner was highlighted by a comment from the lecturer quoted above:

> *Just recently I was marking some scripts and with this particular student everything she had written was 'This was done as per hospital policy.' ... The student didn't understand what I was getting at... If you've got policies and procedures and protocols then you're not individualising the care... they use procedures and policies and protocols... and they think somehow that is safe. The protocol legitimises it...*

> (Midwifery lecturer)

As this lecturer notes, there may be a spurious assumption that a protocol is the last word on a subject. However, if the protocol does not reflect best practice, then a midwife may be well within her rights to disregard it. Dimond (1994a: 118) claims that a midwife's 'independent professional judgement can never be replaced by reliance on a set procedure.' The potential danger of having routine procedures is obvious: some procedures which are considered arcane today were once standard. It is not so long ago that routine shaves and enemas were given in many units upon admission in labour. In the postal survey some midwives said they were delighted when a woman refused these, because it meant they didn't have to carry out a procedure which they considered to be barbaric and unnecessary.

It is important to distinguish between routine practices which are sound and evidence-based, and those which are grounded in nothing deeper than habit. In theory, and with all the available published research, there should be few routine procedures which are not soundly based. This is not to deny that getting agreement, even (or maybe especially) at local level, may be very difficult. One consultant obstetrician noted how different consultants within one unit would have very different ways of approaching something as commonplace as induction of labour:

> *I'll be on call this weekend, and for all I know, they all will be induced on Friday, Saturday and Sunday, and I am responsible for whatever happens... I hope I'm not tempted to, but it wouldn't amaze anyone if I was to say 'Gosh, I wish they hadn't started this patient's labour off today.'*

(Consultant obstetrician 4)

In another hospital a manager told me:

> *We had one consultant who induced everybody, everybody on the dot, at forty weeks... Something in the past, you know, he had a bad experience.*

(Midwifery manager)

Although this may be a very natural reaction, it is important not to become hidebound by one or two instances, however tragic. This 'tyranny of extreme experience' was discussed in *Chapter 4*. No one wants to see a tragic outcome replayed, but the desire to prevent this can – as in this case – lead to an over-reaction. With regard to induction of labour, there is a drive to standardise practice, partly to avoid the acrimony which can ensue when there is disagreement between clinicians and the situation ends in a poor outcome, and partly to help junior staff to know where they are. The Royal College of Obstetricians and Gynaecologists (RCOG) has produced a guideline which concerns induction of labour.

If protocols are allowed to become out-of-date then they will be worthless. It is a lot of work to maintain an awareness of all the research, and keep all the policies and protocols within a unit up-to-date. Nevertheless, this is what is being required of us. The RCOG 'Green-top' guidelines have a review date (a 'shelf-life') of three years.

Deviation from protocols and guidelines

From the previous discussion, it is evident that there is a danger that protocols and guidelines may be too prescriptive. Dally, who fell foul of the GMC in 1987 for failing to follow 'guidelines laid down for good clinical practice' (she had prescribed methadone when this apparently was not considered correct), claims that: 'In medicine, guidelines drawn up by the establishment are all too easily converted into regulations and a means of punishing dissenters.' (Dally, 1990: 27) It will be remembered that the Commission for Health Improvement will have some scope for sanctions against those who do not follow set guidelines.

There is evidently a fear among some junior practitioners that deviating from the unit line will be thought unacceptable. However, single protocols must enjoy the support of the staff who implement them. The scope for disagreements to induce dissatisfaction about which procedure to follow were noted by this consultant:

> *You find juniors or midwives saying to patients 'Well, under normal circumstances I would do this, but Dr X doesn't like it, so we won't'. Now, I think that produces an anxious patient, and litigation is never too far away there.*

(Consultant obstetrician 4)

The desire to avoid litigation is obvious, and the possibility that guidelines may provide a yardstick for judging allegations of negligence is considered below.

To say that we will standardise something is of course to put it strongly. Within any agreement there must be an awareness that local or individual circumstances may call for a different approach. Being allowed to deviate from the line, then, is essential: there is no such thing as a standard labour any more than there is a standard pregnant woman. Attempting to have everything uniform would be impossible to police, not least because certain midwives would see to it that they broke the rules. There is a terrible danger not only in having a 'straightjacket of clinical conformity', but also in believing that we can extract the individual from decision-making. Professor Whitby of Cambridge (Whitby, 1946) put this well over 50 years ago when he said 'if the profession be robbed of its individuality, the soul will go out from it.'

While it is reasonable to conclude that some deviation from a guideline or protocol may be permitted, the extent to which one may deviate may not be so clear. There is some evidence that midwives are particularly likely to disapprove of the breach of a protocol, regardless of outcome. Doctors, on the other hand, 'took the outcome into consideration more, and judged the violation of a protocol to be appropriate providing the outcome was successful. Even in the case when a violation leads to a bad outcome, doctors judged the behaviour of colleagues fairly leniently' (Parker and Lawton, 1999:14).

It is instructive to look to the USA, where the Institute of Medicine (cited by Field and Lohr, 1990:14) stated that deviation is unacceptable when it 'stems from poor practitioner skills, poor management of delivery systems, ignorance or deliberate disregard of well-documented preferable practices. It should not be tolerated when it is a self-serving disguise for bad practices that harm people and waste resources.'

There are potential dangers in deviating from the stipulated line, but there are also dangers in sticking too rigidly to this line. Hurwitz (1998: 77) asks whether guidelines could 'reduce clinical practice to thoughtless activities performed by physician-automata?' Nobody wants to see obstetricians or midwives acting like robots, and yet it has been claimed that some midwives have such a concern to produce neat and comprehensive records, that care can be compromised to the extent that the baby dies (Symon, 2000).

Practitioners all understand the importance of good documentation, but the concern to produce good documentation must never overtake the need to give good care. The proper intention of clinical guidelines is well summed up by the phrase 'Tools, not rules.' Few would advocate 'cookbook obstetrics' or 'cookbook midwifery', in which practitioners, instead of thinking, merely look up a handbook which will tell them what to do.

The standard of care for litigation?

If it is assumed that practices (such as induction of labour) have been standardised to some degree: should these practice parameters be the standard of care in litigation which concerns allegations of negligence (cf. Hirshfeld, 1991; Jutras, 1993)? While practitioners should not assume that practice will automatically go down the North American route, it is instructive to look to the USA for examples of this phenomenon.

In Maine in 1990, a state law was passed to establish 'standards of practice designed to avoid malpractice claims and increase the defensibility of the malpractice claims that are pursued.' The following year a Code of Rules was established, which devised detailed practice parameters for specific obstetric eventualities; caesarean deliveries, tocolysis, ectopic pregnancies, breech deliveries, perinatal herpes simplex virus infections, intrapartum fetal distress, and prolonged pregnancies.

There is a state Board of Registration which can adopt guidelines as rules; if half the doctors in the state agree to abide by them, then a doctor can cite them as a complete defence to a charge of malpractice. This is sometimes called the 'affirmative defence'. Furthermore, a dissatisfied patient cannot point to a doctor's failure to follow the guideline as prima facie evidence of negligence. However, in a US-wide analysis of clinical guidelines Hyams *et al* (1995: 454) concluded that 'our most significant finding is that guidelines are clearly being used for both inculpatory and exculpatory purposes.'

In other words they are double-edged swords: they may be used to blame or to excuse. They can be founded upon by a doctor in his/her own defence, but also by an aggrieved patient seeking to establish that the requisite standard of care has not been met. Reflecting this concern, Murphy (1997: 147) advises practitioners to 'use guidelines as a recommendation only, to avoid having the guidelines used against them in a malpractice case.'

What are the implications for Britain? While guidelines can be introduced as evidence in a court, they cannot be used as a substitute for expert testimony which can be subjected to cross examination (this is discussed in *Chapter 5*). The law, by and large, is well aware that protocols and guidelines are subject almost constantly to review and re-drafting. One protocol or guideline may have considerably more force than another: the court must determine whether it sets out minimum reasonable standards, or whether it codifies customary standards, or whether it recommends best practice. We have to distinguish between reasonable care and a 'gold' standard of care. But there is little doubt now that with the growth in protocols, and the expectation that they are based on sound research, the courts may consider them when deciding what is reasonably expected of practitioners. It has to be remembered that a guideline is just that: it is not a rule. A guideline advises; a rule prescribes.

In the court case relating to Tony Bland, one of the victims of the Hillsborough disaster, the House of Lords accepted the defence's submission of BMA guidelines on the withdrawal of care from a patient in a persistent vegetative state. However, it was also held that since no two cases will be identical, and because guidelines are not etched in stone but will evolve with time, that such a defence would not automatically succeed in the future.

There are certainly difficulties in trying to use guidelines routinely as a yardstick for assessing allegations of negligence. The law has for many years acknowledged that there may be more than one right way of doing something, and has been reluctant to be too determinative of what clinical practitioners should do. It acknowledges that not all practitioners are experts and will judge a practitioner by what he or she could reasonably be expected to have done under the circumstances.

To date, whether or not there has been negligence is decided by reference to two landmark cases. In Scotland there is *Hunter v Hanley* from 1955, and in England *Bolam v Friern HMC* from 1957. While marginally different, these essentially define negligence with regard to what the reasonably competent practitioner would do or know.

Although these two cases remain the legal position, it is only fair to note that Bolam has come in for a good deal of criticism recently. Characterised unflatteringly as 'the doctor's friend', it has also been called 'a hang-over from the Victorian age when Nanny was supposed to "know best"' (Kirby, 1995: 5–8), and 'a medico-legal Jurassic park' (Goldrein, 1994: 1238). If Bolam is ever overturned (and some believe that the Bolitho case in 1997 qualified it to an extent) then the courts may be able to dictate what practitioners should and should not do. This will be a significant retraction of the professional's right to have competence determined by colleagues rather than by lay people. For some in the health service this is desirable; for most (I believe) it is not.

Conclusion

Practitioners are not united about the desirability of having protocols. There is an element of defensiveness in their existence and growth, and yet their *raison d'être* is not to prevent litigation but to promote best (or safest) practice. This is a contentious area, for it seems that some practitioners' concept of safety would in fact preclude any element of choice at all for the pregnant woman. Nevertheless, there is a considerable body of research knowledge which can be used when drawing up and updating unit protocols. Annual revisions are not uncommon, and providing these make use of the available knowledge this ought to help promote optimum practice. Whether staff comply with protocols may be questioned, and balancing a woman's autonomy and the perceived need to follow a protocol is a delicate matter.

Chapter 17

Q Quantum

Quantum literally means 'how much'. The matter of deciding quantum in the law of tort (delict in Scotland), rests on the notion of restoring the plaintiff to the position (s)he would have been in had the tort not occurred. In medico-legal cases damages are intended to compensate for the degree of harm suffered.

This chapter notes the principle of quantum, and then discusses the observations of some of the interviewees. It then examines a number of the legal claims which were investigated in the course of this research.

Most of the interviewees and claims were Scottish, and there are suggestions that the level of quantum may not be as high in Scotland (see below). In this research there were far fewer closed English claims, and to avoid inadvertent identification it is not possible in this chapter to identify those claims which are Scottish and which are English. Cross-Border comparisons are, therefore, limited.

The principle of quantum

There are two categories of damages; 'special' and 'general'. 'Special damages' designate the amount of financial loss between the time the negligently-caused harm was sustained and the trial (or settlement); these include lost earnings, expenses for medical and nursing care, and reimbursement for the purchase of special equipment. 'General' damages include six heads of claim (Payne-James *et al*, 1996: 131):

1. Pain and suffering from the injury ('solatium')
2. Reduced enjoyment of life ('loss of amenity')
3. Future loss of earnings
4. Loss of earning capacity
5. Loss of pension rights
6. Future expenses

The heads of claim that tend to receive most attention are those which concern cerebral palsy. Such claims – if successful – represent the most costly settlements from the health service's point of view, largely due to the general damages referred to above. However, as was seen in *Chapter 7*, there are many other heads of claim within perinatal litigation, and the bulk of successful claims obtain far less than those that receive most attention.

An interesting feature related to the likelihood of receiving compensation is noted by Brennan *et al* (1996). They found that the severity of disability was the best predictor of a damages award, not the occurrence of an adverse event or actual negligence. In their study, several claims in which no adverse event was noted achieved a financial settlement, as did several in which there was an adverse event but no evidence of negligence.

In the USA there are some distinctions that ought to be noted. The notion of 'punitive' damages is that a practitioner who has been found guilty of gross negligence may, in addition to being liable for the compensation award, be punished by a further award. While this category of damages does not exist in Britain, it seems that a similar approach was taken in one claim, as noted by one interviewee:

> *Well, there's a very interesting recent report of an English dental case... where the judge awarded 15% extra for what he called aggravated damages because he held that the dentist had really deliberately and fraudulently over-treated patients without getting the true consent, and that amounted to such conduct as to justify an award for aggravated damages.*

> (Defence solicitor 1)

Another issue relates to how to calculate an amount for pain and suffering. O'Connell (1971: 39) referred to this concept as 'truly... protean... almost unlimited in the manner in which it can be expanded,' and also criticised the techniques used by some attorneys. In particular he criticised the:

> *... so-called 'blackboard technique' whereby counsel uses in argument to the jury a mathematical formula stating that specific sums per day, hour, minute or even second should be allowed as damages for pain and suffering... Some idea of the astronomical values that such techniques can impart to personal injury cases can be seen from the remarks of the appellate court in* (one) *case, 'If one cent were used for each second of pain, this would amount to* [$36] *per hour, to...* [$864] *per 24-hour day, and to...* [$315,360] *per year... Yet a penny a second for pain and suffering might not sound unreasonable.*

> (ibid: 40–41)

It is clear that if the plaintiff has a long life-expectancy, such a formula could end up being extremely expensive for the defence. Because of the inevitable drain on health service resources there is concern about the level of quantum:

> *There is only one pocket of money. I think that's absolutely true. The money that is spent to cover litigation costs is taken away from somewhere else.*

> (Midwifery manager)

Another midwife offered a redistributive solution:

> *If they didn't spend all that money on the court cases but put it into a fund for damaged babies that would make far more sense.*

> (Midwife 3)

One of the claimed reasons for an increase in litigation in the USA is the notion that it is somehow acceptable to sue 'deep pocket' (ie. rich) defendants (Greene, 1989). However, there is little to suggest that the NHS can absorb the larger amounts of quantum without the service being affected detrimentally:

> *If that case is settled, as it might be in Scotland now for £800,000 or £1m the implications for Trusts are very great. Not that they're paying all the bill, of course..but it's still a large amount of money.*

> (Medical director)

'Not... paying all the bill' refers to the financial arrangements introduced by the Scottish Office in 1990 to help employers meet the cost of large compensation payouts (now replaced by CNORIS, see *Chapter 18*). A different but comparable arrangement exists in England with the Clinical Negligence Scheme for Trusts (CNST), and in Wales with the Welsh Risk Pool.

While concerns about finance appear to be particularly acute in England (NAO, 1997; Beecham, 1997), there appears to be less concern in Scotland:

> *I know in Scotland we're far ahead of what is going on south of the border. The amount paid out here is minuscule because we've got a reasonable Central Legal Office... whereas south of the border the money being claimed is stupid, and money being paid out is ridiculous.*

(Consultant obstetrician 3)

The overall effect of compensation payouts is certainly believed to be significant:

> *I was at a conference... And they had* (someone from) *the new NHS Legal Authority... You know he's talking about £200m... in England – it's nothing like that in Scotland... they're looking at very, very large sums of money and it has to come out of the budget...*

(Defence solicitor 1)

With a population ratio of approximately 10:1 it might be expected that the amount of compensation paid in England and Scotland would reflect this. However, as this solicitor pointed out the amount in Scotland is reported to be 'disproportionately much less', a belief confirmed by limited published data which indicate that the amount paid for medical negligence compensation in Scotland amounts to little more than £4m annually (Scottish Office, 1999; NAO, 1999).

Whatever the total cost (and legal costs need to be added to compensation costs) publicity about compensation awards can be problematic. There is a danger that articles about a handful of atypical cases (there have been reports of awards of £800,000 [Anon, 1997a], £1.3m [Anon, 1996d], and £3.3m [Dyer, 1998]) can generate the notion that litigation is all about claims worth hundreds of thousands or even millions of pounds. In fact many reported obstetric claims are settled for much more modest sums: Anon (1996b and c) refers to claims concerning neonatal death which received £11,000 and £15,000, and Anon (1996a) cites a claim involving perineal damage settled for £17,500.

For most claims examined in this research the high value claims were the exception, a point echoed by this solicitor:

> *This chap* (from the NHSLA) *was saying that, as you would expect, it is a tiny percentage of English claims that cost a huge amount of money, and it's the brain-damaged baby cases which are a fraction of the overall. I mean, the average claim is probably about £10,000 or even less...*

(Defence solicitor 1)

One of the dangers of large sum payouts is that they can in certain circumstances become a 'windfall' to the parents. The calculation of damages includes loss of future earnings, and for this the child's lifespan must be anticipated. If the child dies unexpectedly after the award is made, the parents are left with a 'windfall'. In one such case (Calladine, 1997) the defending health authority tried to recoup the damages (£700,000) when the child died just days after the compensation was awarded. One way round this dilemma is to structure settlements so avoiding the lump sum payout:

> *There is also this move towards structured settlements: if it is what is referred to as a 'bottom-up' self-funded structured settlement, what you're trying to do is produce an annual payment to the child, an annuity, which covers the cost of the care that is needed, and that goes on for its natural life.*

(Legal department official)

When this official noted that 'we're probably talking one and a half million for things which are coming to the boil now', this refers to the cerebral palsy claims. This chapter will show that many successful claims are settled for far more modest sums – an important feature of litigation to bear in mind for it helps to paint the broad picture of perinatal litigation. Although the NHSLA and Scottish Office do not routinely publish figures for compensation awards (either individual or collective) further data on quantum can be found in the AVMA Medical and Legal Journal section of *Clinical Risk*.

One obstetrician pointed out that a knowledge of quantum alone can be misleading:

> *If people get just figures about the amount of money spent –* I think £4.5m last year (in Scotlan*d*), *and that's a tiny figure compared with England and Wales – the amount of money in settlements doesn't tell us anything about the numerical incidence* (of claims).

(Medical director)

The incidence (or rate) of claims, the success rate of the different heads of claim, and the compensation awards for the claims that are successful, are all different parts of the complex jigsaw of perinatal litigation. As stated in the introduction to this book, a definitive picture is impossible, for the features are changing constantly. The remainder of this chapter attempts to augment the understanding of how compensation is calculated. However, in the following summaries only a very brief account of some of the details of each case can be given, and it is not intended that these details necessarily explain the amounts in damages which are quoted. The quantum is cited only to give a 'ball park' idea of the amounts that different types of case may succeed in obtaining.

While the law attempts to restore the plaintiff to a position comparable to the one she would have been in had the negligence and harm not occurred, there are inevitable difficulties in deciding how to quantify the harm. There is also an inescapable paradox in the method of deciding quantum, since the degree of negligence and the degree of harm may not be proportionate. Hypothetically, a marginal degree of negligence, for instance delaying slightly too long before intervening in a labour where fetal compromise develops, could result in a brain-damaged infant, and the quantum could be very high (running into the million-pound range or higher). Gross negligence (persistent delay despite overwhelming evidence of fetal compromise) in this instance could result in the baby being so severely affected that it dies; in this event, damages are rarely more than a few thousand pounds. A solicitor commented on this:

> *In Scotland historically damage awards are very low, particularly for damages for deaths. I don't know* (why). *There are signs of catching up a bit* (with England) *with the new breed of judges.*

(Defence solicitor 2)

It will be seen that the amounts under different heads of claim vary enormously. This range contradicts one solicitor's remark that obstetric legal cases are easy to spot because they have 'a £1m price tag on them' (personal communication). It will be noted that many are settled for much more modest sums. In *Chapter 7* the various heads of claim were noted. The following sections refer to claims and the actual or potential damages awarded. These claims are a very selective sample: it is not claimed that they are necessarily typical of similar claims.

Baby claims

Of all the different heads of claim those concerning cerebral palsy receive the most attention. Here brief details about two such claims are given, so that the calculation of the award becomes clearer.

As noted in the preceding section, loss of future earnings may form a considerable part of a claim. In one case the defence conceded that the child's cerebral palsy was a result of staff negligence. The plaintiffs claimed:

> *Average gross non-manual earnings... The said child is unemployable. But for his said condition, he is likely to have obtained employment and earned a wage well above the national average.*

This child's father was said to earn twice the national average wage and his mother also had well paid work. Another paradox in quantifying harm is that, in such a situation, parents of a similarly affected child who are either low-waged or unemployed would not be able to claim as much, despite the degree of harm being comparable.

It is extremely difficult to put a price figure on cases of harm and distress, but if it appears that damages awards are sometimes conjured out of thin air it should be noted that damages are often quantified in a very precise way. The following claim illustrates the calculation of special damages awards. The child developed cerebral palsy, and the family incurred costs in purchasing equipment and adapting their house in order to be able to give adequate care. However, the child then died. The case was to be conceded, and the defence made the following offer:
General damages £10,000; Bereavement £3,500;
Special damages £24,335.98 (20 items):

1	Solicitors' fees for sale and purchase of house	£939.3 + £1,311.63
2	Building extension and shed	£1,000
3, 4	Suction pump, washing machine and tumble dryer	£745
5	Two pushchairs	£278
6,7	Fan and swing	£70
8	Listening device, no cost given	
9	Car	£3,990
10	Loss of earnings	£4,133
11	Petrol + car expenses	£3,500
12	Baby-sitting	£872
13,14, 15, 16	Bedding and towels, clothing, toiletries, cleaning items	£3,366.81
17	Food	£1,410.24
18	Telephone	£800
19	Gas and electricity	£1,500
20	Toys	£400

This very precise quantification required explicit pricing of goods and services. Such pricing will become more debatable when assessing future or apparent loss of income. As noted in *Chapter 25*, there have been a number of examples where, regrettably, a plaintiff's solicitor has been so lacking in the relevant knowledge and experience that the plaintiff's chances of success are reduced. From the list above it will be seen that 'Special damages' cover a wide area. In one instance (concerning a claim about a child with cerebral palsy) a legal department official noted that the, 'claim for special damages ... was all about parents' travelling expenses. Nothing about the child's loss of earnings, or speech therapy, or what you will.'

Many of the claims about stillbirth or neonatal death were similar to those concerning cerebral palsy in that they related to inadequate monitoring. While this usually referred to fetal heart rate monitoring, in one case it referred to monitoring of blood antibody levels. A Rhesus-negative woman was given Anti-D immunoglobulin after delivery, but the dosage was insufficient. In her next pregnancy she developed antibodies which were not detected through combined hospital and GP errors. As a result, her child was stillborn. In this case £4,000 was awarded.

Just how a financial package is intended to compensate for the loss of a baby is difficult to understand. In another case, in which a registrar evidently failed to deal competently with a situation in which the cord was around the baby's neck at birth, the baby subsequently died. Damages were demanded under two heads of claim: firstly for solatium (damages given by way of reparation for injury to feelings), and secondly for loss of society (for the parents not being able to 'enjoy' their baby). Damages were awarded under both heads of claim: £3,000 for solatium; and £4,500 for each parent for loss of society, making a total of £12,000. The difference between this and the previous case is that loss of society can only be awarded once the person in question (the baby) has enjoyed full legal personality. To achieve this, the baby must be born alive; loss of society therefore cannot be claimed for a stillborn baby. The difference between a stillbirth and a baby who is liveborn but who dies moments after birth may appear marginal, but in the law this distinction is very significant (questions of inheritance, for instance, may also depend on a baby being born alive, even if only for a short time).

Another difficulty in deciding quantum lies in trying to predict the likely course of a condition over what may be a long time:

Case: After an apparently normal delivery the baby developed Erb's palsy. Nothing in the case notes indicated any difficulty with the delivery, and it was concluded that the injury must have resulted from excessive force. The plaintiffs suggested £10,000 in damages. The problem in determining a figure was because obtaining a long term prognosis was difficult.

Maternal claims

As with the baby claims, there were several heads of claim, the most common of which was perineal trauma. In one case concerning an episiotomy which was allegedly repaired negligently, the woman claimed she was unable to return to work because of this. Loss of future earnings are an entirely legitimate aspect of a claim for damages. However the legal department questioned whether she had actually intended to return to work after having her baby – the firm for which she worked didn't seem sure, and nothing about her intentions was documented. Although the clinical basis of the case was conceded, the claim could not be settled for some time because of the argument about loss of earnings.

What might at first appear to be very similar claims; for example, 'retained swabs' cases may be settled for very different amounts: the attempt is always to quantify the degree of harm caused. In one such case, the swab was removed after ten days by the GP; it was argued that the patient suffered little except discomfort, and £400 was agreed between the two sides. In another case, the swab was not removed until the postnatal examination at seven weeks; in this instance, £2,000 was awarded. If the plaintiff can show that she suffered extreme distress because of infection caused by such a retained swab, then she may be able to claim a higher figure. Such distinctions show the limitations of studies which only identify the principal reason for raising a legal action.

In an attempt to decide quantum, very often case law will be examined. If similar cases have succeeded in obtaining a certain amount in damages, then it makes sense to follow that precedent.

> **Case:** A swab was retained after a forceps delivery. Because it was thought that the woman suffered little serious discomfort as a result of this, £200 was initially offered. The woman's solicitors described this as 'derisory... little more than a nuisance value settlement.' The defence then offered £400. The solicitors replied by claiming £1,000, citing *Edmonds v Bains*. Having read this case, the legal department then cited two others (*Quinn v Bowie* and *Paton v BSC*), and on the basis of these offered £600. This was negotiated up to £700, which was agreed upon.

It will be seen that a considerable degree of negotiation regarding quantum occurs between the defence and plaintiffs in a case which is conceded or which the plaintiff wins. Mansell's (1997) acerbic views of this process were referred to in *Chapter 6*. The problem with looking to case law is that only a handful of medico-legal cases get as far as the court stage, and so finding a case which is directly comparable may be difficult. In those cases decided out of court – the majority – there is usually no publication of the decision or the amount in damages; a case may be reported in the media, but even then the matter of quantum is not usually disclosed. Because of the lack of case law, those solicitors specialising in this area have to acquire an anecdotal knowledge of the likely level of damages. However, case law is preferable: in one case the lack of a similar claim led to delay:

> **Case:** After delivery the woman suffered a severe haemorrhage, leading to hypovolaemia and severe adult respiratory distress. She was admitted to intensive care, but had recurrent bleeding, and then collapsed. In Theatre, a 'substantial piece of placental tissue' was removed. Upon routine checking, staff were initially doubtful about the placenta, but then documented that it was complete.

To have missed the fact that a 'substantial' piece of placenta had been retained was held to be negligent, and the case was quickly conceded. Unfortunately the matter of quantum took some time: the plaintiffs, claiming £10,000, cited *Kralj v McGrath*, in which an obstetrician had attempted an internal cephalic version of a second twin; the procedure failed, and the baby subsequently died of its injuries. The legal department claimed that there was no case which paralleled this one. Damages of £6,000 were eventually awarded.

Even allowing for the fact that each side knows it will probably have to negotiate to some extent, at times the estimates of damages were sometimes far apart:

> **Case:** A cervical tear occurred at emergency caesarean section. The registrar sutured this with routine closure. The experts for each side disagreed profoundly, and the case went to court. The initial writ in the Court claimed £50,000.

Although the plaintiff lost this case, the Court had some sympathy with her and modified her contribution (for legal costs) to nil under the terms of the Legal Aid Act. To help the determination of future cases the court stipulated the damages the woman would have been awarded had the claim been successful; these were £6,250.

The difference between what was claimed and would have been awarded in this case had the plaintiff succeeded was considerable. Quantum may cause lengthy arguments, even in relatively minor injuries. It is sometimes argued that the plaintiff may bear some responsibility herself, in which case the amount of damages should be less:

> **Case:** A woman who had an allergy to a particular form of sticking plaster (this was clearly stated in her notes) nevertheless had such an adhesive dressing placed on her arm to secure an intravenous infusion. The plaintiffs claimed £3,000. £192 was claimed for loss of the husband's wages – he had to take time off work because his wife could not look after the baby with a swollen hand.

The defence claimed that the plaintiff did not bring the matter to their attention quickly enough, and therefore should bear some responsibility. She was drowsy at the time.

In this case there was difficulty in establishing a suitable amount for such a relatively minor injury. The defence offered £275. The plaintiff's solicitors replied that this was unrealistic: £800 would be fair, but they would accept £500 in order to settle quickly.

Conclusion

Quantum is certainly a problematic area of the law, with the possibility that apparently similar cases may receive hugely different amounts in damages. Among clinicians there must be an awareness that even a minor clinical error may in fact lead to large financial losses. However, because of the chance elements involved (such as whether people decide to sue or not) there is a danger that raising clinical awareness in this way will only lead to a rise in defensive practice. The fact that the degree of negligence and the degree of harm may be hugely disproportionate is a negative feature of a fault-based system, and does not help clinicians to connect their actions with possible future legal proceedings.

This chapter has demonstrated the wide variation in the amount of compensation that may be awarded to a successful plaintiff. Even allowing for the apparent lower level of award in Scotland, it is important to bear in mind that perinatal litigation is not all about million pound claims. The question of how the health service can absorb the cost of compensation is considered in *Chapter 23*.

Chapter 18

R   Risk

At the end of the second millennium, there remains a mistaken
belief that science can and should be used to eliminate risk.
Politicians and voters share the blame.

(Bridges, 1999: 22)

Risk, it seems, is everywhere, and its management (or attempts at management) appears to be a growth industry. Risk and the need for safety are talked of in almost every sphere of modern life. Furedi (1997: 1) claims that: 'Hardly a week now passes without some new risk to the individual being reported, and another safety measure proposed.' The upshot of this approach, he continues, is that we have developed a 'culture of fear', in which society views the taking of risks as undesirable. One theory holds that this increase in our sense of danger has accompanied the exponential growth in information about the world around us. As the mass media rush to bring us news of the latest disaster, we are made aware of the scale of suffering and devastation in both near and far flung places. It is not known whether the incidence of child abduction has increased, but we are guaranteed that television and newspapers will carry such reports to a wide audience. The fear then becomes widespread because, as Beck (1992: 24) claims that, 'Risk society is a **catastrophic** society. In it the exceptional threatens to become the norm' (original emphasis). It is debatable whether such fear or awareness of risk are justified. Furedi (1997: 15) claims that, 'Often people's perception of what constitutes danger has little to do with the real likelihood that they will suffer misfortune from that source.'

If the belief that we have overestimated fear and the chance of risk is accurate, it calls into question much contemporary thinking. Nevertheless, as noted in *Chapter 4*, while perception and reality may differ, it is the perception that shapes what we do. The concept of risk is so broad that in one chapter I could not hope to provide a comprehensive description of its features. Concepts and social theories of risk (cf. Renn, 1992) are beyond the scope of this chapter, which restricts itself to examining a number of views about the role of risk and risk management within maternity care.

The growth of risk awareness

The widespread use of the term 'risk' may debase its meaning. The view of one midwife in an earlier interview was that (Symon, 1994):

We don't take risks so much now – although risk isn't quite the right word.

This suggests that while there may be a perception of danger (ie. an awareness of risk), there may not be clarity of understanding. Leaving aside the debate about whether (or why) risk has increased, there is also a view which holds that concern about risk in the health service has only come about because people have, in the last 20 years or so, learnt to sue. Walshe and Sheldon (1998: 18) claim that, 'It has been largely the financial pressure from legal actions for clinical negligence which has driven the NHS to take risk and risk management seriously.'

This view maintains that because the cost of mistakes was largely borne by those outside the NHS (ie. the affected person, their family, and perhaps their employer) there was little impetus among health professionals to control risk. There is little doubt that concerns about medico-legal risk have arisen to a large extent because of obstetric litigation. Few obstetricians and midwives will be unaware that maternity care has been the area most heavily implicated in the rising cost of litigation. Because figures are not routinely published concerning the exact incidence of litigation, it is difficult to conclude what an appropriate response should be. Data in *Appendix II* demonstrate that the upward trend in litigation seen in the 1980s was not irreversible. The cost of litigation, however, continues to increase, and so concerns about maternity care (the most expensive area within the health service) remain.

That there has been a rapid growth in the awareness of risk can be seen from the health-related journals launched in the last few years which include the term in their title. These include the *Health Care Risk Report* (launched in 1994) which aims to inform health care managers, senior clinicians, and lawyers of the management of risk within the health service; and *Clinical Risk* (which was launched in 1995 and which incorporates the AVMA Medical and Legal Journal), which focuses on the prevention and management of clinical risk. In addition to these there are non-health journals such as *Risk and Human Behaviour* (produced by the Economic and Social Research Council); *Risk Decision and Policy*, which examines issues of decision-making in the context of business and government policy; and *Risk Analysis*.

Explaining risk

One aspect of how health service practitioners discern risk was discussed in *Chapter 4* in relation to the perceived risk of litigation. How practitioners convey a sense of risk to women is another matter: there are concerns that imparting an unjustified sense of danger is a mechanism for scaring pregnant women into accepting levels of monitoring and intervention which they would otherwise not tolerate (Jane, 1996; Hoy, 1997). The dangers of an uncritical use of technology include a rise in morbidity as intervention rates increase.

The availability of information about the incidence of procedures and their associated risks may be poor (Waterson, 1993), although the Changing Childbirth Information Project aims to redress this (Kenney and Macfarlane, 1997). However, the striking reduction in the level of maternal (and infant) mortality, due in part to advances in modern medicine, has meant that it may be very difficult to convey a sense of risk about rare occurrences such as maternal death. While deaths do still occur (as the confidential enquiries note), the very low incidence, when comparing vaginal and caesarean delivery, can lead to the claim that even a two-fold increase in risk of death is acceptable because 'twice nought is still nought.'

Related to the notion that people today do not appear to expect things to go wrong in relation to pregnancy, there is a danger that mentioning risks of poor outcomes may cause undue concern:

> *I've had this situation where people have been coming in to the pregnancy assessment suite because they've had a problem and they've mentioned morbidity and things like that, and I've been able to quote figures to them and sort of say 'Now let's get this in perspective. This is the number of babies who die'... but I've had people asking me about cerebral palsy and I have been quite blunt about the figures... I don't know how you make it more realistic without terrifying the life out of people. That's the big problem we have.*

(Midwife 6)

One obstetrician explained how different practitioners could put a very different slant on things:

> *If I see a patient in a clinic who has a breech presentation I will put* (it) *to her that in a well managed breech delivery her chance of a healthy baby delivering normally is 95%, whereas by Caesarean section it's exactly the same. Another person would say that in his or her opinion the elective Caesarean section is better for her – from her point of view and from her baby's point of view – and that's how it differs...*

(Obstetric registrar)

Even conveying an appropriate sense of the prospect of litigation appears to be problematic:

> *One of my clinical colleagues said to me 'How many more days on legal issues are we going to get?' The people that go get the information, they come back and panic the people that don't go.*

(Midwifery lecturer)

Practitioners can only impart an appropriate sense of risk if they themselves are aware of the reality of risk. This applies as much to the possibility of litigation as to the risks of a poor outcome, and it is hoped that the discussion in *Chapter 9* and *Appendix II* will help in this respect.

Staff perceptions may be affected by reading publications, local knowledge, and personal experience, and it appears that some practitioners overestimate certain risks while underestimating others (Woloshynowych and Adams, 1999). Difficulties may also be encountered when trying to impart knowledge of risk, especially when dealing with large numbers (*ibid*). How a risk rating is explained may affect how it is perceived: people may not understand if told that the risk of maternal death (ie. death during or within a year of a pregnancy) in the UK is 0.005% because a tiny fraction of a percentage point is rarely used. Being told the risk is 5 per 100,000 pregnancies may make it easier to understand, although some experience difficulty in understanding such large numbers; who, after all, can picture one hundred thousand pregnant women? As one clinical risk manager (and mother) came to realise, statistical predictions can be unhelpful: 'What I wanted to know.. .was "will it happen to me?"... To a large extent, the interpretation of the statistics comes down to whether you are an optimist or a pessimist' (Quilliam, 1999: 282).

Risk management

As Dickson (1995) points out: risk is part of everyday life, and risk management, whose origins are in manufacturing and process industries, is the mechanism whereby we try to manage our exposure to risk. Risk management is a part of the current requirement to implement clinical governance, although, as Quilliam (1999) states, the essential components of risk management have been practised by midwives for years. The process involves the identification, analysis and economic control of those risks which 'threaten the assets or earning capacity of an enterprise' (Dickson, 1995: 19). Within maternity care the financial aspects are perhaps more prominent than in many other areas of health care risk management.

Rommal's (1996: 1) claim that, 'perinatal care providers cannot escape risk in their everyday work environment' sums up the perception of an ever-present threat for those involved in maternity care. Even within a maternity unit there are multiple areas of risk, and anything which impacts on staff performance or the care given to women and their babies may be covered by some aspect of a risk management programme. Topics that might be covered include (in no particular order); health and safety, infection control, a policy on latex allergy, adult and neonatal resuscitation training, and baby security. This list is, of course, not exhaustive.

While risk management is a very broad subject, what people are concerned with is clinical risk management: a very useful blueprint for developing a clinical risk management programme is described by van Liew (1997). Such a focus was stressed by one senior doctor:

> *The Trusts will all have a risk management committee now, and they argue about all kinds of issues, from the working of the boilers to clinical matters. But in truth the area that they really should be concentrating on would be the running of the labour ward if they have a maternity hospital, because a single obstetric claim could be so punishing.*
>
> (Medical director)

The large number of articles and books which have appeared on how best to manage clinical risk are testimony to the belief that risk must be controlled and contained. This is not a universal view; one commentator believes that the fear of risk and the challenges that it brings diminishes us all (Hutton, 1998). The issue of whether or not it is desirable to aim for a risk-free society was noted in *Chapter 8*. Nevertheless, it seems to have been accepted – despite the concerns of certain academics and commentators about the overuse of fear – that risk management is implicitly a good thing. A sense of perspective, as noted in the section above on 'Explaining risk' (*p. 151*), is essential; and yet the lack of available and comparable data means that the development of risk management in health care has been patchy and dissimilar.

There appear to be several different versions, each of which reflect local concerns, needs, and experience. Whatever the approach – and it is entirely legitimate that the focus will vary from one unit to another – it is clear that time and resources must be allocated to such groups. This involves dedicated resources: various computer packages have been developed for data collection purposes, and many of these are CNST-compatible. Dedicated staff time (ie. a salaried risk manager) is also essential, although the level of experience and training of risk managers varies greatly (Dimond, 1998a). As one interviewee pointed out:

> *Expertise and experience are patchy across the country. Some Trusts and authorities have not reacted to the increase in litigation and the introduction of NHS indemnity by employing people of adequate intelligence, adequate calibre to handle these things. Sometimes they've dropped it on a senior nurse: 'You can be Director of Quality Assurance and Whatnot and now you're going to handle legal claims as well'...*
>
> (Legal department official)

Risk management will cost money to be effective: there is a good deal of investment required, and returns – however they are measured – may be slow in coming. While spending money in the short term may be unpalatable (given the indistinct prospects of a return on this investment), it is worth noting the costs that may be incurred by not spending wisely. These include the cost of claims and litigation, possible fines, and loss of reputation (Webb, 1999).

Quality – legal

Clinical risk management appears to be based (sometimes rather uneasily) on two concepts, which may be termed 'quality' and 'legal'. This tension can best be illustrated by noting some of the features of risk management programmes that have been published or reported at conferences. The two approaches are not mutually exclusive, and it is not suggested that a clinical risk management programme will only fit into one or other category, but the apparent difference in intention is worthy of examination.

Vincent (1995: 74) notes that, 'risk management is fundamentally a particular approach to improving the quality of care which places special emphasis on occasions in which patients are harmed or disturbed by their treatment.' The US studies cited in *Appendix II* noted that far more patients experience harm than ever initiate litigation. Since the bulk of poor outcomes will not feature as legal claims, to focus only on trying to reduce the incidence of claims, while no doubt valid in terms of lessening the cost of litigation to the NHS, is to risk ignoring the reality of clinical practice.

There are two possible approaches here: the proactive line will involve induction and educational programmes which are designed to ensure that all staff working within a unit are competent. The reactive approach is to measure (sometimes as part of an audit programme) how often poor outcomes occur. While the former is distinctly 'quality' in approach, the latter may be either 'quality' or 'legal', since an awareness of the prevalence of poor outcomes may either help to direct the educational agendum, or be used as a screening tool for the legal department.

Continuing Medical Education (CME) and Post-Registration Education and Practice (PREP) are the formally designated ways in which, respectively, doctors and midwives maintain and improve their skills and knowledge. Davis *et al* (1992) report that CME has been shown to benefit patient care, and a suggested in-service education programme is offered by Beard and O'Connor (1995). In some units (including my own) the attendance at certain in-service training sessions, such as cardiotocography updates and neonatal resuscitation is mandatory for all practitioners working in the labour ward. Offering such education and training is hardly controversial; the salient issues are described by Drife (1995).

Several years ago Ennis and Vincent (1990: 1365) claimed that the 'systematic investigation of accidents in medicine is extremely rare,' and went on to note that while audits of practice were common in hospitals, providing information on errors and accidents was uncommon. However, they acknowledged that, 'obstetricians are more forward looking in this respect than most clinicians' (*ibid*). The collection of data concerning critical incidents or poor outcomes is now in widespread use, in part because it is a basic requirement for Trusts in the CNST scheme. That this represents a culture shift is noted by Clements (1995: 131), who states that 'a risk management reporting system will inevitably be resisted by doctors. Doctors perceive adverse incident reporting as a threat to their reputation and their professional integrity.' Nevertheless, Vincent and Bark (1995) note that detailed analysis of critical incident reporting can uncover common themes.

An example of such a scheme is the Critical Adverse Incident Reporting (CAIR) system in Kettering (Defreitas *et al*, 1999). The idea is to find out the kind of things that go wrong and address the underlying issues. This is not just a headcount of, for example, the number of asphyxiated babies, or the number of women with a massive haemorrhage. It is instead an attempt to identify why things have gone wrong, and then to help prevent a reoccurrence.

The examination of accidents using 'human factors analysis' aims to identify those causes of accidents which are preventable. This process aims to detect the 'active failures' of individual practitioners working at the 'sharp end', and also the 'latent failures' arising out of 'fallible decisions usually taken within the higher echelons of the organisation or within society at large' (Reason, 1993: 2). Traditionally, accident investigation has focused on the first of these, an approach which assumes that serious incidents are a result of individual inadvertent error. Walshe and Sheldon (1998: 17) criticise this view, claiming that structural issues and 'intentional patterns of practice which are misguided or misinformed' may be to blame. It is to be hoped that the current emphasis on evidence-based clinical care will diminish the scope for misguided or misinformed practice, but it is acknowledged that however well structured an organisation, and however well trained and motivated the staff, mistakes, whether through error or violation of a rule, will occur. In a bid to minimise the chances of errors occurring, Vincent *et al* (1998) have developed Reason's model to produce a framework for the analysis of clinical practice.

The practice-based approach which examines standards through the 'quality' lens can be contrasted with the legal focus evident in some adverse incident reporting schemes. Beard and O'Connor (1995: 353–4) note that, 'the first step in achieving a consensus view on how to reduce risk in the St Mary's (Paddington) maternity unit was to set up a medicolegal group... (comprising) the clinical director, a senior obstetrician, a paediatrician, an obstetric anaesthetist, the labour ward manager, a hospital administrator, and a solicitor experienced in medicolegal claims.'

The Nottingham maternity risk management group has a similarly legal focus (Senior and Symonds, 1996). It involves senior representatives from the various clinical disciplines and hospital management, as well as a lawyer and the hospital's litigation officer. It meets monthly, which is costly, as the lawyer's attendance has to be 'bought in'. It is a retrospective forum, examining past incidents that have become claims. Claims management is a subset of risk management. In Oxford the Perinatal Risk Co-ordinator identifies poor outcomes, and liaises closely with the legal department. However, there is also a focus on involving staff and encouraging an educational approach.

As noted above, collecting data on critical incidents or actual poor outcomes is common practice, having obvious potential benefits from a 'legal' perspective:

> *It saves us time and trouble hunting people for statements, and trying to find them when they may already have moved on. The real advantage is catching people here and now, on the spot, and getting as reliable a statement as one can.*

(Legal department official)

The failure to identify potential legal claims early on can cause lengthy delays when, years later, a retrospective investigation becomes necessary (see *Chapter 15*). However, there may be tensions between the 'quality' and 'legal' approaches. Staff may feel that they have a sense of ownership of a process that is explicitly designed to improve their skill levels, but may feel daunted by the prospect that information provided by them – in reporting a critical incident – may end up fuelling a legal claim.

There is also the possibility of disciplinary action. In theory a 'quality' approach will focus on identifying why things have gone wrong, and on instigating educational/training processes which help to prevent a reoccurrence. Its tenor is educative and supportive. A 'legal' approach usually involves senior clinical and management staff, and will inevitably have to focus on questions of attribution. In view of the large potential for financial losses this procedure may be seen as less than magnanimous. One senior obstetrician noted:

> *The Clinical Director should not be the one who is making the decision because he's the one that's going to be involved in any disciplinary thing that might arise as a result... the whole risk management business should be seen not as a disciplinary procedure.*

(Consultant obstetrician 2)

There is evidently a tension between the educative requirements of risk management, and the inevitable possibility that poor outcomes may involve some attribution of blame or disciplinary action. While there is a distinction between the two approaches, there is also a considerable degree of overlap. In trying to improve practice so that sub-optimal outcomes are minimised, the 'quality' approach should also in theory minimise medico-legal risk. However, the unpredictability of legal actions makes this protection rather haphazard. Equally, achieving a significant reduction in legal claims, while desirable from the health service's point of view, does not necessarily mean that standards of care have been raised.

In England the Clinical Negligence Scheme for Trusts (CNST) was established in 1995, and is certainly a driving force in attempting to manage medico-legal risk. The Welsh Risk Pool (set up in 1999) has introduced some CNST concepts into Wales, and CNORIS (Clinical Negligence and Other Risks Indemnity Scheme), established in 2000, is the equivalent in Scotland. The comparatively late arrival of the Scottish scheme may suggest to some that Scotland has been less pressured by the experience of litigation. It is arguable that the primary aim of these schemes is to deal with litigation and its costs rather than raise standards. While the CNST's minimum standards include the rapid review of serious incidents and an agreed system for managing complaints, standards concerning continuing programmes of education are optional.

Consensus?

Although each approach has its own distinct logic, the two approaches have identified the same broad areas of practice that need to be addressed. These relate principally to supervision, training, documentation, and communication (both between practitioners of whatever grade or discipline, and between practitioner and the woman concerned). To these areas may now be added the development of clinical practice guidelines or protocols, which were discussed in *Chapter 16*.

Because of this convergence of approach, and despite having apparently different motives, it has been possible to introduce risk management programmes into maternity care. Nevertheless, there appears to be no universal philosophy behind such moves. Some advocate focusing only on the quality of care, stressing that this is the key to improving overall satisfaction levels. It is understandable that those with a direct experience of litigation may prefer the focus to be overtly on medico-legal risk; the danger in taking a purely reactive approach is that practitioners only learn about claims, and not about the overall standard of care. In today's image-conscious world, this may be very significant.

Clements (1995) suggests appointing both a claims manager, and a risk management co-ordinator who is responsible for the critical incident reporting system and for maintaining standards of health records.

The degree of consensus between the 'quality' and 'legal' approaches needs to be matched by a consensual approach from both individual practitioners and the employer. Risk management is concerned both at the micro and the macro level. This means that there is a responsibility on individual members of staff to address problems themselves, and not simply wait for their managers to devise guidelines or policies (although these, too, are important). The UKCC Rules and Code of Practice (1998b) is clear on this issue: except in an emergency a midwife must not provide any care for which she is not appropriately trained or which is outside her current sphere of practice. If a midwife feels she is not sufficiently experienced in a certain practice, and is being required to undertake such duties, then she has a responsibility to seek further training. Equally, a manager who asks a doctor or midwife to do certain things must ensure that the relevant training or education is available.

The 'Towards Safer Childbirth' report (subtitled 'Minimum Standards for the Organisation of Labour Wards') (RCOG/RCM, 1999) detailed a number of areas that need to be addressed. While risk management is not specifically mentioned – the report calls itself a 'guidance document' and refers to the development of clinical governance – its proposals are very much in line with the principles of managing risk.

Conclusion

Clinical risk management in maternity care, perhaps more than in other areas of clinical practice, is concerned with predicting and trying to control risk. The debate about place of birth often centres on this question. Whether or not it is possible to devise and implement a risk scoring mechanism for pregnant women is debatable: Coppens and James (1999) suggest that this should not be done until a well designed randomised trial has demonstrated the benefits and dangers of such an approach. It is encouraging that risk management may bring some benefits in terms of reducing exposure to litigation (cf. Morlock and Malitz, 1991), but it would appear that there is some way to go before it can be said that all maternity units are implementing comparable schemes.

Chapter 19

S Supervision

Within midwifery practice in Britain there is an historical tradition of supervision in maternity care. Local supervising authorities (LSAs), which were accountable to the then Central Midwives' Board (and today to the UKCC), were set up to monitor midwifery standards, and could suspend a midwife from practising (Isherwood, 1995). This tradition grew because of a fear that poor standards of hygiene and practice were putting women and their babies at risk. Because of this tradition many midwives will associate the term 'supervision' with their supervisor of midwives; while this is an important issue, more pressing from a legal point of view is the matter of the clinical supervision of all practitioners, whatever their discipline. Supervision is a crucial aspect of risk management and inadequate supervision, both of junior staff and of patients, has been cited as a feature of poor outcomes (UK Health Departments, 1996; MCHRC, 1997), and of perinatal legal actions (Ennis and Vincent, 1990; Doherty and James, 1994). Maternity care is multi-disciplinary, and this chapter discusses claims relating to midwives, obstetricians and paediatricians.

There is a legal requirement that an employer provides a safe and adequate service (the failure to do so can constitute negligence [*Bull v Devon AHA*]). From this it can be seen that there is a need to ensure that levels (and standards) of supervision are adequate. It is recommended that practices of supervision are audited along with clinical matters (Bark *et al*, 1997). There is also an onus on individual practitioners to alert their senior colleagues to the fact that they need extra supervision if they feel that this is the case. Failures in either approach may contribute to poor outcomes. In the postal survey attitudes towards the amount and quality of supervision (both of patients and junior staff) varied, but it was a matter of concern that a significant proportion believed these were 'frequently inadequate'.

One interviewee who had claimed that some hospitals had acquired a poor reputation in terms of litigation (labelling them 'repeat offenders') noted that poor management was a contributing factor:

> *The whole unit is just not run well. The levels of training, the level of supervision –*
> *often this stems from the consultant at the top and he's not running it properly.*

(AVMA official 2)

A colleague stressed the importance of adequate supervision, both the 'top-down' approach of senior practitioners ensuring that their junior colleagues are practising safely, and the 'bottom-up' requests of the junior staff:

> *Supervision is a big one; consultant absenteeism is always seen as a big factor. You get*
> *cases where the major thing you can see is that that particular obstetric unit has a*
> *culture that, whatever is happening, no one will call the consultant. If you look at the*
> *CESDI, the biggest percentage of cases... were when they'd identified a problem, and*
> *they hadn't called someone.*

(AVMA official 1)

If this is the case then it is easy to conjure an image of a disaster waiting to happen. As this interviewee noted, the Confidential Enquiries have identified supervision (and the failures in communication which lead to inadequate supervision) as important factors. As noted, it is incumbent on junior staff to request supervision if they feel that they are being asked to carry out procedures for which they are not sufficiently trained. Of course, doing so is no guarantee that supervision will be given, as shown in this case in which a baby died allegedly due to the incompetence of a locum paediatric SHO. The expert report stated:

> (This doctor) *was not competent to resuscitate... it is absurd to suggest that all paediatric SHOs on starting a job are expected to be trained and competent in the procedure...* (This doctor) *asked for help and could not get it. It is totally wrong to put all the blame on* (him); *the blame falls on those who put him into such a position.*

The unpredictability of each day's workload in maternity care means that it can be difficult to guarantee that adequate staff are always available for such supervision. Busier units with high stress levels may be more susceptible to high staff sickness rates, and so ensuring that sufficient staff are on duty can be problematic.

There have been calls to establish a dedicated consultant presence on the Labour Ward (UK Health Departments, 1996) in order to ensure that there is senior help available. As one interviewee noted, problems occurring 'out of hours' can leave junior staff feeling unsupported:

> *In obstetrics most of the problems are dealt with by the junior medical staff. Most of the problems happen in the middle of the night and you don't have senior cover.*
>
> (Obstetric registrar)

In the postal survey there was support from about half the consultants for the proposal to ensure consultant cover on the labour ward. However, despite comparatively few junior obstetricians (25%) stating that they felt they could always rely on their consultant to provide adequate support in order to deal with potential or actual problems in the labour ward (echoing the findings of Ennis, 1991), there was little support among these junior doctors for the idea of a permanent consultant presence.

The amount of supervision available, as noted by one of the above interviewees, may depend on the culture of a unit. One midwife noted that different hospitals may have distinct approaches and, when comparing two, claimed that there could be 'a whole different philosophy of care...' In one it was claimed that:

> *The Sister in charge would just come into your room and check your documentation. You really weren't a practitioner, you were a minion, and there was always someone looking over your shoulder, checking what you were doing.* (This) *was quite good when you were learning, quite good when you were training, but as a qualified midwife, it took a long time to get you standing on your own two feet.*
>
> (Midwife 11)

There is a delicate balancing act between ensuring that junior staff are adequately supervised, and allowing and encouraging autonomous practice. However, the failures to provide supervision are all too obvious. The discussion of one of the claims in *Chapter 13* noted that a junior midwife had spent 'many hours in watching a fetal heart monitor which she was insufficiently trained to interpret or understand'. While the discussion centred on the need for adequate training in fetal heart rate monitoring, it is also apparent that better supervision of this junior practitioner would have meant that the problem would have been identified far more quickly than it was.

It should be remembered that supervision is a particular issue when students are concerned. It appears that in some units students have been left unsupervised and unsupported: in one case in which a student had been left to look after a woman in labour, the CTG trace showed persistent problems. Despite the student claiming that she had reported her concerns to two qualified members of staff, the midwifery expert report noted:

The records suggest that the supervision of the student midwife was inadequate.

Another tragic case concerned a junior midwife (qualified for less than six months at the relevant time), looking after a woman in the second stage of labour. The midwife documented a series of fetal heart rates, many of which would be considered suggestive of fetal compromise, but apparently did not inform a more senior midwife or doctor for about an hour. The midwife claimed that she asked for help at a specific time, saying she thought that the woman needed a forceps delivery. She also claimed that she was told by a senior midwife that all the doctors were busy, but did not record this conversation and seems to have waited a further forty minutes, assuming that someone would come when they were free.

The midwife's evident failure to take any further steps in the presence of probable fetal compromise, or at any rate to document that she had done so, left her wide open to criticism.

However, even with a full complement of staff, adequate supervision of juniors may not always occur. This can lead to tragic outcomes:

> **Case**: Without consulting a more senior colleague, a senior house officer (SHO) decided to use oxytocic drugs to speed up a labour, when there was already evidence of fetal compromise. The woman had had a caesarean section and cervical cryosurgery in the past, and had an epidural in situ. The uterus ruptured vertically through the cervix. The baby died six days later.

Unsurprisingly this case was settled by the defence. The question of supervision may be viewed in a number of lights: it may be argued that the SHO ought to have contacted a more senior colleague before taking this course of action or, alternatively, that the relevant registrar or consultant ought to have been keeping a closer eye on this junior member of staff. Protocols establishing a need to inform a senior obstetrician when such procedures are contemplated may help. Criticism may also be levelled at the midwifery staff who presumably did not query this course of action, or demand that a more senior obstetrician attend.

While ensuring adequate supervision levels may be most difficult in the intrapartum period, it is clear that this aspect of the duty of care principle exists to women throughout their contact with the maternity services. An example of inadequate supervision in the postnatal period concerned a woman who had had a forceps delivery, having been delivered by caesarean section in a previous pregnancy:

> **Case**: The expert report criticised the SHOs who were called to examine the woman when she had severe abdominal pain on the second postnatal day. The expert felt that being so called was unusual, and so the two SHOs should have called a senior colleague.
>
> Instead one prescribed intramuscular narcotics, which only masked the woman's pain. The uterus ruptured, and a hysterectomy was required.

In this case there was explicit criticism of junior medical staff for not requesting additional support from a senior colleague, a criticism that could equally apply to a midwife in similar circumstances. The midwifery staff appear not only to have allowed, but to have assisted a regrettable course of action to be pursued, since it was presumably a midwife who gave the injection. Most frequently, the question of inadequate supervision seems to occur when the unit in question is busy. This is of little comfort to those parents who suffer a tragic outcome, as shown by this husband's statement from another case:

There was only one midwife who was looking after (my wife) *and she was also looking after someone else in the room next door. She was not with us all the time but kept popping in and out of the room... I would say that 90% of the time we were on our own.*

In this case, tragically the child developed cerebral palsy, allegedly due to the failure to carry out adequate monitoring in the second stage of labour. If staff are required to look after more than one woman in labour, documenting this in the relevant case notes will help to explain absences.

Just how staff are deployed when a unit, particularly a labour ward, becomes busy is a matter that must be decided by the senior staff member present. Decisions are made in the light of the best available knowledge about patients and their state of progress in labour. However, despite the best intentions, errors may be made or conditions may deteriorate suddenly when the necessary staff are elsewhere.

> **Case:** A woman who had had a previous caesarean section, was for a 'repeat section' because her baby was presenting by the breech.
>
> She went into labour at 38 weeks, and was in the Labour Ward for six hours contracting irregularly. The obstetricians were busy with other patients (one with twins). As the woman was not felt to be in established labour, the membranes were left intact so as not to exacerbate her labour.
>
> When she was operated upon, her baby was found to be asphyxiated, having aspirated meconium. The baby developed epilepsy, a condition shared by the mother.

It was a matter of debate in this case whether the child's problems were familial or as a result of intrapartum asphyxia. Similarly, the matter of supervision is debatable: as the woman was not thought to be in established labour, it can be argued that constant supervision and/or monitoring was not required. With the benefit of hindsight this may be challenged, but staff will be allocated according to the knowledge available at the time.

In investigating the circumstances that give rise to legal claims, the hospital may examine the ward or unit report books to see how busy the unit was, and to help account for the whereabouts of the staff on duty at the time. Some will say that optimum staffing levels are never likely to be met, given cuts in budgets and a drive to reduce 'over staffing'. Just how this can affect the treatment given to patients is shown in the following case (in which the relevant times have been altered).

> **Case**: There was a delay in going to caesarean section (for fetal distress) overnight, since the duty anaesthetist was busy with another emergency. The second 'on call' anaesthetist had to come in from home.
>
> The operation note recorded: 'NB. Patient in Theatre 20 minutes before arrival of anaesthetic registrar.'
>
> The second 'on call' registrar anaesthetist was called at home at 04.38. He arrived at the hospital at 04.53, and was in Theatre by 04.58. The baby was delivered at 05.06

Once the second anaesthetist arrived there was no delay at all, but it appears that the damage had already been done. Whether a second on call anaesthetist should be on site rather than allowed to go home when on call can be debated.

Conclusion

It is clear that supervision is a critical feature of perinatal care, particularly in the intrapartum period. Qualified staff are required to ensure that women under their care are adequately supervised, and that students or more junior staff are not left in situations for which they have not been prepared. Equally, junior staff have a duty to request extra supervision if they feel inadequately supported. Should the unit become very busy this may be difficult to guarantee; in such an event (as in so many others in perinatal care) good documentation may save a practitioner from conclusions, if not accusations, of negligence.

Chapter 20

T   Telling all: communicating, explaining, apologising

Nobody tells me anything.

(Galsworthy, *The Man of Property*)

This chapter examines the role of communication difficulties in instances that lead to perinatal litigation, and discusses the role of explanation and apology when an outcome is known to be poor. In stressing the importance of adequate explanations, Bonnar *et al* (1999: 3) note ruefully that, 'the trusting acceptance of doctors' judgement and decision-making of former times has been transformed into an attitude of questioning, sometimes suspicion or even hostility in the event of a mishap.'

Allegations about staff-patient communication crop up regularly in legal cases, and the importance of good communication in such circumstances has been stressed (James, 1991; Doherty and James, 1994), although Richards (1999: 730) notes that Hilda Bastian ('Australia's consumer champion') claims that, 'communication is still not regarded as a core skill for doctors.' Indeed, failing to provide an explanation is cited by Beckman *et al* (1994) as an underlying reason for suing. At all times improved communication is likely to lessen patient dissatisfaction; the other side of the coin is that poor communication can always lead to mistrust and mistakes and – according to Lord Woolf – to litigation (Woolf, 1997). A practitioner who communicates well is more likely to be seen as caring, a point stressed by Levinson *et al* (1997: 553): 'When faced with a bad outcome, patients and families are more likely to sue a physician if they feel the physician was not caring and compassionate.' Ideally, communication will be proactive, and not just retroactive: it sets the tone of a good relationship between practitioner and patient rather than waiting for the need to explain something that has already happened. Dillner claims (1995: 757) that there is much room for improvement in standards of communication, noting that in a previous Confidential Enquiry into Stillbirths and Deaths in Infancy, 'all professions are criticised for poor communication.' The most recent report notes that the National Perinatal Epidemiology Unit has been charged with reviewing the role of communication failures in poor outcomes (MCHRC, 1999).

In one of the cases examined here the plaintiffs specifically mentioned the distress that the woman suffered when apparently hearing doctors and midwives openly disagreeing about whether or not there was fetal compromise during labour, although in fact the legal action concerned another matter entirely. It is a matter of conjecture that this perception of staff contributed to the decision to sue, but it seems clear that having one's faith in clinical staff undermined in this way may be a factor.

Communication difficulties

Communication will become difficult in times of stress. Trying to ensure that a woman has understood something clearly when she is either in pain or upset because of events, or is under the effects of opiate or inhalational analgesia, is a skill not held by every practitioner. Equally, some of the problem may be due to the woman or her partner being unable to understand or unwilling to accept certain facts. The following sections illustrate some of these points.

Saying the wrong thing

The need to have good communication channels between patient and staff is obvious. Giving information that is inaccurate or poor in quality may have serious consequences. In one case (concerning a child with cerebral palsy) the mother claimed additionally for the pain and suffering she allegedly suffered at the time of her caesarean section. The expert report stated:

> *There has been no medical mismanagement...* (but) *throughout the entire time there has been poor and unsympathetic communication with this unfortunate lady and while this cannot be quantitated in a legal sense it has been the major cause of her grievance.*

Effective communication during deliveries that are problematic for one reason or another is also critical. A patient's ability to take in information will be reduced if she is upset because she has gone into premature labour or is haemorrhaging; careful and sympathetic explanations may be tried, but when staff are themselves stressed problems can arise. In one case a woman, who had fulminating pre-eclampsia, delivered at 29 weeks gestation. Her partner was initially told the baby was stillborn, but then apparently the staff noted a slow heart rate and commenced resuscitation. By 10 minutes of age the baby's Apgar score was still only 1, and the baby subsequently died. The distress caused by being told that your child is dead, and then to see staff trying to resuscitate him, can scarcely be imagined. While no negligence was established in this case, the actions of some staff clearly left much to be desired. This woman declined a postnatal clinic appointment and a further meeting with staff to discuss these tragic events.

The information given by staff working in the neonatal area can critically affect the course of action taken by plaintiffs. In one case the solicitors claimed that the parents were told by the consultant paediatrician that their child's condition was related to his birth. The baby was re-admitted to hospital at eight days of age with a history of fitting. When the paediatrician found no obvious cause for this, he apparently told the parents that the condition was birth-related. With hindsight he said that the boy's problems were:

> *... more severe than can be easily explained on the basis of the forceps delivery.*

In this case the expert report criticised the paediatrician's remark to the parents. Making comments or giving opinions must always be done with great care, particularly in such a sensitive situation. 'Off the cuff' remarks and intended jokes may be misinterpreted and cause offence, forming the basis of complaints or formal legal actions.

Misunderstandings

Misunderstandings may occur at any stage and have very unfortunate consequences. An obvious cause of problems in communication is a language barrier: obstetric jargonese aside, if anyone (the woman, her family, or a staff member) do not speak English well, and are unable to use the services of an interpreter, then problems are much more likely to occur. In one claim there was a failure to send an ambulance to a woman's house, despite her husband stating that he telephoned at least five times. The baby was born at home, and the plaintiffs claimed for:

> *... physical pain and shock and distress.*

The alleged negligence was that the midwife taking the call did not appreciate that delivery was imminent. English was not the family's first language, and, according to the midwife who received the call, in his excitement the husband was barely intelligible. The 'Towards Safer Childbirth' report

(RCOG/RCM 1999) advocates having 24-hour translator facilities; a move that seems eminently sensible in a multicultural society.

The use of medical jargon may confuse those who are not familiar with it, particularly where the same term can mean different things depending on the context. In one case there was a misunderstanding when staff said to a woman who appeared to have an infected postnatal vaginal discharge:

> *We could take a swab from your vagina.*

The woman took this to mean that a gauze swab had been left inside her following perineal repair, and that this had caused an infected discharge. The midwives maintained that it was a misunderstanding due to the use of the word 'swab', saying that they meant they could use a bacteriological swab to identify any organisms causing the infection. A simple misunderstanding in this instance led to the involvement of solicitors. Similarly, in another case which concerned internal haemorrhaging the plaintiff's solicitors claimed that:

> *Our client was advised by* (the consultant) *that her blood pressure was so low that her life was in danger.*

The consultant replied:

> *I did not say that her life was in danger but I did say that further bleeding could be dangerous...*

The stress of the time may predispose towards this difficulty in communication. There will always be room for some disagreement about what was actually said at what might have been a hectic time, and some of the problems associated with recall are examined in *Chapter 22*. In order to reduce the scope for misunderstandings a policy of 'debriefing' after critical incidents has been advocated (Charles and Curtis, 1994), and this is explored below in the section on 'Explanations' (*p.167*).

Resistance to communication

Communication is, of course, a two-way process. Not only must practitioners be able to impart information in a comprehensible manner, but the woman and/or family concerned must be prepared to listen. At times this evidently does not happen: people under great stress may resist information that is distressing or unpalatable. In one case the consultant obstetrician noted:

> *We would be very willing to try further attempts at verbal explanation but feel this should be done with a third party present to support the couple in their understanding. Our reason for saying this is the resistance to explanation and the belligerent attitude particularly of Mrs G which we have encountered.*

The overlap between obstetrics and neonatology can also provide room for mistakes to be made, or for patients to receive conflicting advice. In one case a consultant neonatologist noted that:

> *Difficulties of communication were compounded by threats of legal action against the obstetricians during the phase of critical illness of this infant.*

In cases where the child is severely or even terminally ill, the ability of parents either to accept this, or indeed to take on board any information about the child's prognosis, may be reduced. In one case in which a baby required to be ventilated, the plaintiff's partner claimed that the ventilator was switched off as there was a large likelihood that the baby, if left to live, would be severely handicapped. The consultant paediatrician replied to this charge by saying that the ventilator was switched off only when the baby's heart had stopped beating, and all other signs of brain death were present. Staff also claimed that in discussion with the parents it was mentioned that, had the baby lived, he would almost certainly have been severely physically and mentally handicapped. Such distressing news may well act as a barrier to effective communication, and it is sad that, in addition to their bereavement, the parents concerned had to endure the stress of a legal action.

Acknowledging that stress and distress can create such difficulties, the consultant obstetrician involved in one case noted:

> *It is always difficult to know how much of any explanation of medical practice is understood or accepted. This is particularly so when the outcome is so distressing that normal feelings of resentment are converted into accusation.*

It would appear that many staff have taken on board the lessons of such experiences, and that there is a greater understanding of the stress experienced by patients and their families. Another obstetrician explained how he tried to avoid misunderstandings:

> *I now spend more time with patients compared with what I did five years ago. I explain... step by step, and that has certainly reduced the chance of complaints.*
>
> (Obstetric registrar)

Just as communication is essentially a two-way process between staff and patient, so good communication between staff is vital. Resistance in this area can seriously affect the delivery of a service, but according to one respondent this used to be commonplace:

> *In days gone by there were many two man units up and down this country, and I'll bet you that if you were to go back and talk to the staff and employees there, that the acrimony felt between the two obstetricians, the inability to communicate, was well developed compared to other specialties.*
>
> (Consultant obstetrician 4)

It is self-evident that poor communication such as described here would significantly affect the standard of care. While it might be hoped that situations like this are not still the case, it would appear that in some units there is still evidence of poor communication. In *Chapter 19* it was claimed by an AVMA official that in some units there is a fear among junior staff of calling the consultant. Such a 'culture' of poor communication means errors are far more likely, and in such circumstances, litigation is a very real possibility. In a multi-disciplinary field such as maternity care this is especially important. If practitioners resist the requirement to communicate with each other, their commitment to providing information for those under their care is open to question.

The link with documentation

The importance of good documentation is discussed more fully in *Chapter 14*. This section briefly describes how effective communication is underpinned by the need to maintain an accurate record, particularly of discussion relating to possible complications or prognosis.

In one case, much of the argument related to what women were routinely told at the antenatal clinic. In this instance, despite the woman specifically requesting a particular screening test, the diagnosis of this condition was not made, the apparent reason being that the relevant blood sample was lost. By the time the diagnosis was made by ultrasound scanning, the fetus was considered viable. In response to a letter from the legal department asking for an account of the events in question, the registrar explained that patients undergoing that specific test would be given a standard (rather than individualised) explanation, and added:

> *It is not practice and is not possible to write down in the case note everything a patient is told in the clinic...*

(Obstetric registrar)

This plaintiff was successful. It seems that cases like this have encouraged practitioners to review their level of documentation concerning such discussions; some examples of this were examined in *Chapter 4* in the section on 'Risk reduction' (*p. 46*).

Explanations

It has been claimed that many plaintiffs are not intent on securing damages payments or pursuing a vendetta against staff members believed to have been at fault, but are only concerned to receive a full and frank explanation and, where appropriate, an apology from the relevant staff. Vincent *et al* (1991: 393) note that in a study of 41 cases reported to AVMA, 'Five parents wrote that their primary reason for litigation was to get a satisfactory explanation of how their child was damaged and why.'

The claim that some people sue in order to get an explanation has been made by others (Young, 1990; Genn and Lloyd-Bostock, 1990), and it is one feature of claims management strategies that an early explanation of events may 'substantially reduce the risk that the patient will seek redress in court' (Ritchie and Davies, 1995: 888). Some of the potential pitfalls of such moves are noted by Strunin and Davies (1995). However, in a bid to head off possible claims, many units are now apparently instigating claims management policies that aspire to provide detailed explanations to patients who have suffered loss in some way. Levinson *et al* (1997: 558) note that, 'more laughter and more use of humor... indicate a warmer personal relationship and are consistent with our belief that patients want to be personally connected with their physicians.'

Without knowing the incidence and nature of legal actions before and after initiating such procedures it is not possible to determine their effectiveness, but at the very least they can be seen as helpful in their attempts to reduce formal litigation, as well as being good manners. One study (Vincent *et al*, 1994) found that few patients who had decided to take legal action considered the explanations that they had been given were adequate, a point that may seem obvious (since they had gone on to seek legal advice), but which highlights the care that must be taken over explanations. Sadly, they will not always be completely effective, even when the plaintiff has no real case to pursue. The need to give adequate explanations was stressed in one published legal claim, in which it was established that, 'failure to provide counselling in cases of sensitive interventions can amount to breach of duty' (Wheat, 1999: 7).

Good explanations

Good explanations appear now to be more of a routine than was once the case. One interviewee claimed:

> *We have changed our practice, as I said, the way we speak to the patient, explain things, that was not there a few years ago... and that's a positive thing, it's good for the patient and also good for us.*
>
> (Obstetric registrar)

Such explanations do not wait for the poor outcome to arise, and seek to establish an effective relationship between patient and practitioner. It is just as important that explanations are good when things do go wrong. In one case part of a stitching needle broke and was retained during a caesarean section. The consultant, who was supervising the operation, knew of this. He probed but couldn't find the needle fragment and felt it would be better to retrieve it later rather than continue probing. The needle was located later by X-ray, and the woman given a full explanation of the situation and plan of management. Fortnightly X-rays were carried out to make sure that the needle wasn't wandering and elective surgery performed ten weeks later. The needle was found and the wound healed well. Despite these full explanations, this plaintiff clearly felt that she had a case. However, nothing the consultant did (or did not do) was negligent: a recognised complication, such as a needle breaking, does not indicate substandard care, providing appropriate steps are taken at the time and subsequently.

Given the perceived increase in litigation, legal actions may now be anticipated by staff when outcomes are poor. In one case involving a stillborn baby, the consultant obstetrician noted that he was not surprised to hear that the patient had instructed solicitors. He claimed that he had spent a long time trying to explain the course of events to the patient and her husband, but felt at the time that he was not getting through to them.

In another case the consultant obstetrician personally operated on a woman because he (correctly) anticipated problems at caesarean section. On being informed of the legal proceedings, he noted:

> *It is my opinion that Mrs B has always been a difficult patient to deal with to her satisfaction... When she was discharged she left me with the impression that she was clear about the sequence of events to date, had understood the oft-repeated explanations, and was satisfied with her treatment. It is disappointing but not surprising that she has apparently had second thoughts.*

Explanations can sometimes be made difficult by the problematic nature of perinatal outcomes. While many members of the lay public appear to believe in a relatively simple cause and effect relationship between events and outcome, this is often not the case. In cerebral palsy it is now believed that as little as 10–15% of cases are due to intrapartum events (and not all of them can be held to be anyone's fault).

Poor explanations

However distressing a course of events – and it must be remembered that staff may also become upset when outcomes are poor – there is a requirement to explain things sensitively. The dissatisfaction from one plaintiff's husband in one case where this evidently did not occur was evident:

> *About 4 or 5 weeks* (later) (my wife) *went to see* (the consultant) *to find out what had happened.* (He) *said to her 'it was one of those things'. I cannot tell you how much distress that this conversation caused* (my wife) *and myself.*

In another case which concerned a scar on the baby's cheek (the injury occurring during an emergency caesarean section), the patient and her husband sought explanation from the obstetricians, but felt 'angry at the flippant manner in which the case was treated', and so went to solicitors. Explanations require a degree of sensitivity that does not appear to have been present in this case. Practitioners must be open to such questioning, although it seems that this is not always evident. One interviewee claimed that some patients faced 'a wall of silence' when trying to get explanations from a hospital. Another claimed that there may be age-related differences in the capacity for expressing sensitivity:

> *The younger consultants are OK. It's the older consultants who have problems with dealing with complaints, dealing with* (people) *nicely and saying 'I'm sorry'.*

(Midwifery manager)

She went on to stress how important it is to be frank and open when dealing with people who seek explanations:

> *Once you've lied to somebody... you've lost your credibility...*

Effective communication requires honesty as well as sensitivity; the sincerity of an explanation will be enhanced if the practitioners concerned are seen not to be reticent about imparting information. The next section discusses one pro-active means of giving explanations.

Debriefing

The term 'debriefing' has come into usage recently in perinatal care to denote the procedure by which a patient who suffers an adverse outcome is given the chance (if appropriate along with her husband or partner) to voice her criticisms and concerns, the theory being that many formal complaints and legal claims are based on misunderstandings. A full explanation of this procedure is given by Charles and Curtis (1994), and it appears that many units have adopted this approach. There are, however, concerns about a lack of clarity in the terminology used (Alexander, 1998), and that poorly constructed debriefing programmes may in fact be counter-productive (Northcott, 1998). Despite the unfortunate militaristic overtones of the term, it appears now to be in common use.

It is clear that explanations, while desirable and a crucial part of sympathetic claims management, are not without their dangers. In one case the defence solicitors advised that a particular registrar (who had delivered a baby who subsequently died) should not be present at a debriefing session with the parents, 'because his being upset about the case could be apparent at the meeting and be interpreted by the family as a sign of guilt.'

This suggestion was resisted by the hospital authorities, who felt it entirely proper that the doctor ought to be present. Nevertheless, the feeling of walking on thin ice is strikingly depicted.

There is certainly a greater openness in terms of letting people see the case notes that relate to them (in part because of statutory requirements).

> *In general we try to be as candid as possible... we give them the case notes and talk them through... the evidence, just to make them see there is no cover-up.*

(Midwifery manager)

The aim, as this interviewee went on to note, is in part to prevent disgruntled patients from pursuing a legal avenue:

> *When it becomes a potentially litigious case, before we respond we always get the advice of the legal department.*

Such cases concern evident poor outcomes. There are also moves to initiate debriefing as a routine in the early postnatal period in order to clarify for the woman the events of labour or delivery, whether or not it is believed that she has suffered a poor outcome. In some units anaesthetists have seen the virtue of such a procedure, apparently resulting from complaints made about inadequate analgesia or anaesthesia, particularly from an epidural or spinal anaesthetic. Despite the obvious good sense of asking patients whether they felt they received sufficient pain relief, it is not an infallible procedure:

> **Case**: During a caesarean section for a woman who was noted to have a psychiatric history, the epidural anaesthesia was found to be inadequate, leading to the need for a general anaesthetic. When two anaesthetists went to see her (three and five days post-operatively) she did not complain of having felt pain during the operation: in fact she said the analgesia had been good.

Given that this woman required a general anaesthetic because the analgesia was not felt to be sufficient at the time, her assertion that she had no complaints might have been treated with a degree of scepticism. Some people are intimidated while in hospital, and the likelihood of their asserting their preferences or opinions is low. At home again, and with time to reflect on events, some will feel that they have been hard done by, and may – as in this case – seek legal advice in order to boost their complaint.

Apologies

It has been claimed that very often patients do not want to go through complicated or formal proceedings, but are anxious 'to get some form of apology and expression of concern' (Neuberger, 1992: 53). She went on to add that the medical defence organisations 'have been fairly negative about expressing apologies on the basis that they could, in fact, consist of being an admission of liability of some kind' (*ibid*). The question of apologies is one that can be problematic, as shown by the following comment from a consultant obstetrician:

> *I apologised... because in a mature and understanding world it is proper to express regret to any patient who considers that she has had a difficult time. That apology is not of negligence, it is of understanding and good manners, and let us hope that type of relationship never be lost in this litigation conscious world.*

This sums up very well the tightrope that must be walked between expressing empathy and sympathy, and the desire not to be seen to be admitting guilt when it is not believed that negligence has occurred. Certainly, there have been cases where the expression of regret has been taken as an admission of guilt. One senior registrar put this very well in writing to a senior hospital executive:

> *I did not state that I wanted to apologise for what I had done. I said that I was very sorry that the baby had died.*

Not all staff were reluctant about expressing such feelings, however, in one case the registrar who had performed the forceps delivery (the baby subsequently died) wrote:

> *I saw the patient and family in SCBU (six hours after delivery). I extended my sympathy and apologised if I was to blame...*

Such an open admission may be unusual. One midwife respondent in the postal survey claimed that one of the causes of litigation was an:

> *Unwillingness on behalf of medical staff to apologise – they're so frightened of legal action if they admit liability that they say nothing...*

The dangers of unguarded explanations or expressions of sympathy are well demonstrated in one case concerning a baby who developed cerebral palsy. The midwife who looked after the woman in labour wrote a personal note to the parents three weeks following the birth, expressing her admiration for their courage in coping with the situation. The legal department, upon being informed of this, noted:

> *...although* (this) *does not amount to an apology or an admission of liability, it is probably not wise for midwives to write to patients following disastrous births. My advice is that the* (hospital) *should encourage a policy of not conducting such correspondence with potential litigants...*

The head of midwifery services, replying to a query about whether there was official advice about whether staff should write to parents in such circumstances, said:

> *I could not in all conscience instruct staff not to write to patients in this way... I am inclined to believe that the best policy would be to allow* (staff) *to use their personal judgement, and accept the risk that we might be left to pick up the pieces.*

The legal department retorted:

> *It is all very well for* (her) *to say that 'we might be left to pick up the pieces', but picking up the pieces can cost as much as £500,000.*

This case occurred a number of years ago, and the amount of potential damages mentioned can be adjusted upwards to £1m or more. Quantum was discussed in *Chapter 17*.

Conclusion

Communication is a social skill, and one which is essential to effective clinical care, particularly in a multi-disciplinary field such as maternity care. Unfortunately some practitioners at times display poor communication skills and fail to take account of the barriers to communication that may occur, especially during labour or when the pregnancy or neonatal period become problematic. Paradoxically it is especially in those cases that are not straightforward that communication requires to be optimal, since more staff members from different disciplines are likely to be involved. Good communication between staff members, particularly those from different disciplines, must be maintained. The importance of good documentation is apparent, since memory recall about explanations may not be accurate, particularly when there is a long gap between an event and the subsequent litigation (this is discussed more fully in *Chapters 14* and *22*).

Apologies and explanations are part of sensitive care, and while they may have their pitfalls, such approaches are believed to lessen rather than increase the likelihood of legal involvement when an outcome is suboptimal. It is axiomatic that such communication with patients must be carried out sensitively; from some of the examples given here it is apparent that this is not always the case. In more than one of the instances given the patient has gone on to sue successfully, and in one it was explicitly stated that the decision to litigate was initiated by an apparently insensitive explanation by staff. While not denying the patient her legal right to seek compensation, it is unfortunate from the health service's point of view that its (public) funds are used to pay legal fees and damages when it is quite possible that a greater degree of sensitivity on the part of staff may have avoided this.

Apologies are particularly problematic: in an adversarial legal system it is considered unwise to hand any 'ammunition' to the other side. Possibilities for a less adversarial means of dispute resolution in health care cases have been suggested (some of these are discussed in *Chapter 23*). Although a clinical error may not amount to actual negligence, some clearly feel that apologising for such an occurrence may be seen as an admission of negligent conduct if there is any hint that solicitors might become involved.

Chapter 21

U   USA: a transatlantic role model?

To err is human; to sue, American.

(DeMay, 1996)

There have been suggestions made that Britain copies a North American example, and that fashions and trends visible in the USA will in due course appear on this side of the Atlantic. Sir Donald Acheson, then the Chief Medical Officer, made this claim in a speech to midwives in relation to obstetric litigation (Acheson, 1991). As if confirming this view, one respondent in the postal survey, explaining why she thought litigation in Britain had increased mentioned, 'an "Americanised" attitude of, "sue if you think you can get anything for your trouble"'. Another cited 'the American culture of suing', and still another referred to litigation as, 'the American (greed) disease'.

International comparisons have been described by several authors, not just in relation to the USA and Britain: Kritzer *et al* (1991) found several differences between the attitudes of Canadians and Americans (having compared Ontario with five federal judicial districts in the US), and also noted that Fitzgerald found that Americans 'were more likely to seek legal counsel than Australians'(*ibid*: 507). Quam *et al* (1987: 209) do not accept that Britain is in danger of sliding towards a US-style crisis, since access to health care remains throughout life here, and there is no direct cost to the patient for future medical care. The USA has twice the proportion of practising lawyers who also operate under a contingency fee system; and juries sit in negligence cases in the USA, which many believe increases damages awards. For these reasons, the litigation crisis that has hit the USA is not inevitable here, so comparisons should only be made with caution.

Because of the lack of published material concerning perinatal litigation in Britain, reference has had to be made to North American sources, although Quam *et al* (1988) question the validity of doing this. Dingwall *et al's* (1991) thorough review makes extensive use of US data. They admit that despite it being 'widely acknowledged that there has been an increase in the frequency and severity of medical malpractice claims in the UK in the 1970s and 1980s... there is... a dearth of published information on the characteristics or extent of this change' (*ibid*: 7). Drife (1993) refers to the apparent effects of litigation on obstetricians and obstetric practice in Britain, but also uses US data concerning the 'haemorrhage' of clinical practitioners from the specialty. Harpwood (1996), in a legal text concerning obstetrics has to make frequent reference to American cases, although the Medical Law Reports have in recent years covered a number of obstetric cases.

It is difficult to measure how much (if at all) Britain is copying the USA in terms of litigation, and this chapter does not pretend to offer an answer to this question. However, because of these various claims, it is worth considering what has been happening in the USA. Since reference to the USA has (inevitably) been made in other chapters, some of this debate is echoed elsewhere. This chapter aims to summarise some of the main attributes of and developments in the US experience of litigation. It will then discuss whether there is evidence for the view that Britain is following an American lead.

Background

The USA has a fault-based civil law system similar to that operating in Britain, although the award of damages in the USA is higher. There are contingency fees for lawyers, which mean that the lawyers may take up to a third of the award if their clients win the case, and nothing if they lose. Some argue that this gives an incentive to lawyers to make extravagant claims for damages. Juries routinely sit in US courts for negligence cases, which provides a plaintiff's lawyer with the opportunity of playing on the jury's sympathy, a ploy criticised by Relman (1990). In part, the awards need to be higher since the cost of looking after someone with a disability (such as a brain damaged child) must be borne principally by the family, whereas in Britain there is (for the time being at least) the NHS which can take some of the strain through providing respite care, and the Benefits Agency, which administers incapacity benefit (formerly invalidity benefit) for those who are chronically sick and unable to work.

Lawyers are allowed to advertise in the USA in a way that many would find unacceptable in Britain. Manuel (1992: 95), referring to a television advertisement in which a classroom scene sees just one child in the class being inattentive and staring out of the window, paraphrases the advertisement (perhaps caricaturing it) saying, 'If your child has a learning disability, it could have been caused by malpractice during the birthing process, call your friendly attorney.'

An extreme case is noted by Illingworth (1987: 14): in Chicago in December 1986 a plaintiff was awarded $32m for a child's 'brain damage', ascribed to 'failure to monitor the heart adequately.' A possible side-effect of such high awards is that insurance companies may be encouraged to settle 'frivolous' claims out of court rather than risk losing much more after a court hearing. In the USA a jury decides not only the outcome of a case, but also the amount in damages.

Juries

This topic is examined briefly in *Chapter 23*, in the context of possible developments in Britain. In the USA the question of whether juries are the appropriate mechanism for deciding court cases (both criminal and civil) has been debated at length for many years. Over fifty years ago Jerome Frank asserted that 'the jury applies law it doesn't understand to facts it can't get straight' (Frank, 1945), and Vidmar (1989) notes that Chief Justice Warren Burger complained in 1971 that 'juries are not competent to deal with the complex issues that come to trial in the federal courts' (Burger, 1971). In appraising Kalven and Zeisal's seminal work 'The American Jury' (which only reported on criminal cases), Hans and Vidmar (1991) note that many of the criticisms levelled against juries; for example that they are unable to understand complex cases, have not been borne out by any empirical data. Kalven and Zeisal's (1966) analysis was based on work carried out in the 1950s, and Hans and Vidmar (1991: 349) concede that, 'Their important conclusions that juries understand the evidence and wage only a modest and polite war with the law could be time-dependant.' This acknowledgement reflects the developments in jury selection since the 1950s, with the composition of juries being changed to reflect more accurately the local community. However the process of jury selection still remains controversial. Vidmar (1996: 97–8) notes that, 'Jurors today are often selected on the basis of their lack of knowledge of the crime, rather than their stated ability to be impartial; or selected on the assumption that they will be inclined to view themselves as representing the perceived interests of their own racial, ethnic, or gender group, rather than deciding the case on the basis of the trial evidence.'

In general, there are three specific criticisms that have been levelled against the jury system: firstly, they are thought to be unable to understand complex evidence; secondly, they are believed to be biased against defendants, particularly 'deep pocket' defendants; and thirdly, they are said routinely to award large amounts in compensation. With regard to the first criticism, Hans and Vidmar (1991: 348) concede that, 'Juries of the 1990s... face much more scientific, technical, and expert evidence than they did three or four decades ago.' It is appreciated that not everyone will be able to absorb complicated evidence, for example, about degrees of neonatal asphyxia or encephalopathy and their likely neurological sequelae. Vidmar and Schuller (1989: 142) note that Rosenthal (1983) claimed that in complex cases jurors may, 'ignore the evidence and instead rely on the credentials and demeanor of the expert and what they perceive to be her or his conclusions.' However, Rosenthal's conclusions were based on interviews with only eight jurors, and on reviewing other literature Vidmar and Schuller disagree with this finding: 'Jurors do not appear to suspend their own judgment in deference to the expert. The expert's testimony is evaluated in the light of the juror's own experience, common sense, and recognition of the adversarial nature of the trial process' (Vidmar and Schuller, 1989: 173).

With regard to the questions of pro-plaintiff jury bias and exorbitant damages awards, Daniels (1989) claims that the attacks on juries are part of an agenda constructed by (among others) the insurance industry. 'Horror stories' are used in insurance industry advertisements to depict juries as biased against defendants: 'This imagery clearly intends to instil fears and anxieties which can be eliminated only through civil justice reform' (*ibid*: 285). Such 'agenda-building' is intended to deflect attention away from the real cause of recurrent malpractice crises which, says Daniels, is the insurance industry's boom and bust business cycle: 'The sheer outrageousness of the stories summarises the crisis and the causal role of juries and the civil justice system. The horror stories evoke a widespread feeling among citizens that a system permitting such anomalies to take place must need immediate and fundamental reform' (*ibid*: 294). Vidmar *et al* (1994) found in an experiment that compared attitudes towards iatrogenic and motor accident injuries that juries did not penalise physicians unduly when assessing damages for pain and suffering. Greene (1989) points out that in fact little is known about how juries calculate awards. While acknowledging that juries may sometimes be biased against corporate defendants, and 'may fuse their sentiments about liability with decisions about damages,' she goes on to assert that jurors' reasoning is frequently involved and sophisticated, and is not the simplistic 'single sum' approach advocated by some critics (*ibid*: 246).

While Daniel's claim that the debate about a 'crisis' is led largely by the insurance industry has some merit (in his article he includes ten advertisements by insurance providers that make this point), the absence of obstetric provision in certain areas of the USA, due to a lack of insurance cover (see below), is difficult to describe as other than critical for those who need such a service. Calling for a large scale jury study along the lines of Kalven and Zeisal, Hans and Vidmar (1991) conclude that there is no empirical data to confirm many of the attacks made on juries.

Incidence of error and litigation

The perceived (or constructed) litigation/malpractice crisis must be examined in context, with the vital question being how often people sue. A study in California in the mid-1970s showed that only 10% of hospital patients suffering negligence due to medical staff filed claims, and only 40% of these (ie. 4% of the total injured) received any compensation (Danzon, 1986). This apparently low incidence of litigating was reflected in the large-scale Harvard Medical Practice Study, which examined over 30,000 case records to determine the incidence of medical negligence. It concluded that accidents were far more likely (by a factor of ten) to occur in hospitals than in other workplaces. There was one disabling injury for every 100 admissions to hospital, and one in four injuries was caused by negligence, but only one in eight victims of negligence actually filed a claim.

Reporting the study, Brennan *et al* (1991) concluded that adverse events occurred in 3.7% of hospitalisations in the state of New York in 1984 (a total of 98,609 adverse events). 27.6% of these (n=27,179) were thought to be due to negligence, which, the authors point out, could all have led to successful litigation. However, they acknowledge that this assessment could only identify the incidence of injuries caused by negligence, and not the incidence of negligence itself: 'Our figures reflect not the amount of negligence, but only its consequences' (*ibid*: 373). With regard to the views of medical staff, they note that 'in the records with evidence of negligence, physicians disagreed frequently about the extent of substandard care... (they) find it difficult to judge whether a standard of care has been met' (*ibid*: 374). These results, which indicate a significant lack of awareness among doctors about what constitutes an acceptable level of care (and, implicitly, what might constitute grounds for civil legal action) are reflected in the studies by Hupert *et al* and Shapiro *et al* (considered below).

Leape *et al* (1991), also reporting the Harvard study, concluded that a majority of the adverse events (58%) were attributable to management error. Acknowledging that not all adverse events are preventable, such as an unpredicted reaction to a drug, or bone marrow suppression following chemotherapy, they concluded that reducing the risk of adverse events requires several different approaches. Among these are on-going research into illness and its causes and treatments; the effective dissemination of guidelines and standards for practice, in part through in-service education; and 'the development of better mechanisms of identifying negligent behaviour and instituting appropriate corrective or disciplinary action' (*ibid*: 383).

Leape *et al* (1991:383) also acknowledged that error prevention requires, 'attention to the systemic causes and consequences of errors, an effort that goes well beyond identifying culpable persons.' Human factors analysis, as described by Reason (1993), was noted in *Chapter 18*. The analysis of error in the hospital setting has been examined by Bosk (1979) and Daniels (1992). Daniels notes that, 'The dynamics surrounding the organisation of medical work are themselves another source of uncertainty in the work environment as well as often being an impediment to the management of error' (*ibid*: 123). He goes on to point out that an error is only so labelled in retrospect, and that there are a variety of methods of dealing with an error, depending on its perceived severity. These range from a 'private talk' with the person responsible ('reading the riot act') to public admonition (eg. on a ward round), formal reprimand and invoking of the disciplinary procedure, and even dismissal (*ibid*: 133). He asserts that the complexity of the organisation, with different units and subspecialties failing to appreciate each other's needs while jealously guarding their own autonomy, creates uncertainty and makes errors more likely. The interaction of personnel from different disciplines also creates a situation where disagreements over the organisation of care (and nursing staffing levels are a particularly acute example of this) can lead to error.

Bosk (1979) examined the role of 'superordinate' surgeons in controlling the mistakes of junior colleagues, and in reviewing the performance of their peers. He found that there was a significant distinction between errors deemed to be technical, and those thought to be 'moral': 'Technical errors are the occasion for restitutive sanctions, while moral errors are an occasion for repressive ones' (*ibid*: 169). This aspect of morality is picked up by Hupert *et al* (1996: 4) who found in their survey that, 'A larger number of respondents equate competence not with expertise but with character – namely, the **moral** character of the practitioner' (original emphasis), and that consequently doctors who were sued viewed the legal action as an attack on their integrity. Bosk's study examined how errors were labelled and dealt with 'in-house' and how the surgical superiors in the hospital approached the matter of their juniors' performance. It is important to stress that this study did not look at cases of negligence only: negligence is in fact a small sub-set of the category of errors. What patients think about such errors is not reported, although one conclusion of the Harvard study was that, 'Contrary to doctors' impressions, injured patients do not sue at the drop of a hat, encouraged by juries who bend over backwards to dip into the deep pockets of malpractice insurers in order to do something for needy victims' (Weiler, cited by Gray [1993: 478]).

Despite such reassuring evidence of an apparent reluctance among patients to sue, other data appears to confirm an upward trend in litigation: Whelan (1988: 71) notes that between 1970 and 1986 the number of claims per insured physician in the USA went up by more than four times. A reason for the higher rate of claims is suggested by Quam *et al* (1987: 1597): 'Patients who have paid directly for their care, through a mixture of insurance premiums and contributions out of pocket, seem more likely to feel aggrieved when treatment fails.' However, this does not account for the recent increase. Sloan *et al* (1989: 3291) found that, 'physicians with relatively prestigious credentials had no better, and on some indicators, worse claims experience', concluding that those who were sued were less likely to make subsequent changes to their practice, so contradicting one of the supposed educative roles of a fault-based system. But it is not in doubt that litigation is a matter of serious concern (Freeman, 1992).

A survey carried out by the American College of Obstetricians and Gynecologists (ACOG, 1988) showed that 71% of their members had been sued for negligence at least once, and 26% had experienced three or more claims. These figures accord with those of Danzon (1986), who reported that 73% of obstetricians had been sued at least once. Dworkin (1989) claimed that the increased tendency to litigate resulted from a growing awareness of the power of the law as a force for good, which stemmed largely from the civil rights movement of the 1950s and 1960s.

Baldwin *et al* (1991: 1050), who found that the overall rate of obstetric malpractice claims for 1982–88 was one claim per 3125 deliveries, claim that insurers should 'consider basing obstetric malpractice premiums on numbers of deliveries rather than specialty.' Ward's (1991) analysis of 500 obstetric and gynaecological malpractice claims found much the same reasons for suing as the reasons identified by Capstick and Edwards (1990) and Doherty and James (1994), reported in *Appendix II*.

It is possible to attempt comparisons in the rate of litigation between Britain and the USA. Baldwin *et al's* calculation of one claim per 3125 deliveries compares with Capstick and Edward's (1990) figure of one per 2500 (referring to ten English health authorities for whom they acted as solicitors); and Law *et al's* (1996) figure of 1.7 per thousand births (ie. 1 in 590) in the West Midland region of England. My own data (mostly Scottish, but some English) ranged in medium-sized hospitals from one claim per 690 deliveries, to 1 per 9000 (Symon, 1997). However, size of unit was a significant factor: in very small units (those with a delivery rate of less than 250 per year), just one claim can suggest an extremely high rate of litigation. The highest was one claim per 228 deliveries, using four-year periods to even out year-to-year fluctuations. These British figures call into question the received wisdom that litigation is much more prevalent in the USA. Comparisons should only be made with caution: data are rarely comprehensive, and even the definition of a legal claim may make a big difference.

Midwives in the USA have also been implicated, although Robinson (1986) claims that this is unfair. She describes how an 'insurance crunch' has hit midwives, despite the fact that only 6% of midwives have been named in malpractice suits, compared with the much higher figures for obstetricians noted above. Midwives tend to work with women who are deemed 'low risk', and, it is claimed, they develop closer links with those in their care: they (midwives) cite a breakdown in the doctor-patient relationship as contributing to malpractice suits. There is increasing specialisation and subspecialisation within medicine that greatly alters the doctor-patient relationship: doctors are now strangers, no longer family friends. In addition, some commentators claim that the greater role of technology has meant a greater potential for mistakes. 'Consumerism and somewhat unrealistic expectations about the capacities of modern medicine,' Robinson notes, 'have combined to make patients less trusting and more willing to blame the doctor for an adverse outcome' (*ibid*: 1017–8).

That the name of American midwives should be tainted by malpractice because the obstetricians are having difficulties may be unfair, but it appears that the problem lies in the availability and cost of insurance. Danzon (1986: 2001) reveals that by 1986 on Long Island neurosurgeons were paying premiums of more than $100,000; and that in protest at rising malpractice liability 234 Massachusetts physicians withheld their care for two weeks. This 'strike' strategy was not the first of its kind: Browning (1986) reports that in 1976 thousands of southern California doctors had walked off their jobs in protest at a 327% increase in premiums. Massive increases in premiums have been reported elsewhere: Bonnar *et al* (1999) note that in the professional lifetime of many Irish obstetricians indemnity rates have gone from £2 to £34,000. One option is for the midwives to self-insure under the aegis of the American College of Nurse-Midwives (ACNM) which, since it is not a profit-making body, can keep the premiums low. The relatively infrequent number of malpractice claims against midwives should lend a certain stability to the scheme, since it has been the suits against doctors that has made the insurance field unstable.

Effects of litigation

More worrying from the point of view of doctor-patient relationships is the report that a senior member of the American Medical Association claimed that, 'Physicians are increasingly seeing every patient as an adversary' (Browning, 1986: 39), and the claim by Casselberry (1985) that family physicians are being squeezed out of maternity care by the threat of litigation. The study by Hupert *et al* (1996) concluded that physicians were often unaware of the true legal test for negligence, and (for this reason and others) frequently viewed legal actions as an attack on their moral character. As a result of this they resented the legal intrusion into their working lives, and perversely refused to accept the supposed 'deterrent effect' of the tort process: 'Torts may anger honest physicians who feel unjustly accused. This may lead physicians to reject negative tort verdicts and actually subvert constructive deterrent teachings of the tort trials' (*ibid*: 8).

The large Wisconsin study by Shapiro *et al* (1989) found some significantly divergent attitudes about litigation when comparing the responses of sued physicians, non-sued physicians, and patients who had sued. While 96% of suing patients believed physician error was a reason for malpractice action, only 20% of sued physicians agreed with this; the divergence was even more marked with regard to physician negligence (as opposed to error) – 97% and 10% respectively. Responses towards questions of the openness and honesty of the pre-claim relationship between doctor and patient, and to the question of respect for one another, also showed large differences in outlook. Non-sued physicians seemed to believe that personal conflicts between patient and doctor were a much more likely cause of malpractice action than either physicians who had been sued or litigant patients. With such differences in outlook, there is clearly room for an improved mutual understanding of the issues at stake in patient dissatisfaction and subsequent litigation.

Other effects of the litigation 'crisis' have been referred to, for instance the increased use of tests; this may be encouraged in a fee-for-service system where the costs of the tests are passed on to the patient, or more accurately the insurance company. Acheson (1991), citing the 1988 ACOG study, notes that defensive medicine appears to be prevalent: 69% of those obstetricians surveyed said the fear of litigation was affecting the way they conducted their clinical practice; 27% had reduced the number of high risk cases they would take on; 13% had reduced the number of deliveries they conducted; and 12% had given up practising obstetrics altogether. In Georgia in 1987 there were 70 counties without a practising obstetrician; two-thirds of the obstetricians in Michigan said that the fear of litigation was their most serious professional problem, and the same proportion in California said that as a result they were now performing more caesarean sections.

Concern about a rising caesarean section rate (20–25% in much of the USA) is not new; Keifer (1993: 1787) cites a distinguished obstetrician addressing an ACOG meeting in the 1950s, at a time when the rate was up to 10%: 'Gentlemen, I hope some day this group may rediscover the birth tract.' DeMott and Sandmire (1990) examined the varying incidence of performing caesarean sections between obstetricians, and concluded that these reflected the individual's response to the threat of litigation. Goyert *et al* (1989), while noting the different rates of performing caesarean sections, concluded from their study that this did not reflect the obstetrician's recent medico-legal experience. Another study (Localio *et al,* 1993), however, concluded that after controlling for other variables, caesarean delivery was positively associated with physician malpractice premiums. Rosenblatt *et al* (1990) found that older physicians, particularly those in urban and solo practice, were most likely to give up obstetrics; recent involvement in litigation was also held to play a part. A deliberate economic move to avoid the increasing overheads of obstetric practice was held to account for some physicians giving up obstetrics (Rosenblatt and Hurst, 1989).

Gould *et al* (1989) found a distinct socio-economic influence in the chances of a woman having a caesarean section; ironically, since caesarean section has a minimal effect on the rate of cerebral palsy, but is significantly associated with increased maternal morbidity, it could be argued that the richest are receiving the poorest care.

The US Institute of Medicine concluded from the ACOG's findings that the poorest sections of society are being deprived of the service of obstetricians, since the areas the obstetricians are least prepared to work in are those where the risks of an adverse outcome are greatest (Acheson, 1991). This view is echoed by Dingwall (1986) who claims that a US obstetrician can expect to be sued eight times in a 35-year career. With regard to income levels, Rostow *et al* (1989: 1058) note that there is a widespread belief that the poor are more likely to sue, but conclude from their study that there is no evidence for this.

Black (1990) also describes this aspect of risk avoidance, highlighting the perceived need to avoid specialities, procedures and patients which allegedly carry a high risk of leading to a malpractice claim, and he cites a study which claimed that up to 49% of doctors who had been sued reported that they now refused litigious patients. Hengstler (1986: 20) cites one obstetrician who refused to accept either a lawyer or the legal firm's clerk after that firm had initiated suits against him: 'We're not refusing to treat anyone connected with a law firm. Previous reports about that just aren't true. We are refusing to treat lawyers who sue us. We can't have a decent doctor-patient relationship with a lawyer who is suing us. What if she goes into labour a week before the malpractice trial is set and there are complications in the delivery room? What if she were to die on the operating table? It's rare, but it could happen. How would that look?'

Baldwin *et al*'s (1995) study, while noting that 'surveys of physicians have reported substantial changes in obstetric resource use in response to the malpractice environment and physicians' claims experience' (*ibid*: 1609), nevertheless found no association between an individual's malpractice experience and an increase in antenatal testing or rate of caesarean section in low risk women. Such claimed risk reduction strategies (also discussed in *Chapter 4*) are noted by DeKay and Asch (1998: 19) who state that, 'defensive testing necessarily reduces the overall quality of patient care', and who go on to criticise the subordination of patients' interests to those of physicians, which, they claim, is inherent in defensive practice. Other studies have indicated that the fear of litigation has discouraged doctors from collecting clinical information for audit.

Effects on the legal system

Symonds (1992: 9) also reports that in West Virginia and Florida a system of no-fault compensation had to be introduced for claims concerning birth-related injuries as a result of the virtual breakdown of the obstetric services, which seems to confirm the frightening view that many women are at risk of having obstetric services denied them. Taylor *et al* (1992) report North Carolina's introduction of an 'obstetrical care incentive program' that encouraged certified nurse-midwives to practice, providing the service that had been the responsibility of (no longer practising) obstetricians.

The Virginia Birth-Related Neurological Injury Compensation Act came about partly due to O'Connell's work on no-fault insurance. In the 1970s he had examined automobile insurance, and concluded that a no-fault mechanism was preferable to a tort-based system. The existing system, he argued, served plaintiffs poorly but lawyers well; in particular, he criticised the contingency-fee method whereby a lawyer's fees could 'take a savage cut out of the victim's payment – keeping in mind that all of the payment is designed, in theory at least, to reimburse the victim for his loss, with no extra amount being tacked on for attorney's fees. Thus the contingent fee almost literally comes out of the plaintiff's hide' (O'Connell, 1971: 42).

Maintaining the principle that had been introduced for car drivers and in workers' compensation, O'Connell continued to argue for a no-fault system in certain forms of medicine: 'as long as the system requires that claimants prove fault on the part of health care providers (with or without caps) and entails payment to claimants for pain and suffering, the system would be unworkable as an insurance mechanism for both claimants and defendants' (O'Connell, 1988: 1476). In the proposed Act, 'no-fault payments (would) be traded for economic loss in a defined set of serious obstetrical cases' (*ibid*: 1478). In liaising with the Medical Society of Virginia he stressed the need to make proposed changes palatable to avoid being watered down or rejected outright; however, it was an insurance crisis rather than reasoned argument in favour of a more equitable system that proved to be the catalyst for the Act, as Fisher (1990: 640) notes: 'In 1986 one of the major insurers in Virginia, the Pennsylvania Hospital Insurance Company, withdrew from the market after a judgement of $8.3 million dollars was made in favour of an infant... As a result 23% of the State's obstetricians were left without cover.' Of the two other insurance companies that provided cover for Virginia obstetricians one stopped offering cover to new practitioners and the other confined its cover to groups of ten or more. Acknowledging that it was an insurance crisis which had brought about the political will to accept a no-fault proposal in Virginia, and despite the fact that his preferred 'early offers' approach (that had also been considered in Massachusetts) was turned down by the Virginia legislature, O'Connell accepted the amended (and less flexible) no-fault provision claiming that he was persuaded to back it 'as an alternative to be tried and from which to learn' (O'Connell, 1988: 1482).

Under the scheme babies damaged during delivery by hypoxia or mechanical injury who subsequently became either permanently disabled, aphasic, incontinent or non-ambulatory, or who were predicted to require close supervision for the rest of their lives, would be compensated. The scheme was to be financed by the state's obstetricians (about 600 in number) who would each pay $5,000 annually; additional income would come from physicians not practising obstetrics ($250 p.a.) and from Virginia's hospitals and insurance companies. However, according to a former president of the Virginia Trial Lawyers Association, the scheme, despite circumventing the requirement to prove fault, still requires that the plaintiff 'prove the doctor caused the injuries. And causation has always been the battle ground in tort cases' (cited by Blodgett, 1988: 35). Further criticism comes from Epstein (1988: 1469), who points out that there is now evidence that a baby may be neurologically damaged if its mother has one 'hit' of cocaine in the first trimester of pregnancy, 'even though it might be very difficult to trace the results thereafter... It seems most unlikely that the Virginia no-fault plan was intended to be a compensation program for victims of maternal drug abuse. Yet that is the risk it creates.'

Claiming that the no-fault scheme cannot be shown to be any better than the system it replaced, Epstein (1988: 1474) argues that the correct response to 'the blunders of the present malpractice system' is a market system in which patients and doctors will contract out of the tort process. Another argument levelled against no-fault schemes is that they will inevitably become too expensive to run; but as Lamb (1992: 28) notes about the Virginia scheme. 'Forty infants a year were supposed to be compensated. Three years into the scheme none had been compensated as all claims had foundered on the tight definitions of causation...'

Danzon (1986: 2004) claims that the tort system in the USA does in fact work quite well, although she believes that patients do not sue often enough to deter negligence and she advocates capping claims since she believes juries award too much in the way of damages.

Conclusion

The US experience of litigation has been held up as an example of what Britain may face unless changes to the legal system are introduced. For the reasons identified in this chapter comparisons should be made with caution. It cannot be assumed that the USA is an automatic role model in this area, a claim that has come about in part because of the dearth of data in Britain detailing the incidence and nature of litigation. It is to be hoped that the increase in available data here will keep the debate focused. Comparisons will continue to be made, and some will be justified; but the assumption that British experience will eventually mirror the American experience is wrong. There has been no evidence to date of a haemorrhage of practitioners from obstetrics in Britain, and so the impetus for radical change is not present. The different structures involved in medical insurance, and the distinctions in the operation of the civil law, will also ensure that the development of litigation in Britain takes its own distinctive course.

Chapter 22

V   Versions of the truth

There was things which he stretched,
but mainly he told the truth.

(Twain, *Huckleberry Finn*)

This chapter examines the theme of recollections and discusses how different versions of the truth may be seen in a legal claim. The investigations of allegations of negligence become unnecessarily time consuming and expensive when memories are poor – factors that are not helped when the case notes are inadequate. It is not suggested that those involved in litigation deliberately lie, only that versions of events may be demonstrably untrue.

One of the most noticeable features of legal cases is the time that they frequently take to arise. This is beyond the control of those who work in the health service, although it could be argued that a well publicised facility for patients who wish to obtain information or express their dissatisfaction may have some effect. The debriefing/counselling sessions described by Charles and Curtis (1994) allow for those who feel their care has been in some way substandard to see their case notes and to air their feelings or grievances. The process of becoming formally legal may become accelerated in a proportion of these cases, and while this may not seem to be in the best interests of the health service, these sessions may in fact prevent a larger number of legal cases from being initiated. If any do become formal legal cases more quickly, then the deleterious effect of prolonged delay on the investigation of a case will be largely avoided.

Patients' versions of the truth

It should be noted that most legal actions which concern the mother must be made within three years of the event in question; this three-year limit is known as the triennium. Exceptions are cases in which the alleged injury is not immediately apparent; and cases which concern brain damaged children may be made effectively without time limit – Halle (1997) notes one such case which took 27 years to arise.

Memories can become distorted over time, and while those patients who experience a poor outcome should now in theory be given a chance to express their views (whatever they may be), all the good communication with and targeted debriefing of patients may not be enough to convince some people that they have no justified cause for complaint.

Of course, those who do have justification for their grievances are perfectly entitled to seek legal advice and, where appropriate, compensation. It will be remembered from *Chapter 7* that the success rate for litigants in this area is low; in fact much lower than that found in most personal injury litigation (cf. Fenn and Dingwall, 1989).

The recollections of staff may be as inaccurate as those of patients, but in the case of staff they usually have case records to help jog their memories. Patients are unlikely – at the time the initial allegation of negligence is made – to have contemporaneous accounts of the events in question, although having made such allegations their solicitors will usually secure access to copies of the relevant case notes. Statutory entitlement to access health records is provided by the Data Protection Act 1984, the Access to Medical Reports Act 1988, and the Access to Health Records Act 1990.

The combination of an inadequate grasp of details at the relevant time and the effect of distorted memories over a period of time may produce some strange accounts.

Recollections of conversations and explanations

This first section examines some claims in which a patient's version of events is challenged by staff. In some it is apparent that the woman has not grasped the facts of the case, perhaps because the explanation offered by staff was inadequate. In two claims the woman's seeming misunderstanding was first voiced after a visit to her GP. In one she claimed that her GP told her the placenta had been left in the uterus following caesarean section. Although she did require a 'D+C' (dilatation and curettage), no retained products of conception were found. In another case in which a swab was retained following perineal repair the woman wrote:

> (My GP) *was extremely angry about this and said that it was a wonder it did not kill me.*

In fact the level of agreed damages in this claim was not high, suggesting that, while distressing for the woman, there had been little physical damage caused. The six-week postnatal check – usually carried out by a GP – is a time for discussing events of the pregnancy or labour. Clearly the GP must have adequate information to hand so that (s)he can explain things appropriately; the dangers of inadequate explanation are clear.

Plaintiffs have also apparently misunderstood explanations by hospital staff. In one claim the plaintiff's solicitors stated:

> (The consultant) *insisted upon lecturing her that as she was a smoker her child would definitely be backward and mentally deficient which caused her great anxiety.*

Memories concerning which staff members have cared for the woman may also be poor, according to one midwife who had been involved in litigation:

> *The woman complained that she hadn't seen a consultant, that she hadn't seen any medical staff, and that she'd been discharged home still without seeing a consultant. And in actual fact the consultants had entered two episodes of care for her and documented them; also that she'd been discharged home by the consultant... So that didn't tie up for the way they were claiming.*

> (Midwife 11)

Recollections of the time of labour in particular may be affected by several factors, including exhaustion, the effects of opiate or inhalational analgesia, and the outcome of the pregnancy. It is accepted that information given to labouring women must be tailored to take account of these factors. a consultant wrote in some exasperation of one patient:

> *Mrs H complains that she was not kept fully informed, but very experienced and dedicated labour ward staff are well aware that during labour patients are not receptive to detailed information...*

The need to give sensitive and appropriate explanations is discussed in *Chapter 20*, while the requirement to document such explanations is stressed in *Chapters 4* and *14*.

Recollections of clinical events

Just as the versions of a conversation may differ, so may versions of clinical incidents and events. Many relate to the labour or delivery period, as in one case concerning a caesarean section. The writ stated that the plaintiff, 'screamed throughout the operation'. The consultant obstetrician (who was not present at the time) claimed that this could not true, since it would be:

> *Intolerable to the surgeons, anaesthetists and nursing staff.*

He also asserted that, contrary to a claim in the writ, there was no general anaesthetic given. The registrar who operated said he remembered the woman from a previous pregnancy and thought that they had a good rapport. He also said it was absolutely untrue that she complained she was in pain at any stage during the operation. In fact, she had been given intravenous thalamonal (an analgesic) after the baby had been born. It appears that this analgesia was so effective that the woman believed she had had a general anaesthetic. Since it was almost three years before the complaint was made, it is a distinct possibility that poor memory had a confounding effect in this case.

In another claim the solicitors stated:

> (In order to deliver the placenta) *we understand that Mrs C was sat upon and thereafter a rather amateurish attempt was made to remove the afterbirth itself.*

In another case the plaintiff claimed that an unsupervised student performed an episiotomy and then repaired it without anaesthetic; the records showed that a staff midwife had carried out the episiotomy, that a midwifery sister was also present, and that a registrar repaired the perineum.

The presence of case records can do much to support the actions of staff; in one case the expert noted that:

> *Mr P alleges that after his wife's waters broke... they were left alone again. This is not borne out by the case records...*

Being sat upon certainly sounds extreme. It is more probable (and this was the staff's explanation) that fundal pressure was used by a member of staff, and this was remembered afterwards as having been sat upon. A lengthy delay between event and legal notification cannot be blamed for an apparent misperception in this case (the claim was unsuccessful), since the solicitor's letter was written less than a month after the birth.

Case records are not proof *per se* of what happened: just because something is written down does not necessarily mean that it is true but, in practice, courts have relied heavily on such records, providing that they are contemporaneous and consistent with the recollections of staff members and of other documents. In one case the plaintiff claimed that after an initial hospitalisation she was discharged home, but came back a week later and insisted on readmission, which took place. The case notes did not bear this out: as planned, she was seen two weeks later for a repeat ultrasound scan and was then readmitted. In this case she had gone to see her GP five years after the events in question, and it was another five years before she consulted a solicitor. In this situation, it is small wonder that memories can be inaccurate.

It is possible that the desire to find a cause for some distressing outcome may blunt one's memories. In one case a woman sued claiming that her dyspareunia was due to her episiotomy repair (claiming the stitching was too tight) – her case records noted that she had presented with this condition six years before her first pregnancy. Memories can become distorted over time, particularly when the outcome is tragic. In one case which unfortunately resulted in a stillbirth a woman was admitted with a possible antepartum haemorrhage, which staff appeared to believe was just 'show'. The consultant wrote:

The records would suggest that her initial bleed had been of a minor nature and that there was no indication to keep her in hospital at that stage. However on subsequent discussion she... described the bleeding as having been at least an egg cup full... on review some two months later her memory of the amount of the bleeding was vastly increased and she described this as having been pints of blood that soaked her bed clothes.

The tragedy of losing her baby may have conspired to make the memories more vivid than the actual events. Questionable recollections of the amount of visible blood also formed part of another claim, in which the plaintiff alleged that, following delivery, she had been transferred to the postnatal ward 'covered completely in blood.' In another case in which a child was diagnosed as having seizures when he was four months of age, his parents initiated the complaint when he was eleven years old. The consultant paediatrician who saw the baby at this time noted:

I saw the parents repeatedly and at no time subsequently did they describe to me what they now claim happened at the child's birth.

Understandable distress at the turn of events may colour perceptions. In one case a plaintiff claimed that she had begged the obstetrician to perform a caesarean once the fetal heart rate dropped. In fact it had stopped altogether and this was confirmed by ultrasound scan, hence the consultant's refusal to carry out a caesarean. The consultant asserted that he did not speak to the husband when he came in, so the husband's claim to have begged the consultant to operate on his wife was untrue. At no point was the fetal heart rate noted to be slow: It was present and normal at the morning check, but not later that morning when further monitoring was attempted.

Just how memories and interpretations can be affected by subsequent events was shown in another claim in which the plaintiff's solicitors stated:

Our client had to be stitched after delivery and was surprised that while this was taking place Dr J decided to whistle while conducting the work. Our client did not object to this light-hearted approach at the time but unhappily it appears to demonstrate the cavalier approach of Dr J to his work.

In another claim the registrar wrote:

I went to see Mrs H early (the following morning), *and informed her that we had sutured up the uterus, and therefore she could still have more children if she wished. Somewhat emotionally she stated 'I don't want to have any more children'. I followed this with what I thought was a logical comment at the time, to dissipate her anxiety by saying if she really felt strongly about that she could always be sterilised. Unfortunately her memory of this was that I advocated she be sterilised.*

In another case in which a premature baby unfortunately developed cerebral palsy, the Summons stated:

(The plaintiff) *felt the baby starting to be born. There was no doctor present at this time. A nurse arrived, and appeared to attempt to push the child's head back into the birth canal...* (She) *thereafter required to have her vagina incised in order to facilitate the birth of the baby.*

The contradictory nature of this claim appears to escape the plaintiff's solicitors, for if the nurse (sic) was attempting to delay the delivery by 'pushing the child's head back into the birth canal', then an incision to facilitate the delivery would have been completely unnecessary if not impossible. The consultant obstetrician pointed out that controlling the delivery of the head to prevent sudden decompression is routine, and that episiotomy in the case of premature delivery is commonplace. He added:

> *Mrs N had received analgesia about two hours before the delivery which could have impaired her memory of events. I do not see how a ludicrous claim can be made that there was an attempt to push the child's head back into the birth canal. No one would contemplate such a manoeuvre – it could not be done.*

In fact there are documented instances of 'cephalic replacement' (known as the Zavanelli manoeuvre), particularly as a method of dealing with shoulder dystocia (O'Leary, 1993). It must be said that this was not the case here: the baby was premature, and weighed little more than 2 kg.

The recollection of lengths of time can vary when distress is present. One patient who was given the wrong baby to breastfeed during the night, told staff immediately that she had fed the baby for a minute. Once at home she found that the mother of the baby she inadvertently fed lived close by, and she developed an anxiety condition. In her claim she said that she had fed the baby for ten minutes and not one.

The perceived reasons for what occurs in the delivery room can also affect recollections and may be used by plaintiffs to explain subsequent developments. In one tragic case in which the baby developed cerebral palsy it was claimed that the midwife examined the woman internally and attached a fetal scalp electrode, and then ran to the sink 'heaving'. The woman was taken soon after to Theatre for a caesarean. The plaintiffs appeared to believe that something occurred during the internal examination which caused the cerebral palsy, and which was so nauseating that it also caused the midwife to vomit. It was explained that, although the midwife had no memory of running to the sink 'heaving', she was herself pregnant at the time and suffering from nausea, and that this was the more likely reason.

Patient recollections at times may clearly be inaccurate, and may be affected by several factors. In labour the ability to comprehend detailed information is generally held to be reduced; extreme tiredness and the side-effects of analgesia make perception problematic. When the issue is complicated by reinterpreting events in the light of subsequent outcomes or the distorting effects of time on memory, the scene may be set for unfortunate confrontation. One way of reducing this possibility is to offer 'debriefing' sessions to postnatal women and, where appropriate, their partners, particularly in cases where the outcome is known to be poor.

From this discussion it can be seen that a patient's recollections may be held to be inaccurate for a number of possible reasons. It ought not to be concluded that a patient's account of events will be treated automatically with suspicion, only that there is the possibility that certain confounding factors may distort perception and recall.

Practitioners' versions of the truth

Staff are not immune to many of the factors described in the first section of this chapter. Full and contemporaneous records (see *Chapter 14*) will usually provide a good indication of the course of events, and are invaluable in helping those involved to recall situations. While it is true that patients – at least initially – will not usually have contemporaneous records to aid their memories, and that staff ordinarily do, this does not necessarily mean that the memories of practitioners will be any the clearer. This section notes that the memories of staff sometimes vary. While the information presented here may not be representative of the ability of staff to recall events more generally, the evident lapses of memory indicate potentially serious difficulties in investigating allegations of negligence.

It can of course be argued that the patient herself (or her partner) may have particularly vivid memories of the time in question, and that to expect staff to remember every patient they look after is unrealistic, especially when there is a long gap between events and a legal action being raised.

The previous section also noted how memories may become distorted or at least made more vivid by knowledge of the clinical outcome. Another example makes this point:

> **Case**: An SHO sutured the perineum, but it became infected, and required resuturing and eventual reconstruction. The patient later claimed that the SHO continued stitching even when she was 'begging for analgesia'.
>
> The SHO dictated a letter to the GP immediately after suturing, because of a piece of tissue being sent for histology. He wrote, 'This delightful lady', and stated that he, '... would not have spoken in these terms had there occurred in the room the kind of conflict that Mrs H alleges. I recall her as a woman who at the time was very happy at the way she had been treated.'

Perinatal legal cases may take several years to come to light; while those affecting the patient herself will usually be governed by the statute of limitations and so must be made within three years, cases involving the child can take many years (in cases where mental incapacity is present there is effectively no time limit).

The relevant legal office will forward copies of the case records to staff in order to help their memories of the events in question, but this is not always effective. In one case the following three statements were given by midwives:

* 'I confirm that it is my handwriting in the... notes... I have no recollection of the incident.'

* 'On reading the notes... I have no recollection of the case.'

* 'Following refreshing my memory about this lady by reading her case notes I find that I remain unable to recollect this situation.'

These were all dated eighteen months after the relevant incident. In another case five midwives' statements all began with the phrase, 'I have no recollection...'; such an uncanny similarity of phrase might raise suspicions that an element of collusion was present. One midwife's entire statement was, 'I have no recollection of this particular case', which could not be faulted on grounds of brevity, but did little to clarify the course of events. This case concerned a stillbirth; seeking to explain the collective amnesia the Director of Midwifery stated:

> *Staff do not remember the lady, and there have been 38 stillbirths* (in the 30 months since).

A prolonged delay between an event and the initiation of a legal action clearly cannot help. As noted in *Chapter 15*, many cases were brought just before the expiry of the triennium (the three-year limit by which time most personal injury litigation must be initiated). One claim, made 35 months after the birth, alleged that a failed forceps delivery had caused a baby's squint. The midwife's statement read:

> *On reading the notes... I see I was present... I have no recollection of this patient and cannot comment further.*

A slightly more helpful (and typical) instance of staff recollections occurred in a case concerning extensive perineal trauma; there was a gap of sixteen months between the relevant time and the requests for statements being made. There were statements made by two midwives:

* 'I have no recollection of this lady. I have made my statement entirely from my entries in the midwifery notes.'

* 'I have little recollection of Mrs C, but on reading the case notes I recognise my handwriting and signature.'

While the quality of the staff's actual recollections are little different in this case, they appear to have been more prepared to provide the legal office with an account of events based upon their respective case note entries.

When the case notes themselves are lacking in detail (or even lacking any entries whatsoever), the legal debate may centre on what a patient will usually be told in certain circumstances. In one case concerning information given at an antenatal clinic, the registrar wrote:

> *I must state that it is impossible to recollect exactly what was said over 15 months ago, but virtually the same things are repeated to patients undergoing that test. It is not practice and is not possible to write down in the case notes everything a patient is told in the clinic, so I would imagine that the answers to your questions cannot always be supported by what is written down in the notes.*

While it is unreasonable to expect every single piece of information given to a pregnant woman to be noted down in her case notes, there were times when the lack of such a record adversely affected the defence's case.

Antagonism can occur when the recollections of staff and patient differ markedly, as in this case concerning a waterbirth (the relevant times have been altered, but the length of time between events is accurate):

> **Case**: The woman claimed she had an urge to bear down at 11.15 while in the pool; she requested pain relief, got out, was given opiate analgesia, was then examined a few minutes later, with the baby being born minutes after.
>
> The midwife asserted that she examined the woman at 9.45, gave her analgesia at 10.15, and said she only got out of the pool at 10.45, with the baby being born at 11.09.

In such circumstances the courts are likely to favour the defence in terms of deciding relevant times if the case notes are both clear and consistent with other documents. Times given in entries in the labour ward delivery and controlled drugs registers would clearly be of particular importance in such a case.

It should not be assumed that staff are never able to recollect patients or events. One midwife described her memories with a representative from the legal department:

> *I remember the case vividly, it's the worst night I ever spent... My midwife's sixth sense told me there was a sick baby who should be got out as soon as possible... a junior doctor assessed her as fully dilated, but she wasn't... after I took over the CTG trace was rotten.... there were other signs of fetal distress, like meconium staining, and the fetal blood gases were borderline rather than reassuring...*

This vivid description illustrates the clarity with which staff may remember particular events (in this case it was 16 months between the relevant date and the action being raised). Whether or not their recall is judged to be accurate will depend on the evidence presented: courts have not always accepted the claims made by staff. Easterbrook (1996) notes that in *Parry v North West Surrey HA* the court rejected the claims made by the doctor and midwife as being untrue, also rejecting the testimony of the midwifery expert.

It is unrealistic to expect practitioners to remember details about events which occurred many months or years earlier; recollections can only be helped by full and detailed contemporaneous documentation. While many staff appear to believe their standard of documentation is high, the prevalence of inadequate clinical records (Cetrulo and Cetrulo, 1989; James, 1991) in legal cases indicates that this is not always the case.

Conclusion

When allegations of negligence are made, a retrospective enquiry will aim to establish the course of the events in question. Staff recollections are essential in trying to do this, but they have on occasion been distinctly poor. Although it is unreasonable to expect staff to remember all the patients with whom they have contact, certain cases of collective amnesia strain the credulity. Clear and detailed case records will often do much to help staff to recall both a particular patient and a specific sequence of events.

Patients will not usually have their own record of events, although access to health records is now much speedier. There may be a need to explain entries in the case notes: poor handwriting, and the use of jargon or technological terms may be baffling to the lay person. Sensitive explanations, carried out as soon as possible, may do much to clarify the events in question. This may help to prevent the sort of apparent misapprehensions noted in the first section of this chapter. However, one of the most important factors associated with inaccurate recall is the length of time between the event and subsequent legal notification. This is something largely beyond the control of the health service, although a well publicised 'complaints and explanations' service may go some way towards improving this.

Chapter 23

W Where next?

Throughout this book a number of criticisms concerning the process and conduct of litigation have been aired. These are wide-ranging, including references to the need to establish fault (*Chapter 6*); difficulties with the legal process, especially causation (*Chapter 12*) and the delays involved (*Chapter 15*); and a lack of the necessary experience on the part of some plaintiff solicitors (*Chapter 25*). Arising out of these and other issues there has been a broad debate about the merits and failings of the current system. Several different suggestions have been made as to how to improve matters. This chapter briefly summarises the debate about the current system, and then discusses some of the suggested alternatives.

Problems

Establishing fault

Medical negligence litigation is part of the civil law of 'personal injury'. A plaintiff can only succeed if it is admitted (or can be shown) that a practitioner has been guilty of negligence and that damage has resulted from this. The need to prove fault was examined in *Chapter 6*, and it will be remembered that there has been some debate about whether a fault-based system is the best way of deciding who should receive compensation. The pressure group Action for Victims of Medical Accidents (AVMA) stresses that accountability is the key and that a strict no-fault system, while superficially attractive in that it would allow compensation for a greater number of people, would not be adequate unless it also addressed the matter of accountability. Their proposed mechanism is a specific review process:

> *As an organisation we're committed to putting in an inspectorate... It has to be an inspectorate with reasonable teeth. You get the impression that* (doctors) *they would get away with a hell of a lot more if they could; you have some very cavalier doctors out there; certainly in obstetrics... We're totally opposed to no-fault compensation: if you took away that – albeit not terribly useful – element of accountability, they wouldn't worry at all. You wonder what* (particularly consultant) *obstetricians would feel they could get away with.*

(AVMA official 1)

It would not be surprising to find few in the medical profession agreeing with such sentiments. In *Chapter 9* a medical director and a consultant obstetrician expressed the view that doctors are themselves distressed when things do not go well (*pp.87–88*). Litigation, they felt, was not a good instrument for improving things. However, Fenn and Whelan (1989) claim that it may have some advantages – the fear of litigation may encourage hospitals to employ more doctors and so avoid the mistakes that become inevitable when staff work long shifts (particularly when doing 'on call'). The fear of litigation may also induce greater vigilance on the part of practitioners, and it is possible that 'defensive' practices (examined in *Chapter 4*) may be safer, although this view is specifically rebutted by DeKay and Asch (1998). Hupert *et al* (1996: 7), in explaining how the adversarial legal system militates against such positive lessons, cite an internist in a survey of physicians who claimed that,

'You don't improve health care by punishing people.'

Fenn (1993) notes that removing the need to establish fault can also be said to remove a potentially important source of information about the standard of clinical practice. However, he goes on to caution that, 'This is not to maintain that the fear of litigation is a significant factor in helping to maintain standards of medical practice: that is clearly untenable' (*ibid*:104). The BMA (1987) pointed out that relying on establishing fault may mean that similar cases of injury will be treated quite differently. For example, a child with brain damage due to encephalitis will get no compensation; a child whose brain damage is due to vaccine damage may get £20,000; and a child who is brain damaged due to negligence during delivery may get hundreds of thousands (or even millions) of pounds. The inherent unfairness of such widely differing amounts of compensation led one consultant to comment:

> *I don't think it's fair on patients... who have unfortunate outcomes, that they have to prove negligence in order to claim pay-outs... You would think that there should be some system where you do have a cerebral* (palsy) *case that there is some form of help available.*

> (Consultant obstetrician 2)

In theory there is help available for those in this position in the form of state benefits and NHS-funded care. The very fact that claims that establish negligence may secure large amounts in compensation (Dyer [1998] cites one claim which received £3.3m) indicates that state provision is not comprehensive.

Central to the theory of a fault-based system is the notion that someone who is deemed to have been at fault is held to account. This theory is reduced in health care by the presence of insurance liability (which almost all practitioners have) as well as the vicarious liability of the employer. Not having such insurance – while theoretically placing a practitioner in a position of unqualified accountability – is in practice a serious impediment, as independent midwives have found to their cost (cf. Challans, 1996):

> *If I had indemnity insurance then I would be quite happy to look after somebody, no matter what... not having indemnity insurance puts you in a very awkward situation.*

> (Independent midwife)

Practitioners may proudly assert their accountability, but few would want that accountability not to be cushioned by indemnity insurance as no practitioner could afford to pay the legal costs and damages of a successful negligence claim concerning cerebral palsy.

Establishing causation

A plaintiff must show not only that a practitioner was at fault, but that this fault directly caused damage. Foster (1996: 1098) notes that, 'Expensively proved breaches of duty are of course worth nothing at all unless they can be linked to loss of a type recognised by the law of tort.' Several examples of legal cases where this causal connection could not be established were cited in *Chapter 12*, and causation remains a contentious issue. It might be claimed that difficulties with establishing causation favour the defence in medical claims:

> *When I think 'What am I going to win on?' I think causation is probably the very first thing I would think about, because that is difficult for a* (plaintiff)...

> (Queen's Counsel)

By the very nature of some medical conditions it may be difficult (if not impossible) to define the exact origin of the condition. While this would not apply to claims regarding perineal trauma following delivery, claims regarding cerebral palsy have often failed at this hurdle. The precise aetiology of this condition is not yet fully understood.

Causation is decided on the balance of probabilities. This 'threshold requirement' leads to an 'all-or-nothing' decision, a feature of the law that one senior solicitor believed is poorly understood:

> *Where* (doctors) *have real problems is in causation. They really do, because they're trained, I suppose, scientifically to regard causation as a 100% requirement, whereas we deal with the balance of probabilities.*

(Defence solicitor 1)

The balance of probabilities is of course 'more than half': if it is held that the likelihood of a condition being caused by a specific event is 49%, the claim will fail, whereas if the likelihood rises to 51% the claim will succeed.

A number of suggestions have been made regarding the applicability of this 'threshold requirement'. The concept of a 'material contribution to the harm' was posited in one case (Wardlaw [1956]); and in another (McGhee [1972]) the House of Lords held that a 'material increase in risk of harm' was 'equivalent to a material contribution to the harm.' However these cases concerned multiple possible causes of a disability, and an attempt to develop such approaches received a set back in a later case (Hotson [1987]). The trial judge had held that the loss of a 25% chance of recovery justified awarding 25% of the damages which would have been awarded had the defendant's negligence been the sole cause of the disability. Although this decision was upheld in the Court of Appeal, the House of Lords ruled that to succeed the plaintiff had to show causation on a balance of probabilities. This approach was also followed in (Wilsher [1986]) in which a newborn baby's blindness was believed to have had five possible causes including negligently administered excess oxygen. The Court of Appeal held that the excess oxygen materially increased the risk of harm, and at this stage the claim succeeded on this ground; however, this decision was unanimously reversed in the House of Lords.

A recent Court of Appeal case (Bolitho [1997]), which subsequently went to the House of Lords (see 'The Bolam test' below), saw the question of causation debated at length. Central to this argument was the applicability of the 'Bolam test', which has been used for forty years in England to decide questions of negligence.

The Bolam test

The legal test in England and Wales by which a practitioner's actions are judged is known as the Bolam test; in Scotland the equivalent is *Hunter v Hanley*. The two definitions of medical negligence are not identical, and there is a view that holds that the test for establishing negligence in Scotland is that much harder (Howie, 1983). By and large, the two judgements are considered to approach the question of clinical culpability in the same way. The Bolam test holds that a practitioner's actions are safe as long as they are in accordance with a responsible body of medical opinion (and in this discussion the term 'medical' covers the field of midwifery).

The Bolam approach is sometimes characterised unflatteringly as 'The doctor's friend'; the argument being that if a doctor (or other health care professional) can find colleagues who are deemed to be responsible to say that they would have acted in the same way, then negligence cannot be established. Goldrein (1994, 1237) notes that the Bolam test, 'was nothing more than part of the summing up to a lay jury,' and he goes on to characterise it as out-of-date: 'The Bolam test has remained unaltered from the time before Russia launched a Sputnik, unaltered since the era before electronic calculators, fuel injected turbo charged car engines, dish washers and hi-fi equipment. Is it a medico-legal Jurassic Park – or is it a "truth" which for ever we should hold "self-evident"?' (*ibid*:1238).

The view that the Bolam test is out-dated was made by one interviewee:

> *We are very keen that something is put in place of Bolam. It's been there since 1957... You have, if the judge wants it, a very easy 'Get out'... There's no onus on the defence expert to go out and bring in research papers or anything to back up this nebulous bunch of people who are out there that might be reasonable... It's an easy 'Get out' for the judge really.*

(AVMA official 1)

Phillips (1997: 20) notes that , 'Australian law may be setting an example in asserting the primacy of the court's view of acceptable practice, diminishing the impact of common practice, in the recent decision in *Rogers v Whitaker*.' This approach was not viewed with any enthusiasm by one senior defence lawyer:

> *We're approaching a stage where the court will decide what is reasonable or not... It worries me if courts are allowed to do that. It's all very well if you've got implicit faith in your judges...*

(Defence solicitor 2)

The 'reasonableness' test has indeed been subjected to greater scrutiny more recently. In the House of Lords the Bolitho case still did not succeed, but the 'Bolam test' appeared to be qualified: 'It is only where a judge can be satisfied that the body of expert opinion cannot be logically supported at all that such opinion will not provide the bench mark by reference to which the defendant's conduct falls to be assessed' (Bolitho [1997], per Lord Browne-Wilkinson @10).

While the terms 'reasonable' and 'responsible' have been used in judgements 'to describe a body of opinion which would qualify as a successful defence' (Scott, 1998: 64), the emphasis is now on this reasonableness being obvious to the lay person. No longer will the court take on trust the word of even an eminent expert if his or her argument is not clear to the court. As such, the right of doctors and midwives to determine what a reasonably competent practitioner ought to do or know is qualified. This may make defending allegations of negligence much harder, and it may be assumed that moves to challenge the authoritative position enjoyed up to now by health professionals will be resisted.

Solutions

A number of problems have been identified. Not unexpectedly, a number of solutions have been suggested, including: appeals for more openness on the part of the health service, particularly with regard to giving explanations and allowing access to case notes; procedural changes to speed up the assessment of each case; changes in the way Trusts deal with the financial side of litigation; attempts to encourage arbitration or mediation as an alternative to formal litigation; and the introduction of juries to determine claims.

Openness

Beech (1990) claims that women seeking to find out what happened in their pregnancy or labour typically encounter obstructiveness on the part of hospitals, and advocates immediate access to case notes. In theory this right already exists (under the Access to Personal Files Act 1987; the Access to Medical Reports Act 1988; and the Access to Health Records Act 1990). Despite these theoretical rights, she claims that:

> *Far too many medical negligence cases involve 'loss of evidence', alterations to the case notes, and lying in court in order to protect the hospital or their colleagues* (and sometimes themselves). *It is time that action was taken to charge those involved with perjury... until the injustice of health authority representatives lying and covering up is properly dealt with there should be no discussion of no-fault compensation...* (since) *it will not produce answers,* (although) *it may well produce a smug satisfaction in some quarters, and the hope that people can be bought off and will stop complaining.*
>
> (Beech 1990: 3).

While it may be hoped that since this was written, defendants are more willing to provide copies of the case notes, securing access is apparently not always easy:

> *What we're finding now is that women are not being refused access to records, but things aren't always made easy for them. There's often a payment of at least £10 plus photocopying; sometimes it's quite high for a woman on a low income. Most women are being asked to go into the hospital and go through the case notes with a professional before they take them away, and for some women that's very distressing. They don't want to go back to the hospital, or they don't want to see a professional at that point.*
>
> (Consumer group representative)

Some concern has been expressed at handing case notes over to women or their families without ensuring that adequate explanations of entries are given at the same time. The scope for misunderstanding clinical entries is great, particularly when abbreviations and initials are used (Dimond, 1998b). Even without abbreviations, clinical entries may be difficult to decipher because of technical language or poor handwriting, and an impartial professional or consumer representative may be useful in helping the woman to understand the case notes. Arranging a neutral venue for this initial explanation of clinical records may avoid the evident distress to some women caused by revisiting the place where they presumably believe some trauma (physical or emotional) has occurred. However, it is imperative that such openness exists, for, as Lord Woolf (1997: 265) notes, 'when complaints are met by silence, it is not surprising that patients think the worst.'

Modifying the legal process

The legal process is often lengthy and slow, and a number of modifications have been tried over the years. An attempt to accelerate the process of relatively inexpensive medical negligence claims was started in 1996 (Dyer, 1996). Claims for less than £10,000 were eligible under this pilot scheme, and while this would include some perinatal claims (see *Chapter 17*) this would not encompass claims concerning cerebral palsy. Legal costs – that can mount up and become very significant – were fixed under this scheme.

Another method of speeding up the legal process may be for each side to use the services of the same clinical expert (Clothier, 1989). This would reduce expense (one expert's fee rather than two), and avoid the differences of opinion between different experts which make negotiations more protracted, heightening antagonisms between the respective sides. An expert ought to be impartial, and disinterested as to the outcome of the case, and as such the expert report ought to be entirely objective (see *Chapter 5*). It might be thought that an objective expert report is an ideal method of determining a case, but the value of having the expert cross-examined has been asserted by one commentator (Puxon, 1996a). She notes that a very senior expert in one court case was moved to concede rather more under cross examination than he had in his initial report, which had been submitted for the defence, and for this she praised him: 'He thus showed true independence, as every expert should... unhappily there are still too many experts who go into the witness box as champions of one side or the other, leaving their independence of mind at the door of the court' (*ibid*: 107).

Lord Woolf, in his Access to Justice report (Woolf, 1996), has made use of some of the above suggestions. One of his principal conclusions is that judges should become 'case managers'. For this they need to become much more specialist – just as the 'Jack of all trades' solicitor should not become involved in medical claims (see *Chapter 25*), so judges will need extra training to be able to understand some of the complex issues at stake. Under the Woolf proposals it may be possible to appoint a single joint expert if there is no medical controversy in the claim. Such a move would require a degree of co-operation between the parties, something that is explored in the section, 'Arbitration/ mediation' (*overleaf*).

The Woolf proposals aim to speed up what is acknowledged to be a slow process. A Clinical Disputes Forum could act as a screening process which would prevent non-meritorious claims from getting as far as formal litigation. In theory this will help to prevent the system becoming clogged up with claims that will almost certainly fail. A 'small claims' process (for claims worth less than £5,000) and a 'fast-track' process for claims whose financial value is not considered to be more than £15,000 are available. In both of these the defence has a requirement to respond quickly, and there is a fear that some patients will use this to 'ambush' the defence:

> *If the plaintiff has got competent solicitors they've got their case all done and dusted before we even know much about it, and then we're going to be running like the clappers trying to get witness statements and expert reports to an impossibly short timetable.*

(Legal department official)

In the interests of justice both sides must have time to investigate events. Ideally, there will be collaboration and the investigation will be a joint one.

Financial arrangements

The cost of litigation can be extremely high, and most (if not all) successful plaintiffs have been supported by Legal Aid. Concern about the mounting cost of Legal Aid has led to restrictions on its availability (Montgomery, 1997), and as of October 1999 Legal Aid has no longer been available for routine personal injury claims. The way around this is to allow solicitors to negotiate conditional fee arrangements (CFAs) with their clients, by which the solicitor will receive a percentage of an award if the claim is successful. There is a danger that lawyers will only take on those claims that look certain to be successful, leaving most potential claims unfunded. Brahams (1999: 1) notes that: 'Lawyers, like plumbers, doctors and accountants, prefer to be paid for work they have actually done rather than on condition of success so that they can pay their gas and electricity bills... .' Even if 'fast track' claims are successful, the costs recoverable are limited to 25% of the damages recovered, a maximum of £3,750. For barristers the share of the fee is limited to 10% of the award, as a result of which, claims Foster (1999: 10), '... only very lucrative medical negligence cases are going to be litigated at all. Many badly injured plaintiffs with cases as near rock-solid as medical negligence cases get, are going to get nothing'. This hardly chimes with the notion of 'access to justice'.

If potential plaintiffs face financial concerns, so do those on the receiving end of claims. *Chapter 17* noted the amounts paid in compensation, and the total amount this is believed to cost the health service. Attempts to improve things from the NHS's point of view have been the introduction of new arrangements for reimbursing Trusts in Scotland (Scottish Office, 1993), and in England with the setting up of the Clinical Negligence Scheme for Trusts (CNST) and the NHS Litigation Special Authority (NHSLA) in 1995; the CNST now falls within the authority of the NHSLA. While this approach does not change the essential nature of the way the law operates, it aims to help Trusts spread the cost of payments for large damages actions. Effectively an insurance scheme, it requires Trusts to classify legal actions according to their likely financial impact. The data that must be provided in order to secure reimbursement will eventually allow for a degree of audit into the incidence of litigation, but it will be some time before meaningful data are available. Since membership of the CNST is not mandatory, the picture that emerges may be unrepresentative. The NHSLA does plan to introduce 'league tables' in due course.

'Lump sum' damages payments may be replaced by structured settlements, in which financial compensation is paid periodically (Ashcroft, 1996). This is to avoid the situation encountered in one recent case (Calladine), in which a child with cerebral palsy died unexpectedly just a week after her parents were awarded £700,000 by the High Court. Following the child's death, the Health Authority announced that it would appeal against the settlement (Anon, 1997c).

The anticipation of the scale of litigation (and consequent damages payments) has been criticised by Fenn and Dingwall (1995) who believe that the situation is not as bad as many Trusts appear to believe. They claim that in over-estimating the scale, Trusts are allocating too much of their finances to the new scheme, so reducing the amount of money which goes to direct patient care.

Arbitration/mediation

Such solutions have been advocated for some time. Clothier (then the Health Services Commissioner) suggested a Clinical Judgement Review Board which would act as an arbiter of cases more than ten years ago (Clothier, 1989). In 1991 a Department of Health consultative memorandum (DoH, 1991) suggested the possibility of setting up arbitration panels that would deliberate on cases concerning alleged negligence. The panel would consist of two doctors (one nominated by each side), and a lawyer skilled in medical negligence work; it would work on paper, and have access to case notes and hospital records. Oral submissions would be unlikely, and (it being an English proposal) the Bolam test for medical negligence would be applied. Where there was not unanimity in panel decisions, a majority would suffice, with the lawyer's views carrying greater weight on legal issues. The speed and relative informality of this system were intended to benefit all sides; however, Capstick *et al* (1991: 232) claim that while a specialist panel may appear attractive, it may become 'an arbiter of... practice instead of deciding the issue of liability.' It is unlikely that many practitioners would welcome such a small panel determining standards of care.

Lord Woolf's report has strongly backed the use of mediation (Woolf, 1996). Now commonly used in divorce cases and small scale disputes (such as those between neighbours), it has been introduced to address 'patient grievances' (Saulo and Wagener, 1996). Mediation should avoid the adversarial nature of the tort/delict system. Genn (1999) notes that people who opt for mediation do so in order to avoid confrontation, and in the hope that settling the dispute will be less expensive and less time-consuming. However, faster dispute resolution may not always be what is required:

> (Woolf) *should also put the screws on the plaintiff solicitors... Inordinate delay is not in the interests of either side – or justice. On the other hand, inordinate speed may not be in the interests of justice either. If neither side has got the time to make a proper assessment and get the expert reports and the counsel advice that is needed, then the balance of justice gets skewed again.*

(Legal department official)

A pilot study co-ordinated by the Oxford Centre for Medical Risk Studies, and funded by a number of hospital Trusts, aims to introduce mediation into medical accident or negligence cases, with a neutral third party acting as a go-between. Backing this move, Desmond, secretary of the Personal Injury Lawyers Group, claimed 'The whole thing creates tremendous potential for settling medical negligence claims before they get priced out of all sense of reality' (cited by Dyer, 1995: 770).

Juries

In the USA juries are used to determine medical negligence claims (see *Chapter 21, pp. 174–175*). While there have been few calls for this aspect of North American law to be introduced in Britain, this debate shadows calls for greater openness in such matters. In theory, the jury will bring a sense of fair-mindedness and objectivity to the proceedings, although recent publicity about miscarriages of justice may cast doubt on the wisdom of having a complex case decided by untrained lay people. One solicitor commented:

> *The* (defence) *will fight tooth and nail, as you know, not to have a jury trial, and I thought it had been pretty well accepted by judges that medical cases were too complex... I have never known a medical negligence jury trial in my 25 years.*

(Defence solicitor 1)

Juries, indeed, have come in for much criticism. While it is theoretically possible for a plaintiff to seek a jury trial, such a development was viewed with concern by another interviewee:

> *If anyone ever attempted to get a case before a jury in a medical case we would oppose it as strongly as we could. We have done in the past. We have got a Sheriff court decision that indicated that these are considered to be too complex. A jury would be more likely to decide for a pursuer, particularly in an emotive medical case, without really considering the main issues. With all respect to the ordinary man in the street that's the way it would work.*

(Defence solicitor 2)

In deciding levels of compensation, a judge will be guided by decisions in similar cases. Juries may not feel bound by this – in British libel cases the amounts awarded by juries have varied hugely. Another lawyer commented on this rather vague approach:

> *I suppose they may subconsciously either be punitive to the doctor who has caused it* (a condition) *or sympathetic to the doctor. I don't know. Jury awards introduce... a sort of uncertainty into the process which is always disconcerting.*

(Queen's Counsel)

Conclusion

Procedural and organisational changes seek to mitigate some of the deficiencies of the legal system: they do not fundamentally alter the way in which the law operates. Some of these changes have come about, partly in response to criticism from consumer groups. There is now a much greater openness in terms of rights of access to clinical records than was the case ten or fifteen years ago, and while there are still those who reproach the health service in this matter, considerable progress has been made. Other procedural features, such as mediation, have been piloted, but have yet to be fully evaluated. There are those who claim that these modest proposals are not enough, and perhaps the most radical suggested alternative to medical negligence law, no-fault compensation, was considered in *Chapter 6* (*pp. 61–65*). The pressure behind such calls has diminished in recent years and where we go from here is not clear. The changes that have been inaugurated, particularly following Lord Woolf's report, have yet to be evaluated.

Chapter 24

X   X-border differences

A Scotsman is quite as foreign as an Australian,
and I can't say fairer than that.

(Rushton, 1975)

Cross-border differences have received a great deal of attention in recent months and years. The re-establishment of the Scots parliament in 1999 under the devolution settlement highlighted the sometimes disparate nature of politics in Scotland and England. The British identity has been called into question, and it cannot be assumed that there is necessarily a common viewpoint or experience between the two countries. As noted in the introduction, most of the research reported here took place in Scotland. Some, however, was based in England, and it became clear that there were a number of perceptible differences between the situation in Scotland and that in England. In the light of the developing relationship between Scotland and England, the tendency to assume that research concerning one area of Britain will inevitably apply in another should be questioned.

The first feature to note is that the legal systems of Scotland and England are (and have always been) distinct. The Act of Union of 1707, despite proroguing the Scottish parliament, guaranteed the autonomy of the Scottish judicial system. With the restoration of a national parliament in Edinburgh in 1999, there is even greater potential for cross border differences to emerge.

That English law and lawyers have not always appreciated the distinctions of the Scottish system is apparent. Referring to the Scots law practice of using a married woman's maiden name (as well as her married name) in the papers relating to the action, Wilson (1984: 4) notes that, 'English judges and textbook writers have never quite grasped the system...' In perinatal litigation this could clearly cause confusion, as a large proportion of plaintiffs/pursuers will be married women.

Legal differences

Textbooks concerning medical law have often skipped over cross-border distinctions. In *The Legal Aspects of Midwifery*, Dimond (1994a: 115), in referring to medical negligence litigation, states that 'the courts use a test known as the "Bolam test" to determine the standard expected from professionals.' Montgomery (1997: 169) in *Health Care Law* notes that this standard, 'was established in a case in 1957 called *Bolam v Friern HMC*.' Neither these nor other standard texts such as McHale and Fox (1997) are wrong in as much as they refer to the situation in England. An honourable exception is Mason and McCall Smith's *Law and Medical Ethics* (1999). However, those north of the border purchasing most of these standard texts are misled, since Scots law looks to the slightly earlier case of *Hunter v Hanley* (from 1955). The judgement in this case was given by Lord President Clyde:

> *The true test for establishing negligence on the part of a doctor is whether he has been proven to be guilty of such failure as no doctor of ordinary skill would be guilty of if acting with ordinary care... it must be established that the course the doctor adopted is one which no professional man of ordinary skill would have taken if he had been acting with ordinary care.*

While this position was specifically reaffirmed by Lord Scarman in the House of Lords in the case of Maynard in 1984, Bolam, which followed two years later, has become the test in English courts. In Bolam the definition of medical negligence was laid down by Mr Justice McNair:

> *... the test as to whether there has been negligence or not is... the standard of the ordinary skilled man exercising or professing to have that special skill... He is not guilty of negligence if he has acted with a practice accepted as proper by a responsible body of medical men skilled in that particular art.*

There is a debate about whether or not Bolam has outlived its usefulness (see *Chapter 23, pp. 192–193*). Accepting for now that Bolam and *Hunter v Hanley* remain the tests, the question arises as to whether or not they are the same. Howie (1983) points out that in Scotland the test for negligence (per *Hunter v Hanley*) is that no doctor of ordinary skill would have acted in the way alleged; in England the Bolam principle holds that the act is safe as long as it is in accordance with a responsible body of opinion. In other words, he is claiming that the test in Scotland is tougher than in England.

Another (anonymous) writer echoes this point (Anon, 1990: 326): (s)he notes that while Lord Scarman said in the case of Maynard, 'I do not think that the words of Lord President Clyde in *Hunter v Hanley* can be bettered,' in the later case of Sidaway he referred to Bolam in detail, and tried to equate Scots law with Bolam principles. As the two are not exactly the same, this commentator claims that the law in England is 'in an unsatisfactorily fluid state.' It must be said that this distinction is not a problem which seems to have troubled most writers or judges since the two respective judgements, although, as noted earlier, the applicability of the Bolam test has recently been criticised.

The incidence and nature of litigation

Appendix II details the incidence of perinatal claims throughout Scotland and in two English areas. While it is not known how representative the English data are of England as a whole, there is no particular reason to think that they do not reflect the situation elsewhere. Figures *Appendix II.1* and *Appendix II.2 (pp. 243–244)* demonstrate a similar pattern between the two countries in terms of the increasing and then diminishing incidence of litigation. However, *Table Appendix II.1 (p. 246)* shows that the first English area (for which comprehensive data were available) was prominent in terms of having a high rate of litigation compared with the Scottish health boards. The rate in both the English areas from 1988–91 (when claims about a 'litigation crisis' were in the media) was as high as the Scottish areas with the highest rates. If it is accepted that these English areas are not atypical, this suggests that litigation is more of a concern for England than for Scotland.

As well as an apparently higher rate of litigation, there was one distinctive difference in the reason for suing in the English files: of 117 separate heads of claim in the 108 files, 56 related to CNS damage. At 48% of all English claims, this was far higher than the 21% of Scottish claim which concerned CNS damage. The rate of success for plaintiffs under this head of claim (at 25%) was slightly higher than the rate in Scotland (20%). The overall rate of success of English claims (34%) was much higher than the overall rate in Scotland (25%). Another distinction, as noted in *Chapter 17*, is the scale of damages which is believed to be far lower in Scotland. In part this reflects – according to one interviewee – the expertise of the Central Legal Office (CLO) in Edinburgh, although the lack of expertise of pursuer solicitors may also play a part (see *opposite*)

In England there is no central body which organises the defence of allegations of negligence, although the Central Negligence Scheme for Trusts (CNST) will in time acquire considerable data about the scale and nature of litigation. Trusts who join the scheme will be expected to provide claims data, but there are concerns that this may be incomplete, as there is no legal obligation to do so. Another concern is that the CNST, since it has no financial interest in the claim, may be obliged to reveal certain details under rules concerning civil disclosure. Information about successfully defended actions, or those whose level of damages (if the plaintiffs were to win) is not high, may not always be reported. Because of this it may not know of all successfully defended actions, and so the overall scale of litigation in England may not be apparent. By contrast, the effective monopoly of the CLO (for as long as it lasts) will allow it to collate comprehensive data.

Legal side-effects

The apparently lower incidence of litigation in Scotland (even given its much lower population) seems to have had some effect on the way litigation is organised. One interviewee claimed:

> *You have to say that the lawyers aren't as organised, there's no doubt about it. In Scotland they're not as organised... Overall I don't think the lawyers are as specialised or as organised as they are down here for medical negligence.*

(AVMA official 1)

The reason for this lack of experience or skill in medical litigation was given by another interviewee:

> *We're a smaller country and we have a smaller throughput of cases and therefore a small number of high value cases which make it worthwhile spending a lot of time. I'm pretty sceptical about the claim that Scots lawyers should be specialists in the English sense of specialism of doing only a fairly narrow sort of case.*

(Queen's Counsel)

A solicitor specialising in defence work agreed:

> *It's difficult to specialise in medical negligence if you are a pursuer solicitor. You don't get the cases, and that's the real difference, I suppose, between England and Scotland. There isn't the opportunity to specialise so much...*

(Defence solicitor 1)

The fact that the Central Legal Office is (to use Galanter's phrase) a 'repeat player', so acquiring considerable experience and expertise over the years, may help to explain why the success rate for pursuers in Scotland appears to be lower than that for plaintiffs in England. Not only is there a lack of suitably experienced solicitors (see *Chapter 25*) prepared to act for dissatisfied patients, but there is also a lack of other individuals who are essential for a claim to be successful.

> *A lot of the Scottish lawyers come down to England for experts, but that's quite difficult, because they've got to put an English expert in court, and the judge is going to say 'Where's the good Scottish expert? Why did you have to get this bloke from England?' It's a bit like us importing an American expert here: it would not go down well. The judge's initial view is 'They've had to go to wherever it is to get an expert, they couldn't get someone from here to back up their case.'*

(AVMA official 1)

It may be that, within a relatively small medical establishment (such as exists in Scotland), there is a reluctance to sit in judgement on one's colleagues. Symonds (1992: 3) reminds us that, 'the dividing line between success and disaster can be very narrow, and there is a corresponding reluctance to sit in judgement.' This point was echoed by one of the obstetricians interviewed:

> *We understand... that one of the problems with litigation is criticising your colleagues, and we try not to do that.*

(Obstetric registrar)

These factors appear to be to the disadvantage of people in Scotland who feel that they have a grievance, despite the fact that there are some who wish to push things along. The AVMA official continued:

> *In Scotland we've had a few false dawns. We've got a Scottish lawyers support group, but the... number of people who really are going to put any amount of commitment in is very small.*

(AVMA official 1)

There would appear to be some significant differences in the experience of litigation in Scotland. Some of the possible reasons for these are now considered.

Differing perceptions?

From the preceding section it may be concluded that Scottish maternity care is less prone to litigation than its southern counterpart. This may be due to a number of factors, including (and according to one's taste) a better standard of care; a reluctance on the part of the public to instigate litigation; a lack of the necessary expertise available to those who do sue; or simply what amounts to a conspiracy to prevent people from suing. Some of the interviewees who work with those who have experienced poor outcomes had strong views about this:

> *There is an unwillingness to challenge medical opinion... Mary Cronk says that women in Scotland do what they're told. That's not my experience... but perhaps there is an underlying feeling there.*

(Consumer group representative)

> *I think in Scotland... still there is a great deal of resistance to actually believing that the hospital had done something badly wrong. I think that your hospitals and your doctors are seen in quite a decent light. In England we're slightly more ready and willing to suggest that something might have gone wrong.*

(AVMA official 1)

This view suggests that Scotland can be thought of as a more paternalistic society, in which people (or perhaps women in particular) feel less willing to take on the medical establishment, or less confident about their chances if they do so. A senior lecturer echoed this view about an apparently paternalistic society:

I think the Scots have particularly a feeling of duty of care, and they feel responsible for what they're doing or how they're working. They feel responsible for their client.

(Midwifery lecturer)

This paternalistic relationship is not only to be found (allegedly) between health care professionals and women using the maternity services, but also (apparently) between doctors and midwives. In the postal survey one Scottish midwife spoke of how the midwife-run unit (MRU) in which she worked was:

... heavily dominated by medical staff. As a midwife I feel frustrated by the way medics dictate to us, and they consider the MRU as being tolerated and have a resentful attitude if we refer a case to them. I have worked in London and in Europe as a midwife, and in London midwives have a much higher status and extended role. I think Scotland's medical establishment does not recognise the potential of midwives and therefore we as a profession do not stand up against this due to fear of confrontation, and increasingly litigation.

Questioned about this apparent difference in relationships during a follow-up interview, this midwife stated:

In London you're treated as a practitioner. Up here you're almost like an obstetric nurse. Your skills as a practitioner aren't acknowledged.

(Midwife 9)

The debate about doctor-midwife relationships has been the subject of research in both England (Robinson *et al,* 1983) and Scotland (Askham and Barbour, 1987). Cross-border differences in such relationships were also evident in a 'matched pairs' analysis of views reported in the postal survey. In this, midwives based in Scotland and England were 'matched' in pairs by grade, length of experience, size of unit and area of work. As the English sample was much smaller it was taken as a base, and matching pairs for each respondent were sought from within the Scottish sample. The sample of obstetric respondents was small and a similar analysis was not possible, although cross-border distinctions did emerge. One of these related to the scope given to midwives: whereas 71% of the English respondents said that midwives in their unit were always given full responsibility when managing the labour of a woman deemed to be low risk, only 29% of the Scottish respondents did so. This large difference was also found in the midwifery matched pairs trial: almost twice as many in the English sub-sample said they were always given such responsibility (122 compared with 66). Why there should be such a marked difference in the perceived role and responsibility of the midwife (among both obstetricians and midwives) on either side of the border is unclear, but this may be seen to support the argument that maternity care in Scotland is more paternalist. This in turn may help to explain the lower incidence of litigation.

Respondents in the postal survey were also asked about communication and rapport between doctors and midwives within their unit, both generally, and when something had gone wrong. Apart from the finding that midwives overall viewed such relationships in a much less optimistic light than the doctors, there were statistically significant differences in the matched pairs trial, with the English group more likely to answer 'very good/good' both generally and when something had gone wrong. There was correspondingly a statistically significant difference in the proportion answering either 'poor' or 'terrible' when something had gone wrong. These differences were not replicated in the obstetric survey.

This question had been prompted by the claim made by Sir Donald Acheson, then the Chief Medical Officer, that colleagues were telling him that litigation and the fear of litigation, were starting to 'poison inter-professional relationships in the delivery room' (Acheson, 1991: 165). Although the numbers strongly agreeing with this claim were relatively small, there was a statistically significant difference noted in the matched pairs analysis, with 16 of the Scottish group strongly agreeing, compared to five of the English group. Such comparatively poor relationships in Scotland might in theory predispose to more litigation, given the importance of interprofessional communication. However, given the data revealed in *Appendix II* this does not appear to be the case. The explanation for these interprofessional views may be complex, and certainly warrants further investigation.

Conclusion

It was not the specific intention of this research to identify cross-border differences; nevertheless, a number of these were noted as analysis progressed. Distinctions in legal terminology and case law apart, there would appear to be significant differences in both the incidence and nature of perinatal litigation. The higher rate of litigation in the English areas, and the far greater prevalence of claims concerning cerebral palsy, certainly merit further consideration, although data collection on a comprehensive scale may be difficult so limiting comparisons. There were some differences in outlook between midwives working in Scotland and those working in the English areas which were surveyed. While there were also a good number of similarities in outlook, the differences concerning the doctor-midwife relationship and the suggestion that Scotland has a more paternalistic approach in health care matters warrant investigation.

Chapter 25

y   Your friendly high street solicitor

*The days of the 'Jack of all trades' high street
practitioner are numbered... the experienced
family lawyer should not do a bit of medical
negligence work on the side.*

(Anon, 1997b: 199)

It has been seen that some practitioners (perhaps unsurprisingly) have a jaundiced view of those who initiate legal actions against health service staff. Criticism has also been levelled at the degree of competence displayed by a number of solicitors who have agreed to represent a client in a medico-legal claim. Such criticisms have now led to the situation where 'high street' solicitors are being discouraged from taking on such claims. The Law Society in England has responded by drawing up a specialist panel of medical negligence solicitors which now comprises about 150 practitioners.

This book is written from the viewpoint of a health service practitioner interested in litigation, and it is readily acknowledged that the depiction in this chapter is not wholly representative. Few health service practitioners would appreciate having their profession portrayed by a minority whose expertise is questionable, and the characterisation of solicitors in this chapter should not be taken as a general comment on solicitors. Nevertheless, the discovery of significant deficiencies in knowledge and expertise merits some consideration, since it has been claimed that failing to secure a solicitor with the appropriate experience may be detrimental to a litigant's chances (Genn, 1989).

The evident lack of experience among some solicitors is now discussed. The first section looks at 'language difficulties', since there were some occasions when plaintiff solicitors clearly had difficulty in understanding or using clinical terminology – a pre-requisite for acting in a medico-legal claim. There were also times when health practitioners found legal expressions baffling. The second section examines some of the claims that suggested a great vagueness on the part of the solicitors; and the third explores some of their attempts to be specific which were scarcely more helpful. The final section then looks at several aspects of an apparent lack of awareness of the law relating to medical negligence, and ponders the question of a solicitor's motivation for taking on the claim

Language difficulties

In order to proceed with an allegation of negligence a lawyer must have some grasp of the clinical situation. A poor grasp will increase the scope for confusion and delay. This point is not intended to chastise lawyers – who may in a year's work have to deal with matters as diverse as medicine, engineering, property, contractual disputes and family law – but to show that the approach of a generalist is unlikely to expedite matters. Issues relating to clinical conditions and the disease process may be complex, and especially so when causation is at the heart of the matter.

Solicitors acting for the defence may not be immune to charges of misunderstanding the clinical situation either, although since they act as 'repeat players' (cf. Galanter, 1974; Genn, 1989) they tend to acquire considerable knowledge about clinical matters. In one case concerning cerebral palsy a defence solicitor, noting various findings in a consultant obstetrician's letter, asked why a diagnosis of an early antenatal asphyxial insult – rather than intrapartum distress – would be wrong. He stated:

> *I have a feeling that the answer to the above question may be clear to the members of the medical profession but would be grateful for an explanation for the lay person.*

The impression created is of people trying to understand a foreign language, a process which can work both ways. It may be easy for practitioners to mock the corruption of language evident in some of these files; two examples are a reference to the 'stafforious virus/bacteria' (Staphylococcal [abbreviated to Staph] aureus), and a claim that, 'A pyrennial plaster was inserted' (presumably a perineoplasty, as this referred to a subsequent perineal repair). However, few health service practitioners will be able to converse in 'legalese': just as lawyers have been seen to misunderstand clinical terminology, so health service practitioners may be confused by legal language. In Scots law the term 'writer', although slightly arcane, refers to a solicitor. That this may be confusing is shown in the following correspondence between a defence solicitor and a midwife:

> Solicitor to midwife: *My purpose in writing to you at this stage is to make an initial contact with you with a view to your coming back to the writer.*

> Midwife to solicitor: *I am not sure I understand what you mean by 'coming back to the writer'. I am assuming you mean replying.*

It can be seen that language difficulties are not only the concern of plaintiff solicitors and the temptation to deride such misunderstandings should be resisted.

The plaintiff solicitors must rely on the plaintiff – and sometimes her family – to provide a description of the relevant events (that these were sometimes inaccurate was noted in *Chapter 22*). These descriptions are the common factor in these examples of failing to convey a sense of understanding about what has happened. Given the distress caused to practitioners by allegations of negligence (Vincent *et al,* 1994; and see *Chapter 9*), a pressing cause for concern is the lack of credibility of some of these claims. However absurd an allegation may appear at first, it must be investigated, and practitioners may feel offended by the suggestion that they have acted negligently. At times the wording of a letter was so vague that little sense could be made of it; at other times the depiction of events was quite striking, but still conveyed a sense of not having understood what had occurred. These are now considered.

Vagueness

The initial letter of claim from the plaintiff solicitors should state the reason for the allegation of negligence. It appeared from this research that certain solicitors were unable to grasp much (if any) detail about the clinical circumstances of the claim. In some no specifications were made at all, as in this briefly worded statement:

> *My client... claims damages from you.*

Although the legal department wrote several times requesting further details, no further contact was made, and the case was assumed to have been dropped. Surprisingly, this was by no means an isolated example. In one case the solicitors wrote simply that there was 'a clear *prima facie* case of negligence in the treatment of our client', but failed to specify what the negligence was. Sometimes a letter, despite claiming that a doctor or midwife had acted negligently, was so non-specific that it was seen as a hopeful trawl by the solicitors rather than a case which genuinely believed in its own merits. Such a letter brought this reply from the defence:

> *We... emphasise that you must give us an outline of allegations of negligence against our clients, failing which we will have no alternative but to conclude that* (this) *is simply a 'fishing expedition' for a claim.*

This request is not for detailed clinical explanations, but for a lucid account of the basis of the claim. Asked for such details, one firm replied:

> *We are not in a position to give a detailed specification of the nature of our client's claim as this will be difficult to determine until we receive a report from* (the expert).

An expert report is not necessary to give some specification for the claim. At times the description of events (when these were given) was less than explicit, as in the following initial claims:

> *We understand that Mrs K's baby was living inside the womb in unusual circumstances.*

> *Mrs H appears to have been instructed to 'hold on' for about 20 minutes despite the fact that the child was half born.*

Both claims demonstrate a poor understanding of the clinical circumstances. Because a claim cannot proceed until specific allegations are made the interests of the plaintiff in pursuing the claim are hardly being met, and yet informing practitioners that lawyers have been in contact will at the very least cause some concern.

Another claim began with the following rather cryptic statement:

> *The issue relates to the initial failure to identify the fact that the baby was misplaced in the womb and the lengthy period before action was taken to deliver the child which has resulted in our client suffering from backache.*

This claim was not pursued vigorously, but claims that proceed further may still founder on misunderstandings. This is particularly so when the claim concerns a complicated disease process. In one case concerning an instrumental delivery the solicitors claimed:

> *We... understand that the child stopped breathing prior to birth and this resulted in brain damage and the child is suffering from cerebral palsy.*

Quite apart from the odd belief that the child had been breathing prior to birth, in this case a paediatric report noted that the early emergence of certain symptoms led to the conclusion that the asphyxial insult must have occurred well before the second stage of labour. The patho-physiology of cerebral palsy is certainly complex, and it appears that the courts have taken some time to acknowledge that there is no simple causal connection between signs of intrapartum compromise and subsequent handicap (Stanley, 1994). A comment from a medical defence organisation about a case from 1992 demonstrates this apparent belief in cause-and-effect:

> *The letter from* (the plaintiff's solicitor) *makes no allegations of negligence at all, as required to do by the rules of court, and we therefore have no idea of where they think any negligence might lie. They seem to have proceeded purely on an 'an accident has happened therefore someone must be to blame' basis.*

Such a tactic is extremely unlikely to succeed in terms of securing compensation, but it has been claimed that initiating litigation may sometimes be the only way of finding out what has happened (see *Chapter 10*). Vague expressions of dissatisfaction are unlikely to get the solicitors very far. In addressing this some solicitors have been keen to include very specific details in their claim. However, it will be seen that these may do little to advance their client's cause.

Distorted detail

The examples above of vagueness did little to convey a sense that certain plaintiff solicitors had a good understanding of the essence of the claim. In theory, the solicitor should initiate litigation by setting out the clinical basis of the claim, as well as noting that it is competent in law. Some of the files examined here included clinical details which were less than helpful, being somewhat distorted (examples of this were also noted in *Chapter 22*). In failing to demonstrate even a rudimentary knowledge of clinical issues, a solicitor can be exposed to disparagement. One allegation of negligence included the following:

> *It is our client's belief and understanding that... she had certain parts of her anatomy stitched which did not require such thus resulting in an abnormality which gives rise to her difficulty having sexual relations.*

The evident lack of knowledge about anatomy was a recurrent theme. In another claim concerning a woman who had had a caesarean section the solicitors stated:

> *The wound opened itself and her bowels came out of her stomach and fell into her hands.*

This graphic description does not explain what the woman's 'bowels' were doing in her 'stomach' in the first place. The lay (and incorrect) use of such terms does little to promote an understanding of what has occurred. As with anatomical terminology, so there was often a poor awareness of clinical terms. In one letter the solicitors stated:

> *Our client... asked that her baby be induced to avoid risks of injury as a result of undergoing normal labour.*

In this case the defence replied:

> *If we are to understand that your client is complaining that she was not induced, this is evidently a mistake on her part. As recorded in the notes, your client's labour was induced.*

In another case criticism was made of a doctor for augmenting a labour:

> *Our client was admitted on... 23rd July with advanced labour pains... the houseman broke her waters despite the fact that her baby was not due until 25th July.*

One does not have to be a professional in the health service to know that for a woman to go into labour two days before her due date is quite normal.

These examples demonstrate that some solicitors do not appear to grasp the salient facts, and therefore are poorly placed to pursue a claim. Such deficiencies are compounded when there is an evident lack of the necessary experience in medico-legal work.

Inexperience in the medico-legal process

Throughout this research there were examples of an inadequate grasp of the requirements of medical law on the part of plaintiff solicitors. Employing a solicitor with little or no experience in this area of the law has been claimed to reduce significantly the plaintiff's chances of success since 'repeat players'– ie. the health service – develop expertise over the years in defending such actions.

Letter of claim

A lack of expertise (which may have been a simple clerical error but which did little to convey a sense of competence) came from one firm who wrote:

> *The grounds for our view that you are likely to be a party in respect of subsequent legal proceedings arise from instructions we have from the client, namely: (here, set out clearly and chronologically, the instructions from the client which generate the inference of negligence).*

The letter of claim that sets out the allegation of negligence, is usually sent to the health service legal department, or occasionally to the hospital management team. On one occasion the letter was sent directly to the midwife concerned:

> *A letter came to me from a lawyer, alleging medical negligence. It didn't go to the hospital, it came direct to me. I was really quite shocked.*

> (Midwife 11)

This midwife, quite appropriately, passed on the letter and the claim was subsequently dealt with through the usual channels. This was not an isolated instance and problems have occurred when staff, in failing to appreciate the adversarial nature of the law, have responded directly to the solicitor in such circumstances. In one instance the plaintiff's solicitors wrote to the consultant obstetrician who replied, giving his brief comments on the case. He then acknowledged that he ought to have passed the note to the legal team. His defence organisation wrote to him:

> *I think it unwise for a doctor to enter into correspondence directly with a patient's solicitor unless you have prior authority from the health authority and its legal advisors or from the defence union.*

There is little chance of keeping things informal once a solicitor's letter has been received. The issue is less clear cut when it is the patient who writes to the practitioner. In most instances – particularly now with streamlined complaints procedures – a courteous and frank reply is warranted. However, if it is thought that solicitors are (or might be) involved, it is prudent to allow the health service legal staff to read correspondence before it is sent.

Medical law

Demonstrating a lack of knowledge of the relevant process or even of the law does little to promote a sense of competence. In one claim (relating to a stillbirth) the solicitors did not explain what the reason for the action was, prompting the legal department to ask:

> *Are the solicitors claiming for loss of society of child[1] (incompetent?). Are (they) claiming for solatium[2] for the husband in respect of the wife's experience (incompetent). The only possible claim here would appear to be solatium for the wife.*

When the solicitors made it clear that they were claiming for loss of society for the child, the legal department replied:

> *The child was stillborn and I would contend that your client can not therefore claim loss of its society since it has no legal personality for the purposes of a claim under the Damages* (Scotland) *Act 1976.*

In *Chapter 15* it was noted that many legal claims experience significant delay, sometimes because of an apparent lack of preparedness on the part of the solicitor. Both parties to the dispute should be aware of the need to keep each other abreast of the state of the claim. This does not always happen, as remarked by one employer to the lead clinician:

> *Out of the blue we were served with a Writ and Statement of Claim... the documents were served half an hour before the solicitor intended to appear in court on the subject.*

Clearly this does not give the defence time to arrange for an investigation, let alone carry it out. Just as the solicitor needs to know about the relevant law and its conduct, so (s)he needs to know how to secure the services of an appropriate expert.

Experts

Once the initial claim has been made and a copy of the case notes acquired, the plaintiff solicitors will usually arrange for an expert report to be produced. In the area of securing an expert report a number of solicitors have demonstrated their lack of experience in this field. The expert's fee is paid by the plaintiff solicitors on behalf of the plaintiff, who will be compensated if the claim is successful. One firm wrote to the health service legal department asking for reimbursement for the expert's fee. Another wrote hopefully asking the legal department to:

> *Advise us of the appropriate body in London to write to to obtain the names and addresses of doctors who may be willing to assist.*

This firm seemed unwilling to accept an expert's report which was not favourable to their client:

> *We have already taken an opinion from Dr F... in his opinion there was no medical negligence involved. In these circumstances surely a second opinion is desirable from everyone's point of view to clear up this matter once and for all.*

Another expert might produce a report with a different conclusion, but such moves are usually no more than a hopeful trawl, and are unlikely to do more than prolong an action and increase expense. Some of the issues relating to experts were discussed in *Chapter 5*.

Perinatal claims may be especially complicated as they may relate to more than one speciality. One firm, apparently in the belief that a Fellow of the Royal College of Obstetricians and

---

1   'Loss of society': a claim relating to bereavement
2   Solatium: damages allowed by way of reparation for injury to feeling

Gynaecologists would be the appropriate person to provide an expert report on a case concerning a baby (but which was in fact 'neonatal' rather than 'obstetric'), instructed a professor whose interest was gynaecological oncology.

There are now published lists of those prepared to produce expert reports, but, as one interviewee noted, such information is of little benefit if the plaintiff solicitor does not understand the nuances of the claim:

> *It's not much good, is it, looking at a list if you don't actually realise what sort of specialist you're looking for, and your high street solicitor gets that wrong. I mean, what's the difference between a neurosurgeon and a neurologist?*

(Defence solicitor 1)

Making a mistake in this area can be significant, as another interviewee pointed out:

> *You could easily go to three or four or five different firms who just don't get a grip on it. There certainly have been cases where they've just gone to the wrong experts, and they haven't realised they've got a case.*

(AVMA official 2)

If a meritorious claim fails for lack of a suitably experienced solicitor, then few would argue that moves to discourage such solicitors from taking on medical claims are a bad thing.

Motivation

Given the evident lack of experience of some solicitors, their motivation in taking on a medico-legal claim may be questioned. Certainly there were instances in this research where the clinicians who were involved voiced suspicions about such motivation. It was noted in *Chapter 9* that some practitioners feel almost victimised when a claim is made against them. In one case a senior clinician noted:

> *I would consider that there is absolutely no substance whatsoever in any of the allegations made in the solicitor's letter, in fact there is so little substance that I would go so far as to suggest that they are mischievous.*

In another case, in which the woman had general surgery after her child was born, the surgeon noted:

> *This claim seems to be very much a sign of the times and seems to me to be a piece of financial opportunism both on the part of the patient and more particularly the solicitor.*

(Consultant surgeon)

The financial opportunities for solicitors in England are now defined by the Access to Justice rules produced by Lord Woolf, and unless a claim is potentially worth a large amount, there may be few solicitors willing to take on even those claims that appear almost certain to win.

Although some respondents in the postal survey believed solicitors to be encouraging patients to seek legal redress, not all solicitors appear highly motivated once involved in a claim. In one case the defence solicitor noted to the employer:

> *I don't think we will be pushed very hard by* (the plaintiff solicitor) *as I met him in Court recently and mentioned this file to him, whereupon he threw up his hands in*

> *horror – clearly he regards it as something of a nightmare which he only touches when he has to.*

This description seemed sadly true, because this individual was extremely slow in responding to any developments. Having achieved no response despite several attempts at making contact over several months, the defence solicitor wrote again in exasperation to the employer:

> *It really is terrible that the plaintiff's family are landed with such an idiot as Mr __...*
> *So far as reporting* (him) *to the Law Society is concerned, the... family would have good cause and justification for doing this.*

The need for expertise

The need for accredited legal specialists appears obvious, and it seems that in England (or at least parts of it) there is now a reasonable chance of obtaining the services of a legal representative who has a sound grasp of medical law. In Scotland there is a much smaller number of medico-legal cases, and consequently less scope for lawyers to specialise. A senior Scottish lawyer confirmed this opinion:

> *Unless a person in Scotland goes to, I suppose, something in the order of half a dozen firms... they will get someone who has got only a very sketchy knowledge – and I would include in the firms with sketchy knowledge* (some) *people who are actually prepared to see themselves described... as a medical negligence expert.*
>
> (Queen's Counsel)

While the situation seems to be more favourable to potential litigants in England, the concerns about some solicitors noted by the AVMA official above indicate that this state of affairs may not exist everywhere. As noted in *Chapter 15*, some lengthy delays were caused by the inexperience of the plaintiff solicitor. Some Scottish firms have evidently taken on board the need to acquire specialist knowledge:

> *Over the last couple of years I've noticed a change: they're beginning to get their act together, they're beginning to come together on joint conferences. And there are one or two firms that I would expect to be able to put together quite a formidable case.*
>
> (Defence solicitor 2)

This development in legal expertise is something those in the health service ought to welcome. While it may seem that greater proficiency for plaintiff solicitors may mean a larger number of successful claims against practitioners, it will also lead to far quicker dispute resolution, and this can only help all concerned. As this defence solicitor noted:

> *From a practising point of view it is actually much better to be dealing with a pursuer solicitor who knows what he's doing.*

It seems clear that there is a pressing need to have suitably experienced solicitors acting for plaintiffs.

Conclusion

It is unfortunate that some people apparently believe that the best way of securing an explanation from staff is to make an allegation of negligence. Once started, the adversarial legal process seeks to ensure that – through legal representation – the respective interests of plaintiff and defendant are promoted. However, this will not necessarily establish an understanding of the case since the two may not amount to the same thing, particularly if the plaintiff solicitor is not well versed in this area of the law.

This chapter has identified a number of areas in which plaintiff solicitors have not demonstrated a high degree of awareness of the requirements of medical litigation, or even of the clinical basis of the claim. The situation is improving, and 'high street' solicitors are being encouraged to pass on claims of this nature so that the plaintiff secures the services of someone with the requisite expertise. Adequate publicity about those on the specialist panel is required, since a lack of such awareness will perpetuate some of the failings noted in this chapter.

A mutual understanding of each other's role is the ideal situation when health service practitioners and lawyers meet. The difficulties encountered when the two different professions do not have this shared understanding is well summed up by one doctor involved in a legal claim: 'As a physician speaking to a lawyer, I just had to make him understand that excellent care doesn't always correlate with excellent outcome' (Sacks, 1997: 472). With the development of a growing panel of specialist lawyers, it is to be hoped that the days of the 'high street' solicitor taking on claims of this nature are over.

Chapter 26

Z Zero sum game: an attainable goal?

In the Zero sum game, gains and losses balance out. Compensation is intended to secure this: successful plaintiffs receive damages intended to place them in the position they would have been in had the adverse event not occurred. In this respect (and discounting for the moment the argument about how pain and suffering can be assessed, or just how money is supposed to compensate for the loss of a child) civil litigation aims for the Zero sum game. Certainly there is scope for research into whether successful plaintiffs feel they have achieved this. This, of course, only represents one aspect of litigation, and as this book has shown, it has many different facets. This final chapter assesses whether or not the Zero sum game can be said to have been achieved; firstly in terms of a justice or fairness argument, and secondly in clinical matters. In other words, it gauges the overall effect of perinatal litigation on perinatal care.

Justice

Justice is linked to the notion of accountability. In the formal-rational legal model we are all held to be accountable for our actions (and sometimes for our failures to act). Accountability is highly prized: elected leaders and many of those in positions of power are held to be answerable for their actions. However, the notion that mechanisms of accountability ensure access to justice can be criticised: Marks (1997: 26) notes that 'justice depends on availability. In the United Kingdom, legal remedies are available only to the legally aided or the rich.' With constraints upon the legal aid budget, it may be that fewer people in the former category will obtain access to justice in the civil courts, and that access to such justice will become the preserve of the rich. Such a claim is scarcely novel: Etzioni (1975) points out that accountability is not always equally applied, since those groups with higher status or more power are able to make any system more accountable to them. Lay members of the public are said to encounter difficulties when dealing with professional treatment, because judgements about professionalism are dealt with 'in-house', and are often opaque to the lay person. Nevertheless, claims Mashaw (1983: 28) 'the mystery of professional judgement is... acceptable because of the service ideal of professionalism.' In light of the various claims noted throughout this book it might be questioned whether the 'service ideal' is still a credible argument.

Making an allegation is one way in which practitioners can be held to account, and as I have stated on more than one occasion, this is not something with which health service practitioners ought to quibble, distressing though such allegations undoubtedly are. There have been many assertions about the incidence of complaints and allegations against practitioners. While the distinction between the two was not always immediately obvious in some of the legal claims examined here, there is a difference. Nevertheless, both may act as a vital pressure valve, representing a method of channelling frustration and anger when an outcome is poor, or at the very least is felt to be poor.

In an inclusive democratic society people are expected to participate and not simply act as passive subjects. Having the means to complain and go to a solicitor can be seen as a vital element in this compact. However, as with most other aspects of democratic society, it is expected that such rights will be exercised with responsibility and an appreciation of the consequences. Despite the claim that seeking recourse in the law may be the only way of finding out exactly what happened at a given time, the awareness of a right to sue may raise some questions. The first is whether people actually consider the consequences of making an allegation of negligence, either for themselves (time, distress, and financial outlay) or for the practitioners concerned (time, distress, and possible loss of reputation). This is especially pertinent if the allegation proves to be unfounded. The second is to consider whether publicising a right to complain or sue gives the impression that there will be something to complain about. If people are encouraged to feel dissatisfied and to find fault, then this may lead to a 'blaming culture', which is difficult to depict as a happy one. Accountability and blaming may become indistinct from each other. Blame may be the answer when we cannot cope with adversity.

High expectations (discussed in *Chapter 8*), while posing a challenge to the NHS in terms of service delivery, also suggest a society confident of its right to enjoy life. Far from accepting Hobbes' dictum that the life of man is (among other things) nasty, brutish and short, contemporary society now expects it to be pleasant and marked by a healthy longevity. While there is no written constitution in Britain codifying individual rights, there appears to be an awareness that the civil law is a means of enforcing rights. Quite where this awareness comes from can be debated. Publicity about the experience of the civil law in the USA is almost certainly a factor, and it was a popular perception that 'the media' generally have played a part (sometimes an irresponsible part, it was claimed) in creating high expectations. While high expectations may denote a society confident of its ability to achieve the good things in life, and without contradicting the right to have recourse to the law, it seems to be the case that for some high expectations have been transformed into unrealistic ones.

If the civil law aims for the Zero sum game, it is on the principle that deserving plaintiffs will receive compensation for their losses. It is possible to argue that this holds true as long as the discussion is restricted to successful litigants. However, as shown in *Chapter 7*, the rate of success for those suing the NHS is not high, at least in terms of perinatal litigation. Studies from the USA have also suggested that many more people are entitled to receive compensation than actually sue. As noted earlier, the increasing number of complaints may (among other factors) mean a greater proportion of the legal claims that are received will have some legal foundation. Despite this, the success rate will probably not approach that of other personal injury litigation (said by Fenn and Dingwall to be 70%) because of the very stiff tests for establishing medical negligence, namely fault and causation.

Reasons for settling claims varied. With respect to the time, stress and expense of defending a relatively inexpensive claim, some were undoubtedly conceded because this was felt to be the best approach all round. Far from being seen as giving the green light to would-be litigants elsewhere, this was claimed to be the best method of minimising distress to practitioners and expense to the health service. It is difficult to square this practice with the justice notion that meritorious claims succeed and unmeritorious ones do not, but equally it was difficult to draw satisfaction from situations in which clinical fault had been admitted but compensation could not be awarded because of a failure to establish causation. Equally, some claims appeared to founder because of an evident lack of suitable experience and skill on the part of the plaintiff's solicitors. Again, this does little to promote a sense of justice, although it is to be welcomed that inexperienced lawyers will be encouraged to pass on claims for which they do not have the requisite skill.

While it was beyond the scope of the research reported here to survey plaintiffs, it seems reasonable to assume that the most satisfied would be those whose claims were successful and which were concluded quickly. One of the least appealing aspects of many of the claims examined here was the length of time they took to be concluded. Lord Woolf's reforms, while not applying in Scotland, aim to 'fast track' many claims, and it is to be hoped that this will reduce the pressure on an already over-crowded legal justice system.

It was noted (see *Chapter 15*) that the processing of many claims was delayed and for a variety of reasons. The strain and distress of being named in a legal action was discussed in *Chapter 9*. The variety of emotional responses (none of them pleasant) bears testimony to the effects of, among other things, an adversarial legal system. Again, it seems reasonable to conclude that those who initiate litigation are subject to extremes of emotion, and yet, given the low success rate for plaintiffs, for most of them litigation is not the solution. It seems improbable that a sense of injustice will be assuaged by losing a law suit. For the majority of plaintiffs the Zero sum game is not achieved. Neither are the lawyers happy: quite apart from the involvement of inexperienced solicitors who are most unlikely to be successful, the introduction of conditional fee arrangements and the capping of amounts recoverable by lawyers acting for plaintiffs, may discourage meritorious claims from being pursued.

From the health service's point of view, the Zero sum game is unattainable: even in those claims that are successfully defended (the majority) the price to be paid is high. As noted above, there is distress to the practitioners involved. There is also the possibility of a damaged reputation (both on a personal and an institutional level). If there has been any media publicity about the initiation of a legal claim (and the local press may find such stories to their taste), there will be comparatively little publicity if the claim subsequently fails. There is also the financial cost of maintaining the administrative structure necessary for the investigation of legal claims, and the associated expenses paid to lawyers and experts. A successful defence may well induce some satisfaction, but this comes at a high price, and when weighed together these can scarcely be said to be of equal value.

Clinical matters

As noted, in the Zero sum game, gains and losses balance out. This is the aim of compensation, which is itself the intention behind litigation. However, as noted throughout this book, litigation has many facets even when we are restricted to the consideration of perinatal matters. In view of the apparent effects of perinatal litigation, it is appropriate to assess the impact of these effects. Taken in the round, such litigation appears to have had a number of consequences on the organisation and management of clinical services and so it is pertinent to ask whether these have had a beneficial or detrimental effect or, indeed, whether the good and bad effects balance each other.

On one side, as noted by Walshe and Sheldon (1998) in *Chapter 18*, it may be that the emergence and development of litigation has encouraged the NHS to take risk management seriously. The apparently inexorable rise in the awareness of risk, and the perceived need to control it, are strong contemporary themes. In general terms, risk-taking is frowned upon, although some will be quick to point out that taking risks is an inherent part of daily life in most, if not all, societies. Crossing the road, driving a car, using kitchen utensils, food consumption, sporting activities and most types of employment entail a degree of risk. Whether such harm is theoretically possible rather than statistically probable is a matter for debate, as the arguments about food safety especially have shown in recent years. Nevertheless, it is generally assumed that risk management is, *per se*, a good thing. If procedures or organisational structures can be improved so that the chances of a poor outcome are lessened, then few would argue against such measures. While risk management covers many areas within health care, for practitioners the most important is probably clinical risk management. Even within this, as noted in *Chapter 18*, there are different approaches, although the essence of each is to minimise the chances of a poor outcome. On the organisational level, it is difficult to argue that better (and mandatory) training in clinical skills is not worthwhile. Another, perhaps less common aspect of clinical risk management is the emphasis on multi-disciplinary education in such training programmes. In this way, not only should all grades and disciplines be taught the same things, but communication barriers between the different disciplines should be broken down.

The adoption of critical incident reporting systems goes some way towards identifying the incidence of poor outcomes or errors. However, until comparable systems are widely used, such information will only be of use locally, and it can be argued that one of risk management's greatest opportunities – to establish the incidence of clinical error – will have been missed. A comprehensive national database will allow information to be shared, and, claim Towse and Danzon (1999), effective risk management policies to be developed. The adoption of agreed protocols and guidelines, providing that they are soundly based, should establish minimum standards which promote clinical effectiveness and an equality of care. They may range from specific clinical practices to an emphasis on the importance of supervising junior practitioners, or of the need to maintain good records.

An awareness of the possibility of litigation may, on an organisational level, encourage an employer to recruit more doctors and midwives; few practitioners would argue against an increase in staffing levels. On an individual level, it has been claimed that the fear of litigation may cause practitioners to take more care, even if only in the level and quality of information given to patients and their families.

While, on the face of it, it is difficult to argue against any such measures, this only tells part of the story. Other aspects may be ignored if this rather rosy depiction is taken at face value. Clinical risk management may, as noted, recommend certain practices; at other times it may insist on them. While the RCOG, and the multi-disciplinary 'Towards Safer Childbirth' document (RCOG/RCM, 1999) put the emphasis on 'guidelines', some units apparently produce protocols that are effectively rules, although individual interpretation may still determine the precise course of action taken. This reduces the scope for the pregnant woman to exercise choice, and may even call into question the notion of informed consent. While clinically-based practitioners will be aware that in an acute emergency the capacity to understand detailed information is reduced, the law is quite clear that a mentally competent woman is well within her rights to refuse any treatment or intervention, even if this inevitably results in her own death or that of her baby. There is a potential danger that protocols, policies and guidelines, introduced as part of clinical risk management, may be used as tools of coercion. While completely individualised care is not practicable in a large scale public service, women are being told that they have the right to exercise choice. In busy maternity units (sometimes referred to unflatteringly as 'factories') there may be a tendency to use clinical risk management as a means of getting women to comply with the norm. When asked, practitioners have cited the fear of litigation as the reason for this course of action, although this explanation is unlikely to be given to the woman or her family. The individual practitioner's response to the fear of being sued is one of the keys to understanding some of the potentially detrimental effects of perinatal litigation. While this is famously difficult to assess, particularly in general terms, the findings both of the postal survey and of the interviews (discussed in *Chapter 4*) suggest that individual examples of attempts at risk reduction, far from improving the standard of care, may actually diminish it. Higher levels of CTG monitoring, and a reduced threshold for performing a caesarean section, increase rather than reduce morbidity. It is hard to argue with a practitioner who has been involved in a tragic outcome and who insists on adopting certain practices in order to try and prevent a recurrence of that tragedy. Nevertheless, being bound by one (or even more than one) extreme example is to court being tyrannised by that experience. Practitioners are exhorted to follow clinical standards which are research- and evidence-based; individual experiences, however tragic, should not take precedence over more comprehensive evidence.

In most cases practitioners are responding to the fear of litigation. In a comparatively small number of cases (for midwives at least) they do so in response to the experience of litigation. While the consequences of being involved in litigation appear to change over time, there is little doubt that on both a clinical and personal level, they may have deleterious effects, particularly in the short term. These effects are not helped by the adversarial legal system which effectively ends any chance of *rapprochement* between practitioner and the family concerned; nor are they helped by the apparent lack of suitable support systems in the workplace. That involvement in litigation is harrowing was clear from the emotions described in *Chapter 9*.

Has the Zero sum game been achieved in terms of litigation's effect on clinical matters? It is possible to argue that clinical risk management, if well conducted, will achieve a balance between a woman's expressions of choice and the relevant unit's recommendation that a certain course of action be adopted. It is also possible to claim that any negation of the woman's right to choose is offset by demonstrating an overall benefit to the whole client population. However, it is difficult to argue that defensive responses, which are widely believed to be prevalent, represent either a justifiable use of resources or a means of achieving an overall improvement in standards. For this reason, the Zero sum game fails.

Conclusion

From the available evidence, perinatal litigation has an overall detrimental effect in terms both of the justice argument, and of the clinical reactions of practitioners. This is a rather pessimistic note on which to conclude; but litigation is rarely (if ever) a happy subject. Even those litigants (plaintiff or defendant) who win their claim would probably rather they had never had to go through the whole experience. Given that poor clinical outcomes will continue to occur, and that a proportion of those who suffer these will complain and even sue, it is tempting to conclude that **something must be done**. Reforms of the legal system have yet to be evaluated, and they might go some way towards minimising the damaging consequences of the adversarial nature of the law. Moves to promote mediation are certainly to be encouraged. Better facilities for providing explanations and apologies to people who feel that they have been hard done by are also to be welcomed. Likewise, practitioners need to know that they can report things in confidence without the fear of disciplinary action and ask for counselling and advice without the fear of recrimination. Such measures may help to brighten the outlook, although practitioners will continue to deal with a general public raised to expect great things of the health service and its staff.

There is no magic solution, of course. Diligent explanations, sensitively given, will help to promote a climate of trust and understanding. While this is surely one of the best means of preventing litigation, there are few who would believe it to be the panacea that will stop it completely. We live in an imperfect world, and it may be that practitioners have to accept the degree of antagonism inherent in any accusation of negligence. As one interviewee noted, having a trusting relationship to start with makes the bringing of complaints much less likely. This involves getting to know the women who use the maternity services over a period of time. Meeting the woman and her partner for the first time when she is in labour is far from ideal. Given claims about 'burn-out' and the expense of such schemes it is questionable whether working in small teams or having a small-caseload practice is feasible in the long run. The maternity services have a difficult task in organising themselves so that continuity of care, much vaunted in the *Changing Childbirth* document and the 'Scottish Policy Review', is ensured.

Postscript

It is hoped that the various discussions in this book will have helped to shed some light on the diverse features and implications of obstetric litigation. I have made use of the extensive literature available on the different subjects covered here, but the conclusions that I have reached are necessarily bound by the limitations of the research. The legal files were mostly Scottish, as were the majority of the interviewees. While the Scottish legal files data were comprehensive, stretching back to 1980, the English data may not have been representative of England as a whole. Given some of the findings about possible cross-Border differences, this may be significant. The numerical data concerning the incidence and rate of litigation may be time-dependant, and will in time become out-of-date. In particular, it will be interesting to discover whether the apparent drop in the incidence of litigation continues, or was simply a 'blip' in an otherwise upward trend. Nevertheless, because of the access to the legal files themselves, it has been possible to depict in detail the character of perinatal litigation. This has been augmented by the interviews, which added a great deal of qualitative information. Whether or not this picture changes over time remains to be seen.

The interviews were necessarily subjective: this is the whole point of qualitative research. It was not my intention to produce a comprehensive and consensual picture. Because of changes in the way legal actions are handled, changes in the way the health service is attempting to control the threat of litigation, and differing views about its scale, importance and consequences, it is impossible to create a portrait with which everyone will agree. My own views have inevitably affected the presentation of the data: as stated in the introduction, no research is value-free.

The introduction also noted that this book, while answering some questions about the scale and character of litigation, would pose other questions. There is undoubtedly scope for further investigation in a number of areas. These include how to define normality; how expectations can be made more realistic; how the matter of a woman's choice is dealt with, especially in emergency situations; whether the standard for consent should be 'rational' rather than 'informed'; and whether initiating a legal action helps or hinders the grieving process. This list is not exhaustive: there are the possible changes to the way the legal system deals with allegations of negligence; the way the health service copes with these allegations; and the question of how need is dealt with when the legal system fails to secure compensation. Clinical matters are also important: the possibility that defensive practices may be increasing morbidity is surely a matter for concern. Instances of poor relationships between health care practitioner and the woman and her family were cited on several occasions, and it is clear that there is room for a great deal of improvement in this area. The claims about paternalism in the provision of maternity care were certainly of interest, and I await with anticipation a sociological cross-border comparison.

The views expressed in this book are subjective, so no claim is made that they provide the definitive answer to an intricate and developing phenomenon. Nevertheless, revealing the 'lived experience' of some of those involved in litigation has, I hope, provided valuable insights into this complex subject. The rapidly growing body of literature on this subject may make some of the discussion in this book already appear somewhat dated. Such widespread interest in this subject, while adding to its complexity, also demonstrates the potential for further research. Of particular personal interest are the possible reasons why some people do not initiate litigation even when it would appear that they have a good case to argue.

Litigation is with us, and while this is so people involved in the health service must learn to live with it. It is hoped that this book has helped to throw light on a subject which, while daunting, is also fascinating.

Andrew Symon
April 2000

Glossary

AFE	~ amniotic fluid embolus
Alopecia	~ absence or loss of hair
Amniotomy	~ rupture of the membranes to induce or augment labour
Anti-D immunoglobulin	~ an injection given to a Rhesus negative woman if her baby is rhesus positive, to prevent her forming antibodies
Anuria	~ absence of urine
Auscultate	~ to listen (in relation to the fetal heart rate)
Coccydynia	~ pain in the region of the coccyx
CLO	~ Central Legal Office (of the Scottish Health Service)
CNS	~ central nervous system. In relation to legal claims this usually relates to cerebral palsy
CVA	~ cerebro-vascular accident ('stroke')
D+C	~ dilatation and curettage: an operation to evacuate contents of the uterus (eg. retained products of conception)
Decidual	~ relating to the decidua (lining of the uterus during pregnancy)
Dyspareunia	~ painful sexual intercourse
Dystocia	~ abnormal labour
Endometrial	~ relating to the endometrium (the mucous membrane lining the body of the uterus)
Ex gratia payment	~ a payment made not on the basis of a conclusion of negligence
Fulminating pre-eclampsia	~ a rapid worsening of pre-eclampsia in which fitting may occur
Fundal	~ relating to the fundus (upper part of the uterus)
Gastro-oesophageal reflux	~ reflux of gastic contents into the oesophagus/mouth
Haematoma	~ bruising
Head of claim	~ the stated reason for the legal action
Hypotonia	~ lack of muscle tone
Hypovolaemia	~ low circulating blood volume
Iatrogenic	~ caused by medical treatment
Ischaemia	~ lack of blood supply
Laparotomy	~ exploratory abdominal operation
Ligate	~ to tie off (as in a bleeding blood vessel)
Microcephaly	~ an abnormally small head

Oxytocic	~ relating to drugs or hormones which promote uterine contractions
Parous	~ (of a woman) having had at least one child
Pulmonary embolus	~ a clot in the lung
Perineoplasty	~ re-fashioning of the perineum
Perineotomy	~ an excision within the perineum
Pinard	~ a stethoscope used for listening to the fetal heart
Placenta praevia	~ a placenta sited in the lower part of the uterus
PPH	~ post-partum haemorrhage
Sagittal suture	~ membranous tissue between the two parietal bones of the fetal/newborn skull
Septic osteitis	~ a blood-borne infection of the bone
Sequelae	~ consequences
SHO	~ senior house officer
Sonicaid	~ an electronic means of listening to the fetal heart
SRM	~ spontaneous rupture of membranes
Steristrips	~ a method for achieving skin closure
Syntometrine	~ an oxytocic (q.v.) drug given to reduce blood loss after childbirth
Tort/delict	~ the law of wrongs (in England/Scotland respectively)
Tortfeasor	~ a wrongdoer
Ureteric	~ relating to one or both ureters
X-ray pelvimetry	~ an estimation using X-rays of the internal dimensions of the pelvis

Legal cases

Bolam v Friern HMC [1957] 2 All ER 118

Bolitho v City & Hackney HA [1993] 4 Med LR 381; [1999] 39 Butterworth's Med LR 1

Bull v Devon HA [1993] 4 Med LR 117

Calladine v Nottingham AHA 1997

Cassidy v Ministry of Health [1951] 2 KB 343

Coles v Reading HMC 1963 107 SJ 115

Cooper v Nevill [1961] CLY 5951

De Martell v Merton & Sutton HA [1995] 6 Med LR 234

Donoghue v Stevenson, 1932 SC (HL) 31; 1932 SLT 317

Edgar v Lamont, 1914 SC 277

Edmonds v Bains (Feb 1967) Kemp & Kemp Vol. 2

Gaughan v Bedfordshire HA (QBD) [1997] 8 Med LR 182

Hallatt and Hallatt v North West Anglia HA (CA) [1998] Part 5. Lloyd's Rep Med 197

Hefferson v Committee of the UKCC (1988) 10 Butterworth's Med LR 1

Hotson v East Berkshire AHA [1987] AC 750; [1987] 2 All ER 909 HL

Hunter v Hanley 1955 Session Cases 200

Kelly v Bastible (1996) 36 Butterworth's Med LR 51

Kralj v McGrath [1986] 1 All ER 54

Langley v Dray and MT Motor Policies at Lloyds [1997] Personal Injuries and Quantum Reports, Part 6: P508–P517

Lanphier v Phipos (1838) 8 C & P 475

Le Page v Kingston & Richmond HA [1997] 8 Med LR 229

Mahon v Osbourne 1939 2 KB 14

Maynard v West Midlands RHA [1984] 1 WLR 634

McGhee v National Coal Board [1972] 3 All ER 1008

Miller v Minister of Pensions [1947] 2 All ER 372

Moyes v Lothian Health Board (1990) Scots Law Times 444

Murphy v Wirral HA [1996] 7 Med LR 99

O'Driscoll v Dudley HA (1997) 37 Butterworth's Med LR 146

Parry v North West Surrey HA (unreported; cited by Easterbrook, 1996)

Paton v British Steel Corporation (1983) Scots Law Times 82

Pfizer Corporation v Ministry of Health, 1965 A C 512

Quinn v Bowie [No 1] (1987) Scots Law Times 575

R v Bateman (1925) 94 LJKB 791

R v Prentice and Sullman, reported 2.11.91

re MB (CA) [1997] 8 Med LR 217

Robertson v Nottingham HA (CA) [1997] 8 Med LR 1

Rogers v Whitaker, High Court of Australia [1993] 4 Med LR 79

Rolland v Lothian Health Board, 1981 (unreported)

Sidaway v Board of Governors of the Bethlem Royal Hospital and others, [1984] 2 WLR 778, CA

Wardlaw v Bonnington Castings Ltd [1956] Session Cases (HL) 56

Whitehouse v Jordan [1980] 1 All ER 650 CA; [1981] 1 All ER 267; [1981] 1 WLR 246 (HL)

Wilsher v Essex Area Health Authority [1986] 3 All ER 801, CA

Wiszniewski v Central Manchester HA [1996] 7 Med LR 248

Wood v Thurston, 1951, unreported

References

Acheson D (1991) Are obstetrics and midwifery doomed? *Midwives' Chronicle* **104**: 158–66

ACOG [American College of Obstetricians and Gynecologists] (1988) *Professional liability and its effects: report of 1987 survey of ACOG's membership.* Washington, DC: Opinion Research Corporation

Aitkenhead D (1998) Sue the doctor, grab it and run. *The Guardian*, 6th February: 19

Akazaki RL (1999) Removing the moral sting from medical malpractice litigation: a modest proposal based on the Canadian experience. *Med Leg J* **67**(1): 9–10

Al-Mufti R, McCarthy A, Fisk N (1997) Survey of obstetricians' personal preference and discretionary practice. *Eur J Gynecol Reprod Biol* **73**: 1–4

Alexander J (1998) Confusing debriefing and defusing postnatally: the need for clarity of terms, purpose and value. *Midwifery* **14**: 122–124

Amu O, Rajendran S, Bolaji I (1998) Maternal choice alone should not determine method of delivery. *Br Med J* **317**: 463–5 (see Paterson-Brown 1998; and related correspondence: de Zulueta; Stirrat and Gunn; Idamo and Lindow; van Roosmalen; all 1999)

Anderson T (1994) Trust betrayed: the disciplining of the East Herts midwives. *Midirs Midwifery Digest* **4**(2): 132–4

Anon (1989) Cerebral palsy, intrapartum care, and a shot in the foot. *Lancet* **334**: 251–1252

Anon (1990) Medical Negligence: Hunter v Hanley 35 years on. *Scots Law Times* **325**

Anon (1996a) Maternal injuries – perineal damage – repair of tear: Re E. *Clinical Risk* (AVMA Medical and Legal Journal) **2**: 22–23

Anon (1996b) Delay in performing caesarean section: Griffiths, deceased. *Clinical Risk* (AVMA Medical and Legal Journal) **2**: 24

Anon (1996c) Obstetrics – Neonatal death: Re S. *Clinical Risk* (AVMA Medical and Legal Journal) **2**: 64–66

Anon (1996d) Neonatal care – respiratory distress – cerebral palsy: Ashton-Mackie v Sandwell HA. *Clinical Risk* (AVMA Medical and Legal Journal) 2: 159–160

Anon (1997a) Former midwives' leader pays £0.8m damages for baby with cerebral palsy. *Nurs Standard* **11**(22): 8

Anon (1997b) Specialist advice. *Solicitors' Journal* **141**: 199

Anon (1997c) Bereaved family face legal fight. *The Herald*, 31 May: 9

Apgar V (1953) Proposal for a new method of evaluation of newborn infants. *Anaesth Analgesia* **32**: 260–67

Ashcroft S (1996) Structured settlements come of age. *Solicitors' Journal* **140**: 1101

Askham J, Barbour R (1987) The role and responsibilities of the midwife in Scotland. *Health Bull* **45**: 153–159

Atiyah P, Cane P (1993) *Accidents, Compensation and the Law.* 5th edn. Weidenfield and Nicolson, London

Audit Commission (1997) *First class delivery: Improving maternity services in England and Wales.* Audit Commission Publications, Abingdon

Avis M, Bond M, Arthur A (1997) Questioning patient satisfaction: an empirical investigation in two out-patient clinics. *Soc Sci Med* **44**: 85–92

Ayres-de-Campos D, Bernardes J, Costa-Pereira A, Pereira-Leite L (1999) Inconsistencies in classification by experts of cardiotocograms and subsequent clinical decision. *Br J Obstet Gynaecol* **106**: 1307–1310

B-Lynch C, Coker A, Dua J (1996) A clinical analysis of 500 medico-legal claims evaluating the causes and assessing the potential benefit of alternative dispute resolution. *Br J Obstet Gynaecol* **103**: 1236–1242

Bakker R, Groenewegen P, Jabaaij L, Meijer W, Sixma H, de Veer A (1996) 'Burnout' among Dutch midwives. *Midwifery* **12**: 174–81

Baldwin L-M, Hart LG, Lloyd M, Fordyce M, Rosenblatt R (1995) Defensive medicine and obstetrics. *J Am Med Assoc* **274**: 1606–1610

Baldwin L-M, Larson E, Hart L, Greer T, Lloyd M, Rosenblatt R (1991) Characteristics of physicians with obstetric malpractice claims experience. *Obstet Gynecol* **78**(6): 1050–54

Bark P, Vincent C, Olivieri L, Jones A (1997) Impact of litigation on senior clinicians: implications for risk management. *Qual Health Care* 6: 7–13

Beard R, O'Connor A (1995) Implementation of audit and risk management: a protocol. In Vincent C, ed: *Clinical Risk Management.* BMJ Publishing Group, London: 350–374

Beaton J, Gupton A (1990) Childbirth expectations: a qualitative analysis. *Midwifery* **6**: 133–139

Beck U (1992) *Risk Society.* Sage, London

Beckman HB, Markakis KM, Suchman AL, Frankel RM (1994) The doctor-patient relationship and malpractice. *Arch Intern Med* **154**: 1365–1370

Beech B (1990) Accountability and compensation. *AIMS J* **2**(4): 1–3

Beech B (1992) *Penalties of Obstetric Technology.* AIMS Publications

Beecham L (1997) Over a third of trusts in England face financial difficulties. *Br Med J* **315**: 210

Berlant J (1975) *Profession and monopoly: a study of medicine in the United States and Great Britain.* University of California Press, Berkeley

Black N (1990) Medical litigation and the quality of care. *Lancet* **335**: 35–37

Blackie J (1985) Scotland. In: Deutsch E, Schreiber H-L (eds) *Medical responsibility in Western Europe.* Springer-Verlag, Berlin, New York

Blair E (1993) A Research Definition for 'Birth Asphyxia'? *Dev Med Child Neurol* **35**: 449–455

Blair E, Stanley F (1988) Intrapartum asphyxia: a rare cause of cerebral palsy. *J Pediatr* (Australia) **112**: 515–519

Blodgett N (1988) Baby Ins. *American Bar Association Journal* **74** (Feb): 35

BMA (British Medical Association) (1987) *No Fault Compensation Working Party Report.* British Medical Association, London

Bolaji I, Meehan F (1993) Post caesarean delivery. *Eur J Gynaecol Obstet Reprod Biol* **51**: 181–92

Bolt D (1992) Discussion section. In: *Compensation and Accountability – keeping the balance* [Proceedings of MDU conference] (Wall J, ed.). Mercury Books, London

Bonnar J, O'Herlihy C, MacDonald D, Minogue M (1999) *Providing good standards of care in obstetrics and gynaecology.* Institute of Obstetricians and Gynaecologists/Royal College of Physicians of Ireland, Dublin

Bors-Koefoed R, Zylstra S, Resseguie L, Ricci B, Kelly E, Mondor M (1998) Statistical models of outcome in malpractice lawsuits involving death or neurologically impaired infants. *J Maternl-Fetal Med* **7**(3):124–31

Bosk C (1979) *Forgive and remember: managing medical failure.* University of Chicago Press, Chicago

Bovbjerg R, Tancredi L, Gaylin D (1991) Obstetrics and Malpractice: evidence on the performance of a selective no-fault system. *J Am Med Assoc* **265**(21): 2836–43

Bowles R, Jones P (1990) Medical negligence and resource allocation in the NHS. *Social Policy and Administration* **24**(1): 39–51

Bradley J (1998) Medical negligence and post traumatic stress disorder. *Med Law* **17**: 225–228

Brahams D (1985) 'Informed consent' – the thin end of the wedge. *New Law J* **135**: 201

Brahams D (1997) Expert witnesses under scrutiny. *Lancet* **349**: 896

Brahams D (1999) Access to Justice – let them eat cake. *Med Leg J* **67**: 1–2

Brahams M (1988) 'No Fault' in Finland: paying patients and drug victims. *New Law J* **138**: 678–81

Brazier M (1987) *Medicine, Patients and the Law*. Penguin, Harmondsworth

Bredfeldt R, Colliver J, Wesley R (1989) Present status of obstetrics in family practice and the effects of malpractice issues. *J Fam Pract* **28**(3): 294–7

Brennan T, Leape L, Laird N, Hebert L, Localio AR, Lawthers A, Newhouse J, Weiler P, Hiatt H (1991) Incidence of adverse events and negligence in hospitalised patients: results of the Harvard Medical Practice Study I. *New Engl J Med* **324**: 37–76

Brennan T, Sox C, Burstin H (1996) Relation between negligent adverse events and the outcomes of medical malpractice litigation. *New Engl J Med* **335**: 1963–67

Brent R (1982) The irresponsible expert witness: a failure of biomedical graduate education and professional accountability. *Pediatrics* **70**: 754–62

Bridges G (1999) The public seem to expect their politicians to disinfect the nation's kitchen surfaces. *The Times*, 28 January: 22

Brown C, Smillie J (1991) The future of accident compensation. *New Zealand Law J*: 249–54

Brown P (1990) How to state your case. *Nurs Times* **86**(38): 52

Browning G (1986) Doctors and Lawyers Face Off. *Am Bar Assoc J* **72** (July): 38–41

Burger W (1971) The state of the Federal Judiciary. *Am Bar Assoc J* **57**: 855

Burstin HR, Johnson WG, Lipsitz SR, Brennan TA (1993) Do the poor sue more? A case-control study of malpractice claims and socio-economic status. *J Am Med Assoc* **270**: 1697–1701

Cameron J (1989) *Medical negligence*. Law Society of Scotland, Edinburgh

Capstick J, Edwards P (1990) Trends in obstetric malpractice claims. *Lancet* **336**: 931–2

Capstick J, Edwards P, Mason D (1991) Compensation for medical accidents. *Br Med J* **302**: 230

Carson D (1988) Medical accident litigation. *Health Service J*, 21 January: centre eight section

Carson D, Montgomery J (1989) *Nursing and the Law*. Macmillan Education, Basingstoke

Casselberry E (1985) Forum on malpractice issues in childbirth. *Public Health Rep* **100**(6): 629–633

Cetrulo C, Cetrulo L (1989) The legal liability of the medical consultant in pregnancy. *Med Clin North Am* **73**: 557–565

Challans P (1996) Independent midwives – what happens now? *Midirs Midwifery Digest* **6**: 268–9

Chamberlain G (1992) *How to avoid medico-legal problems in obstetrics and gynaecology*. RCOG, London

Charles J, Curtis L (1994) Birth Afterthoughts: a listening and information service. *Br J Midwifery* **2**(7): 331–4

Charlton B (1999) The ideology of accountability. *J R Coll Physicians Lond* **33**(1): 33–35

Clements R (1991) Litigation in obstetrics and gynaecology. *Br J Obstet Gynaecol* **98**: 423–426

Clements R (1995) Essentials of clinical risk management. *Qual Health Care* **4**: 129–134

Clothier C (1989) Medical negligence and no-fault liability. *Lancet* **333**: 603–5

Cohn S (1984) The nurse-midwife: malpractice and risk management. *J Nurse-Midwifery* **29**: 316–321

Collins D (1993) The impact of no-fault compensation on the regulation of medical practice in New Zealand. *Med Law* **12**: 61–9

Coppens M, James D (1999) Organisation of prenatal care and identification of risk. In: Steer P, Weiner C, Gonik B (eds) *High Risk Pregnancy*. 2nd edn. WB Saunders, London: 11–22

Copperfield T (1996) Taking the law into your own hands. *Doctor*, 9 May: 72–73

Coulson J (1999) NICE work. *BMA News Review*, March 1999: 16–18

Creasy J (1997) Women's experience of transfer from community-based to consultant-based maternity care. *Midwifery* **13**: 32–39

Crowley-Murphy M (1996) Marketing analysis of a maternity service by a consumer. *J Nurse Management* **4**: 219–223

Dally A (1990) *A Doctor's story*. Macmillan, London

Daniels S (1989) The question of jury competence and the politics of civil justice reform: symbols, rhetoric, and agenda-building. *Law and Contemporary Problems* **52**: 269–310

Daniels S (1992) The pragmatic management of error and the antecedents of disputes over the quality of medical care. In: Dingwall R, Fenn P, (eds) *Quality and Regulation in Health Care: International Experiences*. Routledge, London and New York: 113–39

Danzon P (1986) Medical malpractice: theory, evidence, and public policy (book review) *Harvard Law Review* **99**: 2001

Davis D, Thomson M, Oxman A, Haynes R (1992) Evidence for the effectiveness of CME: a review of 50 randomised controlled trials. *J Am Med Assoc* **268**: 9

de Zulueta P (1999) Patients do not have right to impose their wishes at all costs (letter). *Br Med J* **318**: 120

Defreitas F, Chapman G, Norman B (1999) *Midwifery a 'C.A.I.R.ing' profession – Critical Adverse Incident Reporting*. Presentation at RCM annual conference, 23rd April, Glasgow

DeKay M, Asch D (1998) Is the defensive use of diagnostic tests good for patients, or bad? *Med Decis Making* **18**: 19–28

DeMay R (1996) To err is human, to sue American. *Diagn Cytopathol* **15**: iii–vi

DeMott R, Sandmire H (1990) The Green Bay cesarean section study. *Am J Obstet Gynecol* **162**:1593–1602

Dennis J, Chalmers I (1982) Very early neonatal seizure rate: a possible epidemiological indicator of the quality of perinatal care. *Br J Obstet Gynaecol* **89**: 418–26

Dennis J, Johnson A, Mutch L, Yudkin P, Johnson P (1989) Acid-base status at birth and neuro-developmental outcome at 41/2 years. *Am J Obstet Gynecol* **161**: 213–20

Department of Health (1991) *Arbitration for Medical Negligence in the National Health Service*. HMSO, London

Department of Health (1993a) *Changing Childbirth* (The report of the Expert Maternity Group). HMSO, London

Department of Health (1993b) *Changing Childbirth - Part II: Survey of Good Communications Practice in Maternity Services*. HMSO, London

Derham R, Matthews T, Clarke T (1985) Early seizures indicate quality of perinatal care. *Arch Dis Child* **60**: 809–13

Dickson G (1995) Principles of risk management. In: Vincent C (ed) *Clinical Risk Management*. BMJ, Publishing Group, London: 18–30

Dickson MJ, Willett M (1999) Midwives would prefer a vaginal delivery (letter). *Br Med J* **319**: 1008

Dillner L (1995) Babies' deaths linked to suboptimal care. *Br Med J* **310**: 757

Dimond B (1990) *Legal aspects of nursing*. Prentice Hall, London

Dimond B (1994a) *The Legal Aspects of Midwifery*. Books for Midwives Press, Hale

Dimond B (1994b) Reliable or liable? *Modern Midwife* **4**(4): 6–7

Dimond B (1996) Legal issues. The midwife as expert witness. *Mod Midwife* **6**(4): 22–3

Dimond B (1998a) Clinical risk management: is it just a sham? *Br J Nurs* **7**: 813

Dimond B (1998b) Abbreviations, record keeping and the midwife. *The Practising Midwife* **1**(9): 10–11

Dimond B (1999a) Is there a legal right to choose a caesarean? *Br J Midwifery* **7**: 515–518

Dimond B (1999b) *Patients' rights, responsibilities and the nurse.* 2nd edn. Quay Books, Mark Allen Publishing Ltd, Salisbury

Dingwall R (1986) Maternity care at a premium? *Nurs Times* **82**: 38–9

Dingwall R (1994) Litigation and the threat to Medicine. In: Gabe J, Kelleher D, Williams G (eds) *Challenging Medicine*, Routledge, London

Dingwall R, Fenn P (1991) Is risk management necessary? *Int J Risk Safety in Med* **2**: 91–106

Dingwall R, Fenn P, Quam L (1991) *Medical Negligence – a review and bibliography*. Centre for Socio-Legal Studies, Oxford

Divers M (1994) Personal View: Tradition is better than technology. *Br Med J* **308**: 1244–45

DoH – see Department of Health

Doherty R, James CE (1994) Malpractice in obstetrics and gynaecology. In: Bonnar J (ed) *Recent advances in Obstetrics and Gynaecology*. Churchill Livingstone, Edinburgh

Drife JO (1993) Errors and accidents in obstetrics. In: Vincent C, Ennis M, Audley R (eds) *Medical Accidents*. OUP, Oxford: 34–51

Drife JO (1995) Reducing risk in obstetrics. In: Vincent C (ed) *Clinical Risk Management*. BMJ Publishing Group, London: 129–146

Duff L, Kelson M, Marriott S, McIntosh A, Brown S, Cape J, Marcus N, Traynor M (1996) Clinical guidelines: involving patients and users of services. *J Clin Effectiveness* **1**: 104–112

Dunne R (1999) GMC to clear jam of complaints. *Hosp Doctor,* 12 August: 3

Dworkin RB (1989) Law and the modern obstetrician-gynecologist. *Am J Obstet Gynecol* **160**: 1339–43

Dyer C (1990) Pressure for no fault on three fronts. *Br Med J* **301**: 1010

Dyer C (1995) Pilot study could cut medical negligence costs. *Br Med J* **311**: 770–1

Dyer C (1996) Fast track scheme for medical negligence starts. *Br Med J* **313**: 187

Dyer C (1998) Once it was bad luck, now it's get a lawyer and sue. *The Guardian*, 17 October: 6

Dyer C (2000) NHS bill for negligence set to soar again. *Br Med J* **320**: 891

Easterbrook J (1996) Medical negligence update. *Solicitors' Journal* **140**: 381

Ennis M (1990) *The Mismatch between Skill and Confidence*. Unpublished paper at British Psychological Society conference

Ennis M (1991) Training and supervision of obstetric senior house officers. *Br Med J* **303**: 1442–43

Ennis M, Clark A, Grudzinskas J (1991) Change in obstetric practice in response to fear of litigation in the British Isles. *Lancet* **338**: 616–18

Ennis M, Vincent C (1990) Obstetric accidents: a review of 64 cases. *Br Med J* **300**: 1365–67

Epstein R (1988) Market and regulatory approaches to medical malpractice: the Virginia Obstetrical No-Fault Statute. *Virginia Law Review* **74**: 1451–74

Etzioni A (1975) Alternative conceptions of accountability. In: Greenfield H (ed) *Accountability in health facilities*. Praeger Publishers, New York

Evans J (1995) Evidence-based and evidence-biased medicine. *Age Ageing* **24**: 461–3

Felstiner W, Abel R, Sarat A (1981) The emergence and transformation of disputes: naming, blaming, claiming. *Law Society Review* **15**(3–4): 631–54

Fenn P (1993) The no-fault panacea? *Br J Obstet Gynaecol* **100**: 103–4

Fenn P, Dingwall R (1989) Medical negligence and crown indemnity. In: *Health Care UK 1989*. Hermitage Berks Policy Journals

Fenn P, Dingwall R (1995) Mutual trust? *Br Med J* **310**: 756

Fenn P, Whelan C (1989) Medical litigation. In: Dingwall R (ed) *Socio-legal aspects of medical practice*. Royal College of Physicians, London

Field L (1999) Post-traumatic stress disorder: a reappraisal. *J R Soc Med* **92**: 35–37

Field M, Lohr K (1990) *Clinical practice guidelines: directions for a new program*. National Academy Press, Washington DC: 14

Fisher C (1990) No-fault insurance in obstetrics. *Med J Australia* **153**: 639–41

Fleming V, Douglas V, Poat A, Curzio J, Cheyne J, Cheyne H, Stenhouse E (2000) *Examination of the fitness for purpose of pre-registration midwifery programmes in Scotland*. NBS, Edinburgh

Foster C (1999) Woolf and conditional fees. *Health Care Risk Report*, June: 10–11

Foster S (1996) Causation in medical negligence cases: recent developments. *Solicitors' J* **140**: 1098–1100

Frank J (1945) Courts on trial: myth and reality in American justice. (Cited by Vidmar 1989)

Freeman J (1992) Cerebral palsy and the 'Bad Baby' malpractice crisis. *Am J Dis Child* **146**: 725–727

Freeman J, Nelson K (1988) Intrapartum asphyxia and cerebral palsy. *Pediatrics* **182**: 240–249

Furedi F (1997) *Culture of Fear*. Cassell, London

Gaffney G, Sellers S, Flavell V, Squier M, Johnson A (1994) Case-control study of intrapartum care, cerebral palsy, and perinatal death. *Br Med J* **308**: 743–50

Galanter M (1974) Why the 'haves' come out ahead: speculations on the limits of legal change. *Law and Society Review* **9**: 95–160

Gallup C (1989) Can no-fault compensation of impaired infants alleviate the malpractice crisis in obstetrics? *J Health Polit Policy Law* **14**: 691

Genn H (1987) *Hard Bargaining*. Clarendon, Oxford

Genn H (1989) Negotiating the settlement of claims: issues in medical negligence. In: Dingwall R (ed) *Socio-legal aspects of medical practice*. Royal College of Physicians, London

Genn H (1999) *Mediation in action*. Calouste Gulbenkian Foundation, London

Genn H, Lloyd-Bostock S (1990) Medical negligence – major new research in progress. *J Med Defence Union* **6**: 42–43

Gibb D, Arulkamaren P (1997) *Fetal monitoring in practice*. 2nd edn. Butterworth Heinemann, Oxford

General Medical Council (1989) *Professional conduct and discipline: fitness to practice*. GMC, London

General Medical Council (1993) *Annual Report*. GMC, London

General Medical Council (1995) *Good Medical Practice*. GMC, London

General Medical Council (1998) *Good Medical Practice*. 2nd edn. GMC, London

Goldrein I (1994) Exploding the Bolam myth. *New Law Journal* 16 Sept–28 Oct (seven weekly articles: 1237–1481)

Goldrein I, de Haas MR (1992) Handling cerebral palsy/obstetric negligence claims. *New Law Journal* **142**: 934

Gonen R, Spiegel D, Abend M (1996) Is macrosomia predictable, and are shoulder dystocia and birth trauma preventable? *Obstet Gynecol* **88**: 526–529

Goodwin T, Belai I, Hernandez P, Durand M, Paul R (1992) Asphyxial complications in the term newborn with severe umbilical acidaemia. *Am J Obstet Gynecol* **162**: 1506–12

Gould J, Davey B, Stafford R (1989) Socio-economic differences in rates of cesarean section. *New Engl J Med* **321**: 233–9

Goyert G, Bottoms S, Treadwell M, Nehra P (1989) The physician factor in cesarean birth rates. *New Engl J Med* **320**: 706–709

Grant A (1987) Birth problems and long term morbidity. In: Hosking G, Murphy G (eds) *Prevention of medical handicap: a world view*. Royal Society of Medicine Services International Congress and Symposium Series No.112. Royal Society of Medicine Services Limited, London

Grant A, Joy M-T, O'Brien N, Hennessy E, MacDonald D (1989) Cerebral palsy among children born during the Dublin randomised trial of intrapartum monitoring. *Lancet* **334**: 1233–1236

Greene E (1989) On juries and damages awards: the process of decision-making. *Law and Contemporary Problems* **52**(4): 223–246

Greenfield H (1975) *Accountability in health facilities*. Praeger Publishers, New York

Grimley Evans J (1995) Evidence-based and evidence-biased medicine. *Age Ageing* **24**: 461–3

Grimshaw J, Russell I (1993) Effect of clinical guidelines on medical practice: a systematic review of rigorous evaluations. *Lancet* **342**: 1317–22

Halle M (1997) Rise in legal action hits Britain's GPs. *Br Med J* **314**: 326

Hallgren A, Kihlgren M, Norberg A, Forslin L (1995) Women's perceptions of childbirth and childbirth education before and after education and birth. *Midwifery* **11**. 130 137

Ham C, Dingwall R, Fenn P (1988) *Medical Negligence: Compensation and Accountability*. King's Fund Institute, London

Hans V, Vidmar N (1991) The American Jury at 25 years. *Law and Social Inquiry*: *323–51*

Harpwood V (1996) *Legal Issues in Obstetrics*. Dartmouth, Aldershot, Brookfield USA, Singapore, Sydney

Haverkamp A, Orleans M, Langendoerfer S, McFee J, Murphy J, Thompson H (1979) A controlled trial of the differential effects of intrapartum fetal monitoring. *Am J Obstet Gynecol* **134**: 399–412

Haverkamp A, Thompson H, McFee J, Cetrulo C (1976) The evaluation of continuous FHR monitoring in high risk pregnancy. *Am J Obstet Gynecol* **125**: 310–320

Hawkins C, Paterson I (1987) Medico-legal audit in the West Midlands region: analysis of 100 cases. *Br Med J*: 295, 1533–1536

Henderson M (1997) Baby died after doctor used forceps ten times. *The Times*, 21 November: 8

Henderson-Smart D (1991) Throwing the baby out with the fetal monitoring? *Med J Australia* **154**: 576–7

Hengstler G (1986) MDs won't deliver. *Am Bar Assoc J* **72** (July): 20

Hensleigh PA, Fainstat T, Spencer R (1986) Perinatal events and cerebral palsy. *Am J Obstet Gynecol* **154**: 978–81

Herczeg J (1997) High-risk obstetrics, medicolegal problems. *Eur J Obstet Gyneco Reprod Biol* **71**: 181–5

Hewson B (1997) How to escape the surgeon's knife. *New Law J* **147**: 752

Heywood Jones I (1999) Code breakers: the professional disciplinary process. In: Heywood Jones I (ed) *The UKCC Code of Conduct: a critical guide*. NT Books, London: 216–229.

Hirshfeld EB (1991) Should practice parameters be the standard of care in malpractice litigation? *J Am Med Assoc* **266**: 2886–91

Hodgson J (1981) Professional negligence clarified. *New Law J* **131**: 2

Hough M, Mayhew P (1985) *The British Crime Survey, First Report*. HMSO, London

House of Commons (1992) *Health Committee. Second Report: the Maternity Services* (The Winterton Report). HMSO, London:

Howard R (1999) Pregnant women should have choices (letter). *Br Med J* **318**: 122

Howie R (1983) The standard of care in medical negligence. *Juridical Review*: 193

Hoy T (1997) Using antenatal testing to sabotage home birth. *AIMS J* **9**(1): 13–16

Hoyte P (1997) Writing medico-legal reports. *J Med Defence Union* **13**(1): 18–20

HSC (Health Service Commissioner) (1997) *Selected investigations October 1996–March 1997*. HMSO, London

Hull J, Dodd K (1991) What is birth asphyxia? *Br J Obstet Gynaecol* **98**: 953–5

Huntingford P (1990) Obstetrics and Gynaecology. In: Powers J, Harris N (eds) *Medical Negligence*. Butterworths, London

Hupert N, Lawthers A, Brennan T, Peterson L (1996) Processing the tort deterrent signal: a qualitative study. *Soc Sci Med* **43**: 1–11

Hurwitz, B (1998) *Clinical Guidelines and the Law – negligence, discretion and judgment*. Radcliffe Medical Press, Abingdon

Hutton W (1998) Until we learn to love risk, we will always be second rate. *The Observer*, 21 December: 28

Hyams AL, Brandenburg JA, Lipsitz SR, Shapiro DW, Brennan TA (1995) Practice guidelines and malpractice litigation: a two-way street. *Ann Intern Med* **122**: 450

Idama T, Lindow S (1999) Safest option is still to aim for vaginal delivery (letter). *Br Med J* **318**: 121

Illingworth R (1985) A paediatrician asks – why is it called birth injury? *Br J Obstet Gynaecol* **92**: 122–130

Illingworth R (1987) Litigation and birth. *J Med Defence Union* **3**: 14–15

Isherwood K (1995) Independent midwifery in the UK. In: Murphy-Black T (ed) *Issues in Midwifery*. Churchill Livingstone, Edinburgh: 21–40

Jackson K (1994) Preceptorship involves irreconcilable concepts. *Br J Midwifery* **2**: 174–175

Jackson N, Irvine L (1998) The influence of maternal request on the elective caesarean rate. *J Obstet Gynaecol* **18**: 115–119

Jakobovits A (1996) Medico-legal aspects of brachial plexus injury: the obstetrician's point of view. *Med Law* **15**: 175–182

James C (1991) Risk management in obstetrics and gynaecology. *J Med Defence Union* **7**: 36–38

Jane (1996) A visit to the consultant. *AIMS J* **8**(3): 14

Johnson A (1991) *What proportion of cerebral palsy is due to birth asphyxia?* (unpublished)

Jutras D (1993) Clinical practice guidelines as legal norms. *Can Med Assoc J* **148**: 905–909

Kalven H, Zeisel H (1966) *The American Jury*. Little, Brown & Co, Boston

Keegan K, Waffarn F, Quilligan E (1985) Obstetric characteristics and fetal heart rate patterns of infants who convulse during the newborn period. *Am J Obstet Gynecol* **153**: 732–7

Keifer WS (1993) Preparing for obstetrics in the 21st century: Quo Vadis? *Am J Obstet Gynecol* **168**: 1787–90

Kenney N, Macfarlane A (1997) The availability of statistical information to women. What are your experiences? *AIMS J* **9**(3): 9

Kinnes S (1993) Claiming for damages. *Scotland on Sunday* (Spectrum) 5 December: 6

Kirby M (1995) Patients' rights – why the Australian courts have rejected 'Bolam'. *J Med Ethics* **21**: 5–8

Kirkham M (1989) Midwives and information-giving during labour. In: Robinson R, Thomson A (eds) *Midwives, Research and Childbirth* (Volume 1). Chapman and Hall, London:117–138

Klein R (1973) *Complaints against Doctors*. C. Knight, London

Kraus N (1990) Practising nurse-midwifery in the medical-legal climate. *J Nurse-Midwifery* **35**: 307–314

Kritzer HM, Bogart WA, Vidmar N (1991) The aftermath of injury: cultural factors in compensation seeking in Canada and the United States. *Law and Soc Rev* **25**: 499–543

Laisram N, Srivastava VK, Srivastava RK (1992) Cerebral palsy – an etiological study. *Indian J Pediatrics* **59**: 723–8

Lamb B (1992) Cerebral palsy in the wider context. In: *Cerebral palsy: a medico-legal investigation*. AVMA Conference transcript

Lamont L (1993) Why patients don't sue doctors. *J Med Defence Union* **9**(2): 39–41

Law D, Lewington T, Fletcher R, Hawkins C (1996) Allegations of Medical Negligence against Hospitals in the West Midlands Region. *J Med Defence Union* **12**(3): 67–69

Leahy Taylor J (1982) *The Doctor and the Law*. Pitman, London, Marshfield, Mass

Leape L, Brennan T, Laird N, Lawthers A, Localio AR, Barnes B, Hebert L, Newhouse J, Weiler P, Hiatt H (1991) The nature of adverse events in hospitalised patients: results of the Harvard Medical Practice Study II. *New Engl J Med* **324**: 377–84

Levene M, Sands C, Grindulis H, Moore J (1986) Comparison of two methods of predicting outcome in perinatal asphyxia. *Lancet* **327**: 67–68

Levinson W, Roter D, Mullooly J, Dull V, Frankel R (1997) Physician-Patient Communication. *J Am Med Assoc* **277**: 553–559

Lewis C (1996) The expert and the medical negligence action. *Clinical Risk* **2**: 68–70

Lillienfield A, Parkhurst E (1951) A study of the association of factors of pregnancy and parturition with the development of cerebral palsy. *Am J Hygiene* **53**: 262

Little W (1862) On the influence of abnormal parturition, difficult labours, premature births, and asphyxia neonatorum on the mental and physical condition of the child especially in relation to deformities. *Trans Obstet Soc London* **3**: 293–344

Localio A, Lawthers A, Bengtson J, Hebert L, Weaver S, Brennan T, Landis J (1993) Relationship between malpractice claims and cesarean delivery. *J Am Med Assoc* **269**: 366–373

Low J, Galbraith R, Muir D, Killen H, Pater E, Karchmar E (1984) Factors associated with motor and cognitive defects in children after intrapartum fetal hypoxia. *Am J Obstet Gynecol* **148**: 533–9

Low J, Galbraith R, Muir D, Killen H, Pater E, Karchmar EJ (1992) Mortality and morbidity after intrapartum asphyxia in the preterm fetus. *Obstet Gynecol* **80**: 57–61

MacArthur, Lewis M, Knox E *et al* (1990) Epidural anaesthesia and long-term backache after childbirth. *Br Med J* **301**: 9–12

MacDermott (Lord Chief Justice) (1997) A judicial point of view with regard to the testimony of medical experts. *Med Law* **16**: 635–642

MacDonald D, Grant A, Sheridan-Pereira M, Boylan P, Chalmers I (1985) The Dublin randomised controlled trial of intrapartum fetal heart rate monitoring. *Am J Obstet Gynecol* **152**: 524–39

MacFarlane A, Mugford M (1984) *Birth Counts*. HMSO, London

Maclean M (1989) Alternatives to litigation: no-fault or effective social security? In: Dingwall R (ed) *Socio-legal aspects of medical practice*. Royal College of Physicians, London

MacLennan A (1999) A template for defining a causal relationship between acute intrapartum events and cerebral palsy: international consensus statement. *Br Med J* **319**: 1054–59

MacLeod J, Macintyre C, McClure J *et al* (1995) Backache and epidural analgesia: a retrospective survey of mothers one year after childbirth. *Int J Obstet Anaesth* **4**: 21–25

Mahendra B (1999) Keeping up to the mark. *New Law Journal* **149**: 935

Mann L (1986) Pregnancy events and brain damage. *Am J Obstet Gynecol* **15**: 6–9

Mansell W (1997) Tort and socio-legal studies. The road to Damascus: paved with good intentions but few Epiphanies. In: Thomas P (ed) *Socio-Legal Studies*. Dartmouth: Aldershot, Brookfield USA, Singapore, Sydney: 222–238

Manuel B (1990) Professional liability – a no-fault solution. *New Engl J Med* **322**: 627–31

Manuel B (1992) What may happen if there is no change in the UK system? In: Wall J (ed) *Compensation and Accountability – keeping the balance*. Mercury Books, London

Marks P (1997) Fault/no fault compensation – the same thing? *New Law J* **147**: 26

Marlow N (1992) Do we need an Apgar score? *Arch Dis Child* **67**: 765–9

Martin C (1998) Electronic fetal monitoring: a brief summary of its development, problems and prospects. *Eur J Obstet Gynecol Reprod Biol* **78**: 133–140

Mashaw J (1983) *Bureaucratic justice*. Yale University Press, New Haven, London

Mason K, McCall Smith R (1999) *Law and Medical Ethics*. 5th edn. Butterworths, London

May M, Stengel D (1990) Who sues their doctors? How patients handle medical grievances. *Law Soc Rev* **24**: 105–120

McElhaney J (1989) Expert witnesses. *Am Bar Assoc J* **75** (March): 98–9

McHale J, Fox M (1997) *Health Care Law*. Sweet and Maxwell, London

MCHRC (Maternal and Child Health Research Consortium) (1997) *Confidential Enquiry into Stillbirths and Deaths in Infancy*. MCHRC, London

MCHRC (1999) *Confidential Enquiry into Stillbirths and Deaths in Infancy* (6th annual report). MCHRC, London

McKain B (1991) Parents lose £1m action over severely brain damaged boy. *Glasgow Herald*, 27 Sept

McLean S (1988) No fault liability and medical responsibility. In: Freeman M (ed) *Medicine, Ethics and the Law*. Stevens and Sons, London

McNeil P (1998) Legal procedures: preliminary investigation to trial. In: Thomas L, McNeil P (eds) *Medical Accidents Handbook*. John Wiley & Sons, Chichester

McRae MJ (1999) Fetal surveillance and monitoring: legal issues revisited. *J Ob Gynecol Neonatal Nurs* **28**: 310–319

Mildred M (1989) Reforming the tort system. *New Law J* **139**: 124

Minchon P, Niswander K, Chalmers I, Dauncey M, Newcombe R, Elbourne D, Mutch L, Andrews J, Williams G (1987) Antecedents and outcome of very early neonatal seizures in infants born at or after term. *Br J Obstet Gynaecol* **94**: 431–39

Montgomery J (1997) *Health Care Law*. University Press, Oxford

Morlock L, Malitz F (1991) Do hospital risk management programs make a difference? Relationships between risk management program activities and hospital malpractice claims experience. *Law and Contemporary Problems* **54**(2): 1–22

Morrison J, Rennie J, Milton P (1995) Neonatal respiratory morbidity and mode of delivery at term: influence of timing of elective caesarean section. *Br J Obstet Gynaecol* **102**: 101–106

MPS (Medical Protection Society) (1989) *Annual Report*. Medical Protection Society, London

Mulligan J, Painter M, O'Donoghue P, MacDonald H, Allen A, Taylor P (1980) Neonatal asphyxia 2: Neonatal mortality and long-term sequelae. *J Pediatr* **96**: 903–907

Murphy K, Johnson P, Moorcraft J, Pattinson J, Russell V, Turnbull A (1990) Birth asphyxia and the intrapartum cardiotocograph. *Br J Obstet Gynaecol* **97**: 470–79

Murphy R (1997) Legal and practical impact of clinical practice guidelines on nursing and medical practice. *Nurse Pract* **22**(3):138, 147–8

Naeye R, Peters E, Bartholomew M, Landis R (1989) Origins of cerebral palsy. *Am J Dis Child* **143**: 1154–61

NAO (National Audit Office) (1997) *The NHS (England) accounts 1995–96 (HC 127)*. HMSO, London

NAO (1999) *NHS summarised accounts 1997–98*. HMSO, London

Neale G, Clements R, Hudson M, Leigh S (1996) The medico-legal system and the role of the expert. *Clinical Risk* **2**: 196–9

Nelson K (1988) What proportion of cerebral palsy is related to birth asphyxia? *J Pediatr* (Australia) **112**: 572–573

Nelson K, Ellenberg J (1981) Apgar scores as predictors of chronic neurologic disability. *Pediatr* **68**: 36–44

Neuberger J (1992) Discussion section. In: Wall J (ed) *Compensation and Accountability – keeping the balance* (Proceedings of MDU conference). Mercury Books, London

Neutra R, Fienberg S, Greenland S, Friedman E (1978) Effect of fetal monitoring on neonatal death rates. *New Engl J Med* **299**: 324–326

Newman M (1996) The emotional impact of mistakes on family physicians. *Arch Fam Med* **5**: 71–75

NHS Executive (1996) *Listening... Acting... Improving. Guidance on Implementation of the NHS Complaints Procedure*. DoH, London

Nielsen P, Stigsby B, Nickelsen C, Nim J (1987) Intra- and inter-observer variability in the assessment of intrapartum CTGs. *Acta Obstet Gynecol Scand* **66**: 421–424

Norman B, Crowhurst J, Plaat F (1999) All types of anaesthesia carry risks (letter). *Br Med J* **318**: 120

Norrie K (1985) Medical negligence: who sets the standard? *J Med Ethics* **11**(3): 135–137

Norrie K (1987) Reasonable: the keystone of negligence. *J Med Ethics* **13**(2): 92–94

Northcott N (1998) Don't accept the debrief. *Nurs Times* **94**(10): 32

O'Connell J (1971) *The Injury Industry (and the remedy of no-fault insurance)*. Commerce Clearing House Inc, New York, Chicago, Washington

O'Connell J (1988) Pragmatic constraints on market approaches: a response to Professor Epstein. *Virginia Law Rev* **74**: 1475-83

O'Connell J, Simon R (1972) *The Payment for pain and suffering: who wants what, when and why?* Insurers Press Inc, Illinois

O'Meara C (1993) An evaluation of consumer perspectives of childbirth and parenting education. *Midwifery* **9**: 210–219

O'Leary J (1993) Cephalic replacement for shoulder dystocia: present status and future role of the Zavanelli manoeuvre. *Obstet Gynecol* **79**: 883–884

Oliphant K (1996) Defining 'Medical Misadventure'. Lessons from New Zealand. *Med Law Rev* **4**: 1–31

Osborne J (1999) Learning to bear hurt without laying blame. *The Times*, 6 February 1999: 16

Page L (1997) Evidence-based practice in midwifery: a virtual revolution? *J Clin Effectiveness* **2**: 10–13

Palmer G (1994) New Zealand 20 years on. *University of Toronto Law Journal*: 223

Paneth N (1993) The causes of cerebral palsy: recent evidence. *Clin Invest Med* (Canada) **16**: 95–102

Paneth N, Stark R (1983) Cerebral palsy and mental retardation in relation to indicators of perinatal asphyxia. *Am J Obstet Gynecol* **147**: 960–66

Parker D, Lawton R (1999) Attitudes to rule-related behaviour in the NHS. *Risk and Human Behaviour Newsletter* (ESRC) **6**: 11–15

Paterson-Brown S (1998) Should doctors perform an elective caesarean section on request? – Yes, as long as the woman is fully informed. *Br Med J* **317**: 462–3 (see correspondence: de Zulueta; Stirrat and Gunn; Idamo and Lindow; van Roosmalen; all 1999)

Pattison A (1997) Banging your head against a brick wall? The insolvent defender. *J Personal Injury Litigation* 4/97: 264–273

Payne-James J, Smith P (1996) Professional bodies and discipline. In: Payne-James J, Dean P, Wall I, (eds) *Medicolegal Essentials in Healthcare*. Churchill Livingstone, Edinburgh

Payne-James J, Dean P, Wall I (1996) *Medicolegal essentials in healthcare*. Churchill Livingstone, New York, Edinburgh, London

Peach L (1999) *Fitness for purpose. The UKCC Commission for Nursing and Midwifery Education*. UKCC, London

Pearson, Lord (Chairman) (1978) *Royal Commission on Civil Liability and Compensation for Personal Injury*. HMSO. Cmnd 7054, London

Perlman J, Tack E, Martin T, Shakelford G, Amon E (1989) Acute systemic organ injury in term infants after asphyxia. *Am J Dis Child* **143**: 617–620

Phillips A (1997) *Medical Negligence: seeking a balance*. Dartmouth, Aldershot, Brookfield USA, Singapore, Sydney

Powers M, Branthwaite M (1996) Foreseeability and remoteness. *Clinical Risk* **2**: 85–87

Puxon M (1996a) Comment section: *Murphy v Wirral* HA [1996] 7 Medical Law Reports, 107

Puxon M (1996b) Comment section: *Wiszniewski v Central Manchester HA* 1992 W 12365 [1996] 7 Medical Law Reports, 248

Puxon M (1997) Comment section: *Robertson v Nottingham HA* [1997] 8 Medical Law Reports, 1

Quam L, Dingwall R, Fenn P (1987) Medical malpractice in perspective – Part 2: The implications for Britain. *Br Med J* **294**: 1597–1599

Quam L, Dingwall R, Fenn P (1988) Medical malpractice claims in obstetrics and gynaecology: comparisons between the United States and Britain. *Br J Obstet Gynaecol* **95**: 454–461

Quilliam S (1999) Clinical risk management in midwifery: what are midwives for? *MIDIRS Midwifery Digest* **9**: 280–284

Ranjan V (1993) Obstetrics and the fear of litigation. *Professional Care of Mother and Child*, January 1993: 10–12

RCM (1992) *A Philosophy for Midwives*. RCM, London

RCOG/RCM (Royal College of Obstetricians and Gynaecologists/Royal College of Midwives) (1999) *Towards Safer Childbirth: minimum standards for the organisation of Labour Wards*. RCOG, London

Reason J (1993) The human factor in medical accidents. In: Vincent C, Ennis M, Audley R (eds) *Medical Accidents*. OUP, Oxford: 1–16

Relman A (1990) Changing the malpractice liability system. *New Engl J Med* **322**: 626–7

Renn O (1992) Concepts of risk: a classification. In: Krimsky S, Golding D (eds) *Social Theories of Risk*. Praeger, Westport, CT: 53–82

Richards T (1999) Australia's consumer champion. *Br Med J* **319**: 730

Ritchie J, Davies S (1995) Professional negligence: a duty of candid disclosure? *Br Med J* **310**: 888–9

Roberts G (1993) If only a caesarean had been carried out. *J Med Defence Union* **9**: 76–78

Robertson J (1991) Disabled boy's parents lose damages case. *Scotsman,* 27 September

Robertson J (1992) Negligence case settled in advance of judgement. *Scotsman,* 22 January

Robinson G (1986) Midwifery and malpractice insurance: a profession fights for survival. *University of Pennsylvania Law Rev 134*: 1001–1034

Robinson J (1996) Complaining about complaints. *Br J Midwifery* **4**: 323–324.

Robinson J (1998) Dangers of debriefing. *Br J Midwifery* **6**: 251

Robinson J (1999) The demand for caesareans: fact or fiction? *Br J Midwifery* **7**: 306

Robinson S, Golden J, Bradley S (1983) *A study of the role and responsibilities of the midwife*. Nursing Research Education Unit Report No. 1, Chelsea College, London University

Rommal C (1996) Risk management issues in the perinatal setting. *J Perinat Neonat Nurs* **10**: 1–31

Rosenblatt R, Hurst A (1989) An analysis of closed obstetric malpractice claims. *Obstet Gynecol* **74**: 710–4

Rosenblatt R, Weitkamp G, Lloyd M, Schafer B, Winterscheid L, Hart L (1990) Why do physicians stop practising obstetrics? The impact of malpractice claims. *Obstet Gynecol* **76**: 245–250

Rosenthal (1983) Nature of jury response to the expert witness. *J Forensic Science* **28**: 528

Rosenthal A (1999) Maternal age is important (letter). *Br Med J* **318**: 121–2

Rosser J (1999) Women behaving badly. *The Practising Midwife* **2**(8): 4–5

Rostow V, Osterweis M, Bulger R (1989) Medical professional liability and the delivery of obstetrical care. *New Engl J Med* **321**: 1057–1060

Rushton W (1975) *Sassenach's Scotland*. House of Seagram, England

Ruth V, Raivio K (1988) Perinatal brain damage: predictive value of metabolic acidosis and the Apgar score. *Br Med J* **297**: 24–27

Sacks L (1997) Res ipsa loquitur. *J Am Med Assoc* **278**: 471–472

Sandall J (1997) Midwives' burnout and continuity of care. *Br J Midwifery* **5**: 106–111

Saulo M, Wagener R (1996) How good case managers make tough choices: ethics and mediation Part II. *J Care Management* **2** (2): 10–12

Saunders P (1992) Recruitment in obstetrics and gynaecology: RCOG sets initiatives. *Br J Obstet Gynaecol* **99**: 538–46

Savulescu J, Momeyer R (1997) Should informed consent be based on rational beliefs? *J Med Ethics* **23**: 282–288

Scott W (1998) Bolam and Bolitho: a new standard of care for doctors? *New Law J* **148**: 64

Scottish Office (1993) *The provision of maternity services in Scotland: a policy review*. Scottish Office Home and Health Department, Edinburgh

Scottish Office (1997) *Designed to Care*. Scottish Office Health Department, Edinburgh

Scottish Office (1999) *Report on the review of medical indemnity and 'other risks' reimbursement arrangements*. Scottish Office Health Department, Edinburgh

Senior OE, Symonds EM (1996) A do-it-yourself package for managers. *Clinical Risk* **2**: 107–113

Shapiro R, Simpson D, Lawrence S, Talsky AM, Sobicinski K, Schiedermayer D (1989) A survey of sued and nonsued physicians and suing patients. *Arch Intern Med* **149**: 2190–6

Sharp D, Chamberlain G (1992) Doctors' concerns about litigation. In: Chamberlain G (ed) *How to avoid medico-legal problems in obstetrics and gynaecology*. RCOG, London

Shaw GB (1946) *Recoil of the dogma of medical infallibility on the doctor (Preface to 'The Doctor's Dilemma')*. Penguin, Harmondsworth Middlesex

Sheikh A, Hurwitz B (1999) A national database of medical error. *J R Soc Med* **92**: 554–5

Shepperd S, Charnock D, Gann B (1999) Helping patients access high quality health information. *Br Med J* **319**: 746–66

Simanowitz A (1987) Medical accidents: the problem and the challenge. In: Byrne P (ed) *Medicine in contemporary society*. King Edwards Hospital Fund for London, London

Simanowitz A (1992) Discussion section. In: Wall J (ed) *Compensation and Accountability – keeping the balance* (Proceedings of MDU conference). Mercury Books, London

Sloan F, Whetten-Goldstein K, Stout E, Entman S, Hickson G (1998) No-fault system of compensation for obstetric injury: winners and losers. *Obstet Gynecol* **91**: 437–43

Sloan F, Mergenhagen P, Burfiel W, Bovbjerg R, Hassan M (1989) Medical malpractice experience of physicians. *J Am Med Assoc* **262**: 3291–7

Sloan F, Whetton-Goldstein K, Githens P, Entman S (1995) Effects of the threat of medical malpractice litigation and other factors on birth outcomes. *Med Care* **33**(7): 700–14

Slovenko R (1996) Humor in the courtroom. *Med Law* **15**: 589–90

Smith R (1990) No fault compensation: the momentum builds. *Br Med J* **301**: 1350

Springett P, Finch J (1998) Rogers pays for Lloyd's pipes. *The Guardian*, 8 July: 33

Stanbridge R (1999) Make a good legal profit. *Hosp Doctor*, 22 July: 43

Stanley F (1994) Cerebral palsy – The courts catch up with sad realities. *Med J Australia* **161**: 236

Stanley FJ, Blair E (1991) Why have we failed to reduce the frequency of cerebral palsy? *Med J Australia* **154**: 623–6

Steer P (1999) Assessment of mother and fetus in labour. *Br Med J* **318**: 858–861

Steer P, Danielian P (1999) Fetal distress in labor. In: Steer P, Weiner C, Gonik B (eds) *High Risk Pregnancy*. 2nd edition. WB Saunders, London: 1121–1149

Stirrat G, Dunn P (1999) Obstetricians are more than technicians (letter). *Br Med J* **318**: 120–121

Strunin L, Davies J (1995) Candid disclosure is right (letter). *Br Med J* **310**: 1671

Stuttaford T (1988) A poisonous messenger? *The Times*, 20 October: 15

Sureau C (1996) Historical perspectives: forgotten past, unpredictable future. *Baillières Clin Obstet Gynaecol* **10**: 167–84

Symon A (1992) *Litigation in perinatal care: Who's accountable? Who's to blame?* (MA [Hons] thesis). University of Edinburgh (unpublished)

Symon A (1994) Midwives and Litigation 2: a small scale survey of attitudes. *Br J Midwifery* **2**: 176–181

Symon A (1997) *The Rise and Fall of Perinatal Litigation – a medico-legal examination of allegations of negligence in childbirth* (PhD thesis). University of Edinburgh

Symon A (1998) *Litigation – the views of midwives and obstetricians (Who's Accountable? Who's to blame?)*. Hochland and Hochland, Hale

Symon A (1999a) Perinatal litigation in Scotland 1980–95: its incidence, rate and nature. *J Obstet Gynaecol* **19**: 239–247

Symon A (1999b) Inter-professional and peer criticism: a side-effect of litigation? *J Obstet Gynaecol* **19**: 248–252

Symon A (2000) Litigation and changes in professional behaviour: a qualitative appraisal. *Midwifery* **16**: 15–21

Symonds EM (1987) Defensive Obstetrics. *Hosp Update* (October): 846–8

Symonds EM (1992) Medico-legal aspects. In: Shaw RW, Soutter WP, Staunton SL (eds) *Gynaecology*. Churchill Livingstone, Edinburgh

Taylor D, Ricketts T, Berman J, Kolimaga J (1992) One state's response to the malpractice insurance crisis: North Carolina's obstetrical care incentive program. *Public Health Rep* **107**: 523–9

Taylor-Adams S, Lyons D (1998) Do obstetric staff know when to call for assistance. *Healthcare Risk Resource* **1**(4): 2-3

Tharmaratnam S, Gillmer M (1995) The litigation boom in obstetrics. *Obstet Gynaecol Today* **6**(2): 17–20

Tingle J (1998) Negligence is costing the NHS £2.3 billion. *Br J Nurs* **7**: 873

Towbin A (1986) Obstetric malpractice litigation: the pathologist's view. *Am J Obstet Gynecol* **155**: 927–935

Towse A, Danzon P (1999) Medical negligence and the NHS: an economic analysis. *Health Economist* **8**(2): 93–101

Tranter S (1996) Acting as an expert witness: courtroom skills. *Midwives* **109**: 306–7

Truelove A (1985) On handling complaints. *Hosp Health Services Rev* (Sept): 229–232

Tucker J, Hall M, Howie P, Reid M, Barbour R, Florey C, McIlwaine G (1996) Should obstetricians see women with normal pregnancies? A multicentre randomised controlled trial of routine antenatal care given by general practitioners and midwives compared with shared care led by obstetricians. *Br Med J* **312**: 554–559

UK Health Departments (1996) *Report on Confidential Enquiries into Maternal Deaths in the United Kingdom 1991–93*. HMSO, London

UKCC (United Kingdom Central Council for Nursing, Midwifery & Health Visiting)

UKCC (1989) *Exercising Accountability*. UKCC, London

UKCC (1992) *Code of Professional Conduct*. UKCC, London

UKCC (1992b) *The Scope of Professional Practice*. UKCC, London

UKCC (1993) *Midwives' Rules*. UKCC, London

UKCC (1996) *Guidelines for Professional Practice*. UKCC, London

UKCC (1998a) *Complaints about Professional Conduct*. UKCC, London

UKCC (1998b) *Midwives' Rules and Code of Practice*. UKCC, London

van Liew D (1997) Clinical risk management within the NHS. *Nurs Times Res* **2**(2): 88–96

van Roosmalen (1999) Unnecessary caesareans should be avoided (letter). *Br Med J* **318**: 121

Vidmar N (1989) Empirical Research and the issue of jury competence. *Law and Contemporary Problems* **52**: 1–8

Vidmar N (1996) Book Review of Jeffrey Abramson's 'We the Jury'. *Contemporary Sociology* **25**: 97–9

Vidmar N, Lee J, Cohen E, Stewart A (1994) Damage awards and jurors' responsibility ascriptions in medical versus automobile negligence cases. *Behavioural Sciences and the Law* **12**: 149–160

Vidmar N, Schuller R (1989) Juries and expert evidence: social framework testimony. *Law and Contemporary Problems* **52**: 133–76

Vincent C (1995) Clinical risk management: one piece of the quality jigsaw. *Qual Health Care* **4**: 73–74

Vincent C, Bark P (1995) Accident investigation: discovering why things go wrong. In: Vincent C (ed) *Clinical Risk Management*. BMJ Publishing Group, London: 391–410

Vincent C, Martin T, Ennis M (1991) Obstetric accidents: the patient's perspective. *Br J Obstet Gynaecol* **98**: 390–395

Vincent C, Taylor-Adams S, Stanhope N (1998) Framework for analysing risk and safety in clinical medicine. *Br Med J* **316**: 1154–57

Vincent C, Young M, Phillips A (1994) Why do people sue doctors? A study of patients and relatives taking legal action. *Lancet* **343**: 1609–13

Vintzileos A, Nochimson D, Guzman E, Knuppel R, Lake M, Schifrin B (1995) Intrapartum electronic fetal heart rate monitoring versus intermittent auscultation: a meta-analysis. *Obstet Gynecol* **85**: 149–155

Walker D (1981) *The law of delict in Scotland*. W Green & Son Ltd, Edinburgh

Walshe K, Sheldon T (1998) Dealing with clinical risk: implications of the rise of evidence-based health care. *Public Money and Management* Oct–Dec: 15–20

Ward C (1991) Analysis of 500 obstetric and gynecologic malpractice claims: causes and prevention. *Am J Obstet Gynecol* **165**: 298–306

Warden J (1996) NHS repeats its mistakes. *Br Med J* **312**: 1247

Waterson J (1993) Keeping Mum. *Health Service J*, 20 May: 27

Weaver J (1999) Hit Squad. *BMA News Review*, Nov: 18–22

Weaver J (2000) GMC receives its wake-up call. *BMA News Review*, April: 22–25

Webb L (1999) Managing Risk. *Health Services Management*, July: 13

Weiler P, cited by Gray C (1993) Canadian lawyer at Harvard a mainstay behind calls to change response to medical malpractice. *Can Med Assoc J* **149**: 477–8

Wheat K (1999) Commentary section on: 'Appropriate standards of care and causation' (Bridges J, Gardner J) *Health Care Risk Report* **5**(7): 6–7

Whelan C (1988) Litigation and complaints procedures: objectives, effectiveness and alternatives. *J Med Ethics* **14**: 70–76

Whetton-Goldstein K, Kulas E, Sloan F, Hickson G, Entman S (1999) Compensation for birth-related injury: no-fault programs compared with tort system. *Arch Pediatr Adolescent Med* **153**: 41–8

Whitby L (1946) The Science and Art of Medicine. Cambridge University Press, Cambridge. Cited by Kessel N (1988) No more license to practise. *Lancet* **330**: 464–5

Willis J (1996) Failing to make the grade – shortage of midwives. *Nurs Times* **92**(28): 55–56

Wilson W (1984) *Introductory essays on Scots Law*. W Green & Son Ltd, Edinburgh

Woloshynowych M, Adams S (1999) The perception of risk in obstetric care by obstetric healthcare professionals. *Healthcare Risk Resource* **2**(3): 14–17

Woolf (Lord) (1996) *Access to Justice. Final report by the Right Honourable the Lord Woolf, Master of the Rolls*. HMSO, London

Woolf (Lord) (1997) The medical profession and justice. *J R Soc Med* **90**: 364–367

Yoong A, Lim J, Hudson C, Chart T (1992) Audit of compliance with antenatal protocols. *Br Med J* **305**: 1184–6

Young B (1990) The Occurrence. In: Powers J, Harris N (eds) *Medical Negligence*. Butterworths, London

Young G, Spencer J (1996) General practitioners' views about the need for stress support service. *Fam Pract* **13**(6): 517–21

Appendix I

The patient's dilemma

The following is a summary of correspondence between Sandy Kirkman and myself, and is offered in an attempt to further the debate about terminology. Kirkman wrote criticising my use of the word 'patient' in an article in the *British Journal of Midwifery*. Over the next few months we discussed various possibilities along these lines:

Patient

Kirkman: The word stems from the medical model and connotes of disease and waiting to be told what the doctor says you should do.

Symon: 'Patient' does have unfortunate connotations, but no one to my knowledge has come up with anything better.

Client

Kirkman: I am moving more and more to 'client' and I am choosing to disregard the commercial aspect of the word.

Symon: The term 'client' connotes a fee-for-service relationship which is inappropriate in the NHS. Architects, lawyers, and some of those in even less savoury occupations have 'clients'. Midwives, except those in independent practice, are effectively paid by the state. They do not present a bill to, nor demand payment from, those who use their services.

Mothers

Kirkman: All our clients are, or are aiming to be, mothers.

Symon: 'Mother' is too general a term. It may be used selectively, but doesn't fit the bill for the pregnant primigravida; nor does it distinguish the newly-delivered mother from the woman with adult offspring.

Consumers

Kirkman: Still a bit commercial

Symon: 'Consumer' is commercial, as you say. I feel that 'client' suffers in exactly the same way, for the reasons given above. I'm opposed to the marketisation of the NHS, and believe the terms 'consumer' and 'client' insidiously legitimise the place of the market in health care.

Recipients of care

Kirkman: Rather twee

Symon: 'Recipient of care' is a mouthful, and does not distinguish the pregnant woman/new mother from a 'real' patient, an OAP in a home for the elderly, or a special needs child.

Women

Kirkman: Rather general

Symon: Far too general

Parturient

Kirkman: Horribly American

Symon: 'Parturient' only refers to someone about to give birth. I wasn't aware that it was in use anywhere.

Kirkman: It is the sickness aspect of 'patient' which distresses me the most. In the quarter of a century that I have been attached to the world of midwifery I have become convinced that putting women in hospital and treating them as if they were sick, or potentially so, is the single most harmful thing we have done in the name of progress.

Symon: I do agree that 'patient' is not always appropriate, and like you I dislike the sickness connotation. However, the argument that we do not refer to a pregnant woman as a patient on the lines that pregnancy is a normal physiological event is invalidated as soon as something abnormal occurs. The 'client' becomes a 'patient' when she has a minor antepartum haemorrhage; if this settles completely, she becomes a 'client' again, until her blood pressure is too high to be considered normal. She could have her designation changed any number of times. The merit of the term 'patient' is that it is continuous, widely used, and universally understood. The alternatives cannot claim this.

Conclusion

We could not agree on an alternative, and it may be that a single alternative to 'patient' is neither feasible nor desirable. A wider discussion and debate is needed.

Dr Sandy Kirkman is principal lecturer in midwifery/research at the University of Glamorgan

Appendix II

The incidence of litigation

Some claims about the incidence of litigation were examined in *Part I*. This appendix details the incidence of perinatal litigation in Scotland from 1980 to 1995, disclosing the rate of litigation. A limited cross-border comparison based on a smaller sample of English legal files is also described. The reasons for suing and the success rate of each head of claim were described in *Chapter 7*. While the data concerning the English areas provide a snapshot of English litigation, the Scottish data are comprehensive.

The incidence of litigation can be depicted relating either to the year of the relevant event, or the year in which the claim was made. Because of the 'long tail' problem (the length of time between an event and subsequent legal notification) detailing the year of the event (in this case the baby's birth) can be misleading. Probably a truer representation of the picture is to show how often claims are brought. The following charts show the number of claims brought year-on-year in Scotland and the two English areas from 1980 to 1995. It breaks down these claims into 'Maternal', 'Non-CNS baby' and 'CNS' claims.

Figure Appendix II.1: Scottish perinatal claims 1980–1995 (year of claim)

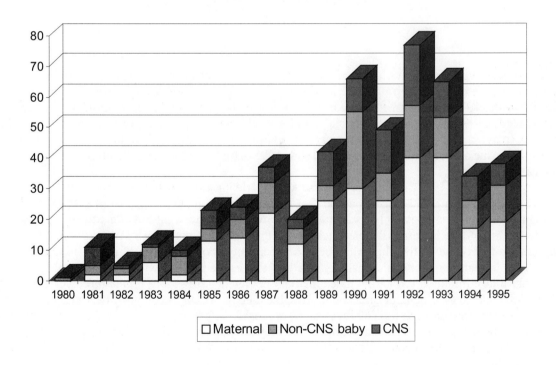

Figure Appendix II.2: English areas – perinatal claims 1980–1995 (year of claim)

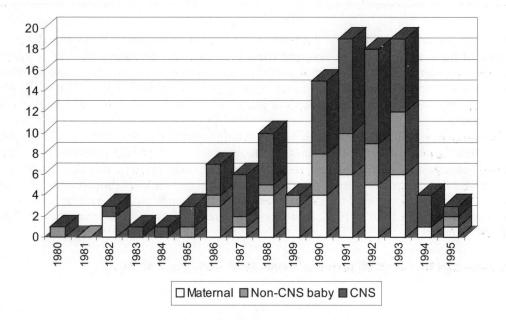

The first few years in both charts will be an under-representation since this research was only concerned with events occurring since January 1980. Actions raised in the early 1980s concerning events in the 1970s (and sometimes earlier) are not included. Changes in eligibility to Legal Aid introduced in 1990, by which the financial position of children is assessed separately from that of their parents, may have contributed to the surge of claims in the early 1990s, but there is a dramatic reduction in the number of actions raised in 1994–1995 in both Scotland and the English areas which is not easily explained.

Montgomery (1997) notes a steep rise in civil legal aid certificates generally in 1991–92, followed by a fall in 1992–93. It may be that the surge in perinatal claims from 1990–92 is partly explained by the greater availability of and publicity concerning legal aid. This further distorts the predictability of the 'lag time' factor which was at this time diminishing (Symon, 1999a). A reduced lag time in theory means that there may be less uncertainty about the scale of future litigation.

The 'limitation of actions' aims to ensure that claims are brought within a reasonable period. In personal injury litigation (which includes medical negligence litigation) this is three years from the date of the relevant incident, or three years from the date on which the plaintiff becomes (or ought to become) aware that grounds for a claim exist. However this is qualified: firstly in the case of children, for whom the three-year period starts only when they reach adulthood; and secondly because mental capacity is required. In some CNS cases this will never be attained and so there is effectively no time limit. While the maternal cases for up to 1991 should be more or less complete (data collection ended in May 1996, and the statute of limitations will bar most actions concerning events before May 1993), much longer will have to pass before it can be concluded that the alleged litigation crisis has passed.

It is feasible that the reduction in the number of claims may be due to better publicity about complaints procedures in hospitals. Many of the claims examined here had little legal merit, a finding echoed in another survey (B-Lynch *et al*, 1996), and it may be that similar incidents, rather than involving solicitors, will now form the basis of a formal letter by the patient to a Trust's 'Complaints Officer'. It is possible to conclude that a fall in the overall number of legal claims disproves, or at least casts doubt on, the theory of a 'litigation crisis'. However, if it is the absence of or reduction in the less meritorious claims that accounts for the fall in numbers, then the situation is no less serious. Indeed, the success rate of claims is likely to rise. It should also be borne in mind that this research only examined perinatal legal claims and this apparent fall in incidence may not be replicated in other areas of medicine. A recent National Audit Office report estimates a 25% annual rise in the cost of medical negligence claims in England and Wales over the next five years (NAO, 1997), which suggests that the litigation 'crisis' south of the Border is far from over. Of course an increase in the cost of litigation is not necessarily inconsistent with a reduction in the number of claims.

Practitioners and managers may prefer to identify how frequently their unit is likely to experience a legal claim. However, as Dingwall and Fenn (1991) note, there are difficulties with determining this. However, a study by Law *et al* (1996) which reported on claims in one English area in 1991, found that obstetrics (not including gynaecological cases) was the medical specialty most likely to receive a claim; the rate was 1.7 per thousand deliveries (ie. approximately one claim for every six hundred deliveries).

Larger hospitals, or, as was the case before Trust status, health boards which contained larger hospitals, might be thought more likely to be sued because they have a greater proportion of high risk patients. This assumes that, all other things being equal, they experience both a higher incidence and rate of poor clinical outcomes. However, as *Table Appendix II.1* shows, there is little consistency between different areas, or even in the same area over time. To even out inevitable year-on-year fluctuations, the data are grouped into four four-year periods and are given by health board/English area rather than by hospital.

While certain areas (and indeed hospitals) featured prominently in this research, this does not necessarily reflect on their standard of care, merely on the apparent inclination of a proportion of those attending that hospital to consult a solicitor. The lack of a necessary link between negligence and a subsequent initiation of litigation was demonstrated in the USA in the Harvard Medical Practice Study (Brennan *et al*, 1991). Little can be concluded about standards of care simply from a knowledge of the rate of litigation, since many factors may be involved in deciding to sue (Vincent *et al*, 1994). It is most improbable that the wide variation in the rate of litigation evident in *Table Appendix II.1* could be ascribed to differences in clinical practice and outcomes over time and between different areas.

Unhappily, there being no obvious pattern to the rate of litigation seen here, there is no formula that will predict how often a maternity unit will experience a claim. For those fearing litigation this is of little comfort, and there is no doubt that the prospect of litigation (however remote) is daunting.

The incidence of litigation has been the subject of a great deal of speculation and comment. From the data presented here it is seen that the apparent belief in an inexorable rise in litigation is misplaced. The dramatic fall in the number of claims raised in the last two years for which data are available cast serious doubt on the presumption that the incidence of litigation continues to increase. There is at present no way of knowing what the incidence of claims has been since data collection ended, and it is possible that the fall in claims in 1994 and 1995 are just a 'blip' in an otherwise upward trend. For such a fall to be seen across Scotland as a whole and in the two English areas would appear to be more than coincidence. As noted earlier, extraneous factors such as eligibility for legal aid may have played a significant part in this fall. The introduction of Lord Woolf's reforms in England will further affect the incidence of full-blown litigation, making comparisons more problematic.

Table Appendix II.1: Deliveries per legal claim: 12 Scottish Health Boards and two English areas, 1980–95[1]				
	1980–83	1984–87	1988–91	1992–95
HB1	N/A	N/A	904	2106
HB2	N/A	4173	1894	1294
HB3	2324	1879	1133	2276
HB4	2598	1342	1160	1618
HB5	2743	1001	824	4836
HB6	3920	1217	948	2115
HB7	6870	2283	1732	3679
HB8	8479	2456	1153	1983
HB9	8880	3548	940	2335
HB10	11550	3691	948	2115
HB11	20536	6865	4067	1086
HB12	24962	8364	4287	3165
Eng 1	1472	1230	885	2799
Eng 2	–	–	733	4787

As shown in *Table Appendix II.1*, discerning a trend when examining data by local area becomes more difficult. It is in fact impossible to predict with great accuracy the likelihood of a claim being received. So many different factors would appear to be involved that predictions are a risky business. Whatever the incidence of claims, their effect on practitioners in terms of their emotional responses may be very significant.

1   This table previously appeared in Symon A (1999a). Permission obtained to reprint.

Appendix III

Cerebral palsy

Nelson (1988) describes cerebral palsy as a category of disability involving patients with one kind of problem – a chronic non-progressive disorder of movement or posture of early onset. Huntingford (1990), also notes that it is not a diagnosis, and summarises it as a non-progressive condition of mental and/or physical handicap that becomes apparent soon after birth.

Cerebral palsy is a complex condition, and one whose aetiology is at best only partially understood, although aetiological studies have been attempted (Naeye *et al*, 1989; Laisram *et al*, 1992). Acheson (1991: 158) points out that cerebral palsy 'results from damage to a brain while it is in the process of development'; this can be 'as early as the first three months of pregnancy or as late as early infancy.' The condition was first described by Little, an orthopaedic practitioner in London (Little, 1862). He did in fact stress the relevance of prematurity in cases of cerebral palsy, but it is his connection between the condition and birth trauma/birth asphyxia which has been remarkably enduring, and which accounts, at least in part, for some of the litigation in the field of obstetrics and midwifery. Puxon (1997: 14) notes that 'this misconception by the layman is doubly unfortunate: it causes untold anxiety to the parents of such children who survive, and it puts a grievous burden on the medical staff involved. The cost to the taxpayer, through legal aid and the coffers of the health service, is a further casualty.' The debate surrounding cerebral palsy's possible link with intrapartum events has been so widespread that there has been a recent international consensus statement regarding this possible causal relationship (MacLennan, 1999).

Hensleigh *et al* (1986: 978) refer to Lillienfield and Parkhurst's (1951) analysis of data from the New York Crippled Children's Program, from which they 'offered a unifying hypothesis of common causation for both perinatal mortality and cerebral palsy'. They also note that 'the incidence of cerebral palsy in developed countries is about 1.5 to 2.5 per 1000 live births. Comparisons between countries show no correlation with the prevailing perinatal mortality rate' (*ibid*, 1986: 978) In other words, intrapartum monitoring measures which were designed to reduce perinatal mortality will have little impact on the incidence of cerebral palsy, since the factors leading to the two outcomes are different. A meta-analysis by Vintzileos *et al* (1995) found that electronic fetal monitoring was associated with both an increased rate of surgical intervention and decreased perinatal mortality due to fetal hypoxia. However, Stanley (1994) notes that obstetric technology has done nothing to reduce the incidence of cerebral palsy – indeed, this has increased slightly, a factor attributed to the survival of low birth weight babies who would not have survived twenty or thirty years ago.

Illingworth (1985) notes that a common feature associated with cerebral palsy is relative infertility of the parents, and that a third of cerebral palsy infants were of low birth weight (less than 2500g). He says: 'The high incidence of congenital anomalies found in children with mental sub-normality or cerebral palsy is a strong indication of a prenatal origin for many so-called "brain damaged" children,' (*ibid*: 124) and notes studies which have suggested that an underlying brain defect predisposes to perinatal problems, especially hypoxia. He claims that: 'It is simplistic to ascribe "brain damage" to single factors, such as breech delivery or hypoxia at birth, without considering the antecedent causes of those factors,' (*ibid*: 122) and in a later article (Illingworth, 1987: 15) goes on to say: 'An implicit pointer to possible prenatal factors in cerebral palsy, rather than perinatal ones, is... that despite sophisticated intensive care and fetal monitoring in the last decade or two, and a considerable increase in caesarean sections, the incidence of cerebral palsy has remained steady or has increased, in contrast to the striking reduction in perinatal and infant mortality.'

Towbin (1986: 932), a pathologist, highlights the role played by 'latent prenatal sub-acute lesions... (caused by) maternal complications during pregnancy.' He claims that the baby with acute cerebral damage stays depressed for a long time, even weeks; the baby with old cerebral lesions is delivered depressed but 'usually responds to attention in the delivery room and is soon alert and active with spontaneous respirations.'

Birth asphyxia

The link with 'birth asphyxia' is problematic because the term 'birth asphyxia' is one which, while frequently used, is defined in several different ways. There is no way of measuring asphyxia directly (ie. measuring oxygen levels on the brain at cellular level). In most clinical settings, indirect measures or markers are used, such as fetal heart rate (FHR) changes, fetal or cord blood pH, or a baby's condition at birth (assessed by the Apgar score) or neurological status in the first few days of life. Paneth (1993: 97) points out that, 'The several asphyxial markers do not identify the same infants (*so*) it is difficult to choose any particular clinical variable as truly representing birth asphyxia... (*it*) is a research laboratory concept, not yet translatable into a clinical measure.' Because of the difficulties in reaching a comprehensive definition, Blair (1993: 449) recommends that, 'the term be dropped in clinical practice in favour of terms referring to clinically observable events.'

The assumed link between cerebral palsy and birth asphyxia is one which Nelson (1988: 572) challenges: to ask what proportion of cerebral palsy is related to birth asphyxia is, he says, just as pertinent as to ask, 'What proportion of mental retardation is caused by Down's syndrome?' The American Collaborative Perinatal Project (a 1960s study) found 21% of children with cerebral palsy had at least one marker of serious intrapartum asphyxia, but a third of these also had a major non-central nervous system malfunction. It found that more than half the children with cerebral palsy and a marker of serious asphyxia also had an indication that the cerebral palsy may have stemmed from pre-labour problems. This issue has been crucial in recent court cases.

Blair and Stanley (1988: 516) found that there was an association between the clinically observed signs of birth asphyxia and spastic cerebral palsy; they concluded that in only 8% of children with spastic cerebral palsy was intrapartum asphyxia a possible cause. There is now, they claim, a questioning of the 'conventional wisdom' that cerebral palsy and birth asphyxia are linked (Stanley, 1994, later notes that courts may be catching up with this belief); they admit there is a weak association, but claim a stronger one between cerebral palsy and 'adverse ante-natal events'. For instance, low birth weight is a major confounding factor since it is associated with both cerebral palsy and birth asphyxia; Acheson (1991) notes that as well as prenatal factors, babies of very low birth weight (less than 1500g) are prone to brain damage due to low blood pressure in the first few days of life. Blair and Stanley (1988) claim that there is no absolute link either way between birth asphyxia and abnormal neonatal neurological signs: severe asphyxia may not lead to seizures, and seizures may occur when there has been no severe asphyxia. They further claim that since the research suggests that few children with cerebral palsy are damaged during birth, efforts to reduce further the incidence or likelihood of birth asphyxia may have little effect on the incidence of cerebral palsy. Asphyxia, they say, may be an early sign of cerebral palsy, 'the effect of ante-natal brain anomaly rather than a cause' (*ibid*: 519). Referring to the probable early antenatal origins of most cases of cerebral palsy, the same authors later comment: 'Obstetricians should realise that they can only promise perfection at the end of labour if there is perfection at the beginning' (Stanley and Blair, 1991: 625).

Freeman and Nelson (1988: 240) state that, 'to attribute cerebral palsy to prior asphyxia with reasonable certainty, there must be evidence that a substantial hypoxic injury occurred and that a sequence of events ensued which would prove the clinical impact of that hypoxic insult. Few cases of cerebral palsy meet these criteria.' The assumption seems to have been that if evidence of fetal distress could be proved, then that would indicate a cause of an ensuing cerebral palsy; one such sign of fetal distress is the staining of the amniotic fluid with meconium, which is observable once the membranes have ruptured. They claim from their study that 99.6% of infants whose birth weight was above 2500g and who had shown meconium staining of the liquor during labour did not go on to develop cerebral palsy. Paneth (1993) estimates that meconium passage occurs in 20% of labours, yet the incidence of cerebral palsy is 0.2–0.25%.

The weight of recent evidence, then, is heavily against an automatic link between cerebral palsy and birth asphyxia, and yet it has been the concern to reduce the likelihood of birth asphyxia which has led to the increase in the caesarean section rate.

The markers

The markers generally used to assess fetal or neonatal compromise have been listed above. Many follow up studies have been carried out to investigate these markers: Neutra *et al* (1978) and Haverkamp *et al* (1979) examined the relationship of CTGs to outcome; Mulligan *et al* (1980), Paneth and Stark (1983), Low *et al* (1984), and Perlman *et al* (1989) examined asphyxiated babies; Nelson and Ellenberg (1981) studied the Apgar score as a predictor of chronic neurologic disability; and Dennis and Chalmers (1982), Derham *et al* (1985), and Minchom *et al* (1987) looked at babies who had had seizures. A brief summary of these various markers is given here.

The Apgar score

The origins of the Apgar score go back to the early 1950s (Apgar, 1953), since when it has become the almost universal method of assessing the condition of the newborn baby. It has, however, not been without its critics (Marlow, 1992).

Henderson-Smart (1991: 576) notes that, 'More children with cerebral palsy had low Apgar scores, and children with low Apgar scores more often developed cerebral palsy. However this association is statistically rather than clinically important.' Grant (1987) notes that the 1960s American Collaborative Perinatal Project found that the 4% of babies with an Apgar score of less than 7 at five minutes contained 25% of subsequent cases of cerebral palsy (a relative risk of between 8 and 9). On the other hand, 98% of babies with an Apgar of less than 7 at five minutes did not develop cerebral palsy. Goodwin *et al* (1992: 1506) claim that even in cases where severe acidosis exists, 'the Apgar score is not highly predictive of asphyxial complications... Our findings suggest that even in the pH range below 7.0 a 5-minute Apgar score less than 3 has only moderate predictive value for HIE.' HIE (Hypoxic Ischaemic Encephalopathy) is discussed below.

Ruth and Raivio's study (1988) found that 81% of those babies defined as at risk because of a low Apgar score will be normal at follow up. Levene *et al* (1986: 68) conclude that, 'The failing of the Apgar score is that it describes the condition of the infant at a particular time; it may not reflect how long the infant suffered intrapartum asphyxia. In addition a low Apgar score may be due to sedation of the infant by drugs given to the mother.'

Blood analysis

Samples of blood may be taken from the fetal scalp during labour, and also from the umbilical cord after delivery. Measuring the pH levels should identify an existing acidosis. Goodwin *et al* (1992: 1506) claim that population-derived statistical lower limits of normal umbilical artery pH range from 7.1 to 7.2, but go on to claim that, 'an umbilical artery pH below these levels is not highly correlated with Apgar score or with evidence of short and long term end-organ asphyxial sequelae.'

Henderson-Smart (1991: 577) notes that, 'scalp pH values of less than 7.2 have been considered evidence of significant acidosis necessitating delivery, and levels of 7.2–7.25 as pre-acidosis indicating the need for continued close surveillance. However, although pH values correlate with altered adaptation immediately after delivery, they are not related to long term neurological outcome.' A study by Dennis *et al* (1989: 213) found several babies with very low Apgar scores but no acidosis, and they speculate that, 'the ability of the fetus to produce an acidosis in response to the stress of labour may be beneficial to long term outcome... the absence of an acidotic shift may be a sign of a compromised fetus.' However they also note that many units aim to deliver babies with no acidosis, and in this pursuit, some now routinely assess the cord blood pH values and record these in the notes, even when there has been no clinical sign that fetal compromise has existed.

Neonatal seizures

Seizures may be one manifestation of a baby with cerebral dysfunction; they are a feature of hypoxic-ischaemic encephalopathy (HIE), but not its only feature. There is a belief that this term should be replaced by 'perinatal encephalopathy', since there is apparently little firm evidence of either hypoxia or ischaemia in many cases. Nevertheless, the term remains in use, and describes the condition of a baby who is believed to have become hypoxic at some stage, and who has developed neurological signs which indicate short and/or long-lasting cerebral damage. HIE is usually described as being mild, moderate or severe, and one of its most striking features is the presence of seizures. Others are irritability, diminished or absent reflexes, and hypotonia.

It has been claimed that seizures in the neonatal period are a much better means of predicting later neurological problems: Johnson (1991) claims that with these there is a 50 to 70-fold increase in the risk of cerebral palsy. Grant (1987) notes that the Dublin trial of electronic fetal monitoring (EFM) found that the group who had continuous monitoring had less than half the rate of seizures as the group who were intermittently monitored. From this it may be concluded that more intensive monitoring could help to prevent seizures and so reduce the incidence of cerebral palsy, but this view is disputed. One author (Anon, 1989: 1252) claims that 'while more intensive forms of fetal monitoring can prevent seizures, this protective effect does not appear to apply to babies whose seizures reflect aetiologies that are subsequently manifested in cerebral palsy. Seen another way, the seizures in some children with cerebral palsy were not manifestations of preventable intrapartum asphyxia', a point accepted by Grant in his paper. The cerebral palsy rates for the two groups in the Dublin trial were the same at four years of age.

Of HIE generally, Hull and Dodd (1991: 953) note that 40% of the babies they studied with this condition had normal deliveries, and 45% of these had no evidence of fetal distress or asphyxia at birth. Henderson-Smart (1991: 577) claims that 80% of babies with moderate HIE, and even 20% of those with severe HIE, develop normally.

Prematurity

While all the individual markers which may indicate that the fetus is, or has been, compromised have been shown to be poor predictors of later handicap, it has also been claimed that their presence in the preterm fetus or neonate is more significant (Low *et al,* 1992: 60). This argument is also complicated: while it is acknowledged that the ability of a preterm fetus to withstand the stresses of labour is less than that of a term fetus, it is debatable whether the onset of premature labour is itself an indication of a fetus who is already compromised. If this is the case, then it is self-evident that the preterm fetus will not fare as well.

Stanley and Blair (1991: 623) note that despite the huge increase in obstetric interventions seen in the last thirty years, the incidence of cerebral palsy has not fallen but has in fact increased slightly. They claim that this rise is 'coincident with increases in the neonatal survival of low birthweight babies'. This view is echoed by Paneth (1993: 95): 'Premature delivery is the single most important antecedent of cerebral palsy, and the increase in survival of very small infants resulting from newborn intensive care may augment this contribution in the future.'

However, while the rate of cerebral palsy is much higher in those babies born prematurely, Mann (1986) points out that two thirds of all babies with cerebral palsy are not in fact born prematurely, so while this variable is probably the most common single factor in the aetiology of cerebral palsy, it can help to explain less than half its occurrence.

Cardiotocography

Cardiotocography (CTG), also known as Electronic Fetal Monitoring (EFM), is the aspect of perinatal care which has probably the most attention from a legal standpoint. Vincent *et al* (1991) claim that deficiencies in staff interpretation of CTGs have at times resulted in poor outcomes and subsequent litigation, and a number of these have been reported: *Murphy v Wirral HA* [1996]; *Wiszniewski v Central Manchester HA* [1996]; *Robertson v Nottingham HA* [1997]. However the supposed benefits of EFM are not universally acknowledged. A study among high risk patients by Haverkamp *et al* (1976: 310) found that, 'The presumptive benefits of EFM for improving fetal outcome were not found.'

The large scale Dublin randomised controlled trial of intrapartum fetal heart rate (FHR) monitoring (MacDonald *et al,* 1985) concluded that continuous monitoring was beneficial in reducing the incidence of neonatal seizures, but suggested this was due to shorter labours in the continuously monitored group. A follow-up of the Dublin study led Grant (1987: 107) to 'conclude that there is little chance of preventing mental retardation by alterations in the management of labour and delivery.'

Ennis (1990) points to a high degree of over-confidence in the ability to interpret CTGs among practitioners, and in the postal survey midwives expressed more confidence in their ability to interpret a CTG trace than the obstetricians. Interpretation of CTGs has been shown to vary not only between individual practitioners, but also when the same practitioner examines the same trace twice (Nielsen *et al*, 1987). With such a low level of agreement about interpretation, it is perhaps surprising that the CTG still forms such an integral part of legal wranglings when the issue is a brain-damaged baby. Further follow-up of the Dublin study led Grant *et al* (1989: 1235) to conclude that 'intrapartum FHR patterns do not seem to correlate with later cerebral palsy... suboptimal intrapartum care, in particular failure to respond appropriately during labour to an abnormal FHR pattern, has been shown to be associated with about a 6-fold increase in the risk of very early (<48 hour) seizures but not with an increased risk of cerebral palsy; and... less than 10% of cases of cerebral palsy are likely to be related to intrapartum care.'

These conclusions do not support a wholesale rejection of cardiotocography, but they do indicate that its use must be tailored – Sureau (1996) suggests that continuous clinical monitoring may be as effective as its electronic equivalent in terms of identifying problems. Nevertheless, Murphy *et al* (1990) note that continuous electronic monitoring has become integral to obstetric practice, 'despite the fact that no clear evidence exists for its efficacy, especially in low risk pregnancy.' Their study found a low degree of specificity (ie. false positives – staff diagnosing fetal compromise when it did not exist), and conclude that this is one of the main reasons for current dissatisfaction with this method of monitoring. They stressed the need to view the CTG in conjunction with other assessments (such as fetal blood sampling [FBS]), and not as the sole indicator of the fetal condition. Despite this, the use of FBS varies enormously, a factor claimed to contribute to non-essential caesareans: Steer (1999: 859) claims that, 'to reduce unnecessary operative delivery for erroneous suspicions of acidosis, it is essential that electronic fetal heart rate monitoring is supplemented by fetal blood sampling with pH and base deficit measurement.'

Keegan *et al* (1985) also found a high degree of false positives and false negatives in CTG interpretation, and Henderson-Smart (1991: 577) claims that, 'Unfortunately heart rate changes during labour falsely indicate asphyxia about 50% of the time. Furthermore, interpretation of the heart rate trace varies markedly between individuals and within individuals.' With regard to inter-observer variability, (Martin, 1998) claims that differences in opinion between experts have contributed to the (perceived) increase in litigation.

Index